THE NOMOGRAPHIC COMPUTATION OF COMPLICATED AND HIGHLY SATURATED MAGNETIC CIRCUITS

THE NOMOGRAPHIC COMPUTATION OF COMPLICATED AND HIGHLY SATURATED MAGNETIC CIRCUITS

PROF. OTTO BENEDIKT
TECHNICAL UNIVERSITY, BUDAPEST

PERGAMON PRESS
NEW YORK · OXFORD · LONDON · PARIS
1962

PERGAMON PRESS INC.

122 East 55th Street, New York 22, N.Y.
1404 New York Avenue N. W., Washington 5 D. C.

PERGAMON PRESS LTD.

Headington Hill Hall, Oxford
4 & 5 Fitzroy Square, London W 1.

PERGAMON PRESS S.A.R.L.

24 Rue des Écoles, Paris Ve

PERGAMON PRESS G.m.b.H.

Kaiserstrasse 75, Frankfurt am Main

Translated
by
G. P. DIENES

Supervised
by
K. SZENDY

Library of Congress Card Number 61—17374

PRINTED IN HUNGARY

CONTENTS

CHAPTER FIVE

CHAPTER SIX

CHAPTER TEN

PREFACE

The publication of the present book in English is a source of great pleasure for its author for two reasons. First, because a large number of excellent specialists, engineers and scientific research workers who, in computing, designing, building and testing electrical machines and devices, frequently find themselves faced with difficulties created by complicated and highly saturated magnetic circuits which seem practically insoluble, will thus become acquainted with our system of nomographic methods. Secondly, because the fact that after the Russian, Hungarian and German editions this book is being published in a fourth language, English, proves, together with the international reception of the earlier editions that the author's criticism of the methods used previously has been supported by many experts, that the importance of the problems raised therein has been accepted by them and that the nomographic methods suggested by the author have been welcomed as an accurate solution.

The system of nomographic methods is the result of theoretical and practical research work of some eighteen years, initiated by the development of a method for the solution of a relatively simple problem. It extended to the discovery of closer connexions to more and more complicated problems and resulted in developing into the generally valid system presented in this book.

These new computation methods were published only after their applicability in practice and their accuracy had been thoroughly tested.

The nomographic investigation of the magnetic circuits of different direct-current traction machines undertaken by the author and other research workers proved the new methods to be highly effective. These were found instrumental in the exact determination of the influence of armature reaction and of the saturation of the pole shoes upon the wave form of the voltage between the brushes. They helped to establish the exact distribution of magnetic losses along the periphery of the armature and to reveal the relation between the changes in the shape of the air gap and the pole shoes, on the one hand, and the distribution of the magnetic values in the machine, on the other. The solution of these problems had been so cumbersome and time-absorbing that some of them seemed practically insoluble with the use of the traditional methods.

On the other hand, the application of the nomographic methods has proved to be extremely simple and has yielded immediate and accurate results.

A representative and convincing example of this is the problem of the distribution of the transverse slot fluxes due to the saturation of the tooth at no load. Eminent scientists like Ollendorf and Dreyfus have undertaken intricate and complicated investigations to achieve an analytical solution of this problem without, however, attaining results applicable in practice. The same problem could be solved by the author's nomographic methods in a very simple manner, yielding results in full agreement with experimental data. Since the slightest changes of the magnetic conditions in the other parts of the machine involve considerable changes in the distribution of the transverse fluxes, the exact agreement between the magnetic conditions in the slots obtained experimentally and those obtained nomographically is a proof of the general validity of the methods.

On comparing the experimental data obtained by the Office of Investigations at the Kirov Works "Dynamo" for the magnetic distribution of the transverse slot flux due to the saturation of the teeth, with the theoretical value obtained nomographically, the theoretical and experimental results were found to be in complete agreement.

Prompted by this fact the author published his system of nomographic methods in 1953 in Russian to make it widely available in practice for the engineers of the Soviet Union. Thanks to the courtesy of the Hungarian Academy of Sciences the opportunity has now been ensured to acquaint my colleagues in Hungary and other countries with this new system.

It is not intended to deal here with the solution of every single problem to which this system can successfully be applied. The author wishes to point out the typical and essential features of the nomographic system. Many examples will be quoted to illustrate the application of the methods to the concrete tasks an engineer may be confronted with in the practice of designing electrical machines.

The fact that most of the examples refer to problems of d.c. machines is obvious since, as has been pointed out above, the correctness of the system of nomographic methods has been checked by comparing the theoretical and experimental results of d.c. machines. Nevertheless the computation methods developed by the author can be applied not only to d.c. machines but to all electrical machines having a saturated magnetic circuit. In addition to this, many problems expounded in this book concern also different electrical devices.

The purposes of this book are:

1. To show that the system of nomographic methods is suitable for solving in a simple manner a large number of complex problems of practical importance occurring in the computation and construction of electrical machines. The author has endeavoured to present the fundamental features of the system in a form to make them readily understandable and applicable in practice, without the necessity of trudging through mathematical difficulties. An endeavour has been made to disclose the principal fields of application of this system by means of concrete examples showing the exactness, the practicability and the simplicity of these methods and to collate the results obtained by them with those that can be achieved by means of the usual methods.

Should the reader wish only to acquaint himself with the practical application of the nomographic methods without going into theoretical details, he will find it sufficient to peruse the chapters marked with an asterisk in the Contents.

2. To draw the attention of engineers and scientific research workers to this system as a means for the solution of a large number of other possible problems enumerated in the last chapter of this book.

The author is convinced that all the possibilities inherent in the methods developed by him can only be exploited by the efforts of many scientific workers. Bearing this in mind, the author has, in all instances, included the proofs of his new statements and quoted demonstrative computations for control purposes showing the exactness of the results with a view to enabling anyone to check the correctness of each method and to have a sound basis for solving other similar tasks or for creating new and improved methods. The text of the proofs is set in small-size type to prevent these parts from interfering with an understanding of the main conclusions, which can be mastered and utilized also without the proofs.

The author hopes that the nomographic system here expounded will contribute to the solution of many problems of the complex magnetic circuits without the necessity of resorting to cumbersome calculations and expensive and time-absorbing experiments, will ensure a better preparation of the indispensable experiments, utilize their results and will further enhance the high quality observed in designing electrical machines and devices.

It is a pleasant duty to express my gratitude to Mr. I. Rácz, professor at the Technical University, Budapest, and to Mr. F. Csáki, professor at the Technical University, Budapest, for their valuable advice, as well as to Mr. K. Szendy, Doctor of Technical Sciences for supervising the English manuscript.

To Mr. G. P. Dienes and the workers of the Academy Publisher I express my thanks for the translation and for the careful work in preparing and setting the English edition and for the attractive form of this book.

The author extends his thanks in advance for any observation or suggestion in connection with the book and requests the reader to kindly forward them to the Technical University, Budapest, XI, Budafoki út 4-6, Chair for Special Electrical Machines and Automatics.

INTRODUCTION

The author wishes to call the reader's attention to extremely important fields in the computation methods of magnetic circuits whose development in recent years has failed to satisfy the growing requirements of electrical engineering. We mean the computation of magnetic circuits containing highly saturated ferromagnetic bodies of complex shape. Such magnetic circuits occur more and more frequently in modern electrical machines as a consequence of their more intensive exploitation. An essential improvement of their computation methods permits the utilization of considerable latent reserves.

The usual computation methods of the magnetic circuits in electrical machines are known to rely on simplified assumptions and to neglect a great many factors. In many instances they neglect the saturation of the steel, assume a uniform or sinusoidal distribution of induction, a uniform air gap around the armature periphery, etc. These simplifications were very useful at the outset because they rendered it possible to lay down the foundation of electrical engineering. Nevertheless, these simplifications represent the vulnerable points of the usual methods which are no longer able to meet all the requirements of modern electrical engineering because the intensified utilization of the machines, the complexity of the configuration of the magnetic circuits, etc. have raised many problems that cannot be solved with these methods.

In calculating electric circuits it can usually be assumed that a linear relation exists between the voltages and current densities. Thus it is easy to find the distribution of voltages if the resistances and currents are given, to determine the magnitude and distribution of the currents if the voltages and resistances are known, or else to obtain, from given voltages the dimensions and form of the resistance corresponding to the given value of the current. It is also easy to solve such tasks by the substitution of one resistance by another having the same value but different form and dimensions, or to replace several series-connected resistances by a single resistance.

In the computation of highly saturated magnetic circuits the conditions are entirely different on account of the complicated non-linear relation of magnetic flux density to field strength. If the usual method is suitable for determining the drop of magnetic potentials by integrating the field strength according to its sections when the flux and the form of the magnetic circuit are given, then the inverse task of determining the magnetic flux for a given configuration of a magnetic circuit and for given differences of magnetic potentials — an often recurring problem — can only be solved at the price of rather complicated and cumbersome methods of repeated attempts and successive approximation.

The problems listed below are not only insolvable with the usual methods but have — as far as it is known to the author — never even been raised owing to their complicated character: *a)* to determine the dimensions and form of a magnetic circuit so that the reluctance should maintain a given value, i.e. that a definite magnetic flux should cross the magnetic circuit at a given magnetic potential difference; *b)* to replace a reluctance by another magnetically equivalent one having different form and dimensions; *c)* to substitute several series-connected reluctances by a resultant reluctance.

In many up-to-date electrical machines the problems are rather involved on account of the non-uniform air gap, the highly saturated pole shoes of complicated configuration or composed of sheets of different form, or owing to the presence of several saturated magnetic circuits exerting a complicated influence on each other.

Thus our engineers are often compelled to apply the usual method in order to obtain approximate results and to correct its defects where it is possible by the methods of successive approximation, checking the results against experiments.

It should, however, be remembered that the methods of successive approximation require too much time and often fail to yield practically applicable results. Furthermore, the lack of simple and exact computation methods makes it difficult to select the appropriate variants of machines to be tested experimentally and to modify the dimensions and configuration of the machine on the basis of experimental results. All this considerably increases the cost of the experiments.

Hence the design and experimental checking of electrical machines having complicated and highly saturated circuits require computation methods which provide, without unnecessary loss of time, exact results for the widely varying cases occurring in practice.

To this end the author suggests the use of the system of nomographic methods developed by him for the computation of complex, highly saturated circuits in electrical machines.

This system not only simplifies the calculation of the distribution of magnetic potentials at a given distribution of fluxes and a given geometrical configuration of the magnetic circuit, but also enables us to solve the inverse tasks successfully: to determine the magnetic fluxes at a given distribution of magnetic potentials and a given configuration and to find the forms and dimensions of the magnetic circuit ensuring the required distribution of the magnetic flux density and the magnetic potentials. For some new problems that can be solved with the system of nomographic methods, let us refer to the determination of the resulting reluctance of series-connected ferromagnetic bodies and fields, each of which consists of teeth and parallel slots, to the location of the geometrical point of the solutions, to the nomographic determination of fields within which the magnetic relations can be regarded as linear, etc..

The usefulness of the system of nomographic methods consists not only in its replacing the methods employed so far, but also in its supplementing and improving them. As an example let us refer to the combination of the nomographic method with the usual one employed for computing the net potential in cases when the distribution and the magnitude of the magnetic field is to be determined in non-ferromagnetic spaces limited by highly saturated ferromagnetic bodies. This combined method is used in this book for determining the magnetic leakage fluxes in the stator of d.c. machines with due regard to the influence of the saturation of the pole upon these fluxes.

For the computation of the distribution and the magnitude of the magnetic field it is often useful to combine the nomographic method with the analytical ones. As an example we may quote the method expounded in this book for the calculation of longitudinal fluxes created in the slot by the influence of the air gap or of the adjacent highly saturated teeth.

The nomographic method can successfully be employed also for the improvement of the well-known and frequently applied analytical methods of determining the magnetic relations in saturated ferromagnetic bodies. These methods, based on the assumption of a linear or some other analytically expressed relation between flux density and the corresponding magnetic potential differences, may yield satisfactory results only if the limits within which this assumption is valid are strictly established. Furthermore, in case of complicated configurations, it is extremely difficult to choose exactly the parameters valid in the range investigated. In such cases the nomographic method may be employed to determine exactly the limits within which the relation of the magnetic values can be expressed analytically, as well as to compute the constants characteristic of this relation. This procedure may be termed the nomographic-analytical method. It has been used in this book for the solution of the following problems:

a) to determine the magnetic relations in the teeth of the armature with due regard to the transverse slot flux set up by saturation;

b) to determine the magnetic potential differences along the pole shoe.

Though this book contains over one hundred examples illustrating the application of the new method, they cover but a relatively small part of the field in which it may be employed. The highly saturated complex magnetic circuits have become widely used not only in electrical machines but also in devices in order to ensure better exploitation and more useful effects.

In addition to this the system of nomographic methods can be used for the solution of the following problems:

a) an exact computation of systems containing permanent magnets;

b) the influence of magnetic saturation upon commutation;

c) the influence of ventilation ducts and other openings upon the magnetic conditions;

d) the influence of the simultaneous change of several geometrical parameters upon the magnetic conditions;

e) the laws according to which the electromagnetic relations change during the transition processes, and for the solution of similar problems.

f) In the application of the system of nomographic methods it must be borne in mind that it is but part of the general theory of electrical machines and devices. This implies that the results thus obtained should be co-ordinated with all the other theoretical requirements applying to electrical machines and devices, as well as with the technological and economical requirements.

CHAPTER ONE

SHORTCOMINGS OF THE USUAL METHODS FOR COMPUTING THE MAGNETIC CIRCUITS OF ELECTRICAL MACHINES AND DIFFICULTIES OF THEIR APPLICATION TO THE SOLUTION OF PRACTICAL PROBLEMS IN ELECTRICAL ENGINEERING

1-1. Usual Methods for Determining the Reluctance of Ferromagnetic Bodies with Continuously Changing Cross-Section

The ferromagnetic parts of electrical machines and devices, in which magnetic flux occurs, display a wide variety of forms.

Beside such forms as parallelepipeds (Fig. 1-1a) or cylinders with constant cross-section, one often comes across bodies with cross-sections varying along their height according to definite rules. Such bodies are, for instance, those illustrated in Figs. 1-1b to 1-1i whose profiles are formed by straight lines (wedge-shaped body in

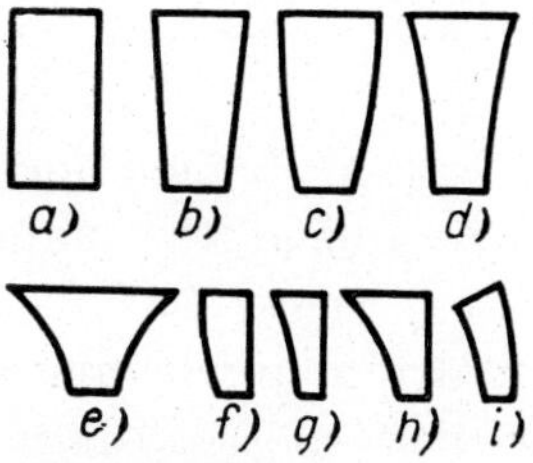

Fig. 1-1

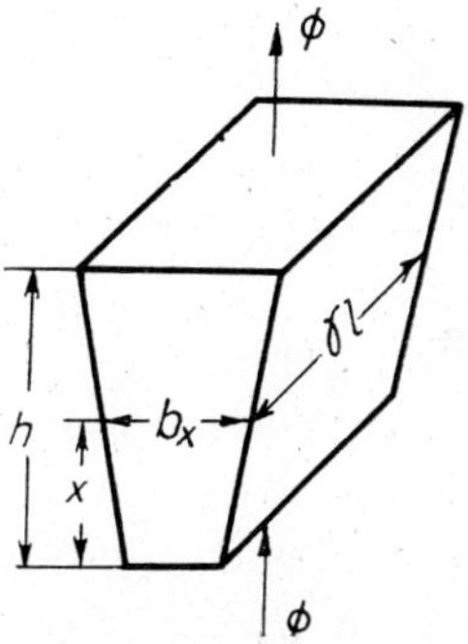

Fig. 1-2

Fig. 1-1b), by convex parabolas (Fig. 1-1c) or concave ones (Fig. 1-1d), by circular arcs (Fig. 1-1e) or by several different curves (Fig. 1-1f to 1-1i).

Let us examine a relatively simple case of magnetic computation when the magnetic flux Φ entering a wedge-shaped body (Fig. 1-2) has a constant cross-section along its entire height. We shall neglect the part of the flux issuing from the side walls and creating longitudinal and transverse flux in the surrounding air space (for instance, in the slots of the armature). Despite the simplification adopted, the computation according to methods hitherto applied involves considerable difficulties. The induction (flux density) B at a distance x from the lower side is

$$B_x = \frac{\Phi}{b_x \gamma l} \tag{1-1}$$

where γ = the filling factor of laminated steel with due regard to the insulation layers between the sheets, if any,
b_x = the width of the wedge-shaped body at a distance x, and
l = the length of the body.

Denoting the field intensity corresponding to this flux density B_x by H_x at a height x, the height of the body by h, the difference of the magnetic potentials is obtained as

$$V = \int_{x=0}^{x=h} H_x \, dx = \int_0^h f(B_x) \, dx = \int_0^h f\left(\frac{\Phi}{b_x \gamma l}\right) dx \tag{1-2a}$$

The ratio V/Φ representing the reluctance of the body can be expressed as

$$\frac{V}{\Phi} = \frac{1}{\Phi} \int_0^h f\left(\frac{\Phi}{b_x \gamma l}\right) dx \tag{1-2b}$$

The Eqs. (1-2a) and (1-2b) clearly show the considerable difficulties involved in these computations even for the simplest cases because it involves integrating quantities whose dependence on x cannot be expressed analytically. The only thing that remains is to integrate each part separately, i.e. to perform a great number of operations, such as the computation of the flux density B_x in several cross-sections of the body and the determination of the corresponding field intensity values H_x accordingly. The number of the cross-sections selected should be the greater, the more the cross-section of the body varies along its height and the higher the degree of saturation. From the field intensity values H_x thus obtained we compute the approximate value V of the magnetic potential difference. The complexity of this method obviously increases with the number of intermediate sections selected.

According to certain opinions, for cases occurring in practice in electrical machines and devices, it is sufficient to divide the body into three sections and assume that the field strength along the height of each section changes linearly. In such cases V is determined by computing B_x and H_x for four cross-sections only.

According to Richter,* the actual distribution of field intensity can be substituted by a parabola, and it is sufficient to determine the value B_x and H_x for three cross-sections, that is, the maximum, the middle and the minimum cross-sections. Then V can be calculated with Simpson's formula.

TABLE 1-1

No. of Ex.	Geo-metr. shape of body	Magnetic values			Values of V computed with the usual methods			
		max. G	min. G	max. field intens. A/cm	A	B	C	D
1	2	3	4	5	6	7	8	9
1		22,100	14,700	1,130	834	867	693	681
2		22,100	14,700	1,130	700	726	504	435
3		24,000	9,600	2,250	1,161	1,194	696	543
4		24,000	9,600	2,250	1,143	1,146	597	306

Let us check now the correctness of these statements with the help of the four examples of Table 1-1. They can be made to cover

* Richter, *Elektrische Maschinen*, I. Verlag Birkhäuser, Basel 1951, p. 189, Eq. 259.

a wide field of practice if the magnetic bodies of different shapes are examined in different magnetic fields. All of the four bodies in Table 1-1 are equal in height, to wit, $h = 3$ cm, and in width, i.e. $\gamma l = 1$ cm. In Exs. 1 and 2 the ratio of the smallest and the largest cross-section is large ($\alpha = 0.666$) while in Exs. 3 and 4 it is small ($\alpha = 0.4$).

In Exs. 1 and 3 the bodies are wedge-shaped and their width changes linearly: for Ex. 1

$$b_x = 1.152 - 0.384 \left(\frac{h - x}{h} \right) \quad \text{cm}$$

while for Ex. 3

$$b_x = 1.92 - 1.152 \left(\frac{h - x}{h} \right) \quad \text{cm}$$

but the smallest width is 0.768 cm for both.

In Exs. 2 and 4 the bodies are limited by convex parabolas and their width changes in Ex. 2 according to

$$b_x = 1.152 - 0.384 \left(\frac{h - x}{h} \right)^2 \quad \text{cm}$$

while in Ex. 4 according to

$$b_x = 1.92 - 1.152 \left(\frac{h - x}{h} \right)^2 \quad \text{cm}$$

Finally, the bodies in Exs. 1 and 2 are subject to a relatively small magnetizing force (the maximum field strength being $H_{max} = 1{,}130$ A/cm) while those in Exs. 3 and 4 are affected by a large magnetizing force (the maximum field strength being $H_{max} = 2{,}250$ A/cm).

The computation should first be performed for the body of Ex. 1 according to Richter's method, which will be referred to as "method A". In the smallest cross-section a flux density of 22,100 G corresponds to the greatest field strength presumed (Table 1-2). On determining flux density and the field strength for the maximum and middle cross-section (at a height of $x = h/2$), the value $V = 834$ A is obtained from the three values of the field strength by using Simpson's formula.

Thereupon the same computation is performed with another usual method which will be referred to as "method B". Let the body be divided into three sections along its height, and the flux density and field strength determined for the same maximum induction of 22,100 G at h, $h/3$ and $2h/3$. By assuming that between each cross-section (i.e. 0, $h/3$, $2h/3$ and h) the field strength changes linearly, we obtain $V = 867$ A. Thus the results obtained by using the above two methods almost coincide. On comparing columns 6 and 7 in Table 1-1 the same agreement is found for the other three examples as well. Hence the methods A and B yield very similar results when applied to magnetic bodies of different shape within a wide range of varying magnetizing force.

TABLE 1-2

Induction G	0	100	200	300	400	500	600	700	800	900
6,000	3	3	3	3	3	3.1	3.2	3.2	3.3	3.3
7,000	3.4	3.4	3.4	3.5	3.6	3.7	3.7	3.8	3.8	3.9
8,000	4	4	4.1	4.1	4.2	4.2	4.3	4.4	4.5	4.6
9,000	4.8	4.8	4.9	5	5.1	5.2	5.3	5.4	5.5	5.6
10,000	5.7	5.8	5.9	6	6.2	6.3	6.5	6.7	6.9	7.1
11,000	7.2	7.4	7.5	7.6	7.7	8	8.2	8.5	8.7	8.9
12,000	9.3	9.6	9.9	10.1	10.5	11	11.3	11.6	11.9	12.3
13,000	12.8	13.4	14	14.5	15	15.5	16.2	16.9	17.6	18.3
14,000	19	20	21	22	23	25	27	28	30	32
15,000	34	36	38	40	42	44	46	48.5	51	54
16,000	58	61	64	67	71	74	78	82	86	91
17,000	96	100	104	108	113	118	123	128	133	139
18,000	145	150	156	163	169	176	183	190	198	206
19,000	213	222	232	242	254	266	278	290	304	319
20,000	330	349	367	390	413	435	462	490	525	555
21,000	595	635	680	725	770	820	870	920	970	1,020
22,000	1,075	1,130	1,185	1,235	1,285	1,340	1,395	1,445	1,500	1,555
23,000	1,605	1,655	1,715	1,780	1,860	1,920	1,990	2,050	2,110	2,190
24,000	2,250	2,320	2,390	2,460	2,530	2,600	2,680	2,750	2,820	2,890
25,000	2,970	3,050	3,120	3,200	3,290					

The above agreement may, at first glance, suggest that the methods A and B are suitable for determining the magnetic relations correctly. This probably accounts for the wide-spread opinion that both methods yield correct results in spite of their being founded on different assumptions concerning the distribution of the field strength. On closer inspection, however, it becomes evident that this opinion can hardly be sustained. It may, for instance, be anticipated that method B would yield excessive results. In reality, the field strength increases more rapidly than flux density, particularly in the range of high induction values. It may, therefore, be expected that the field

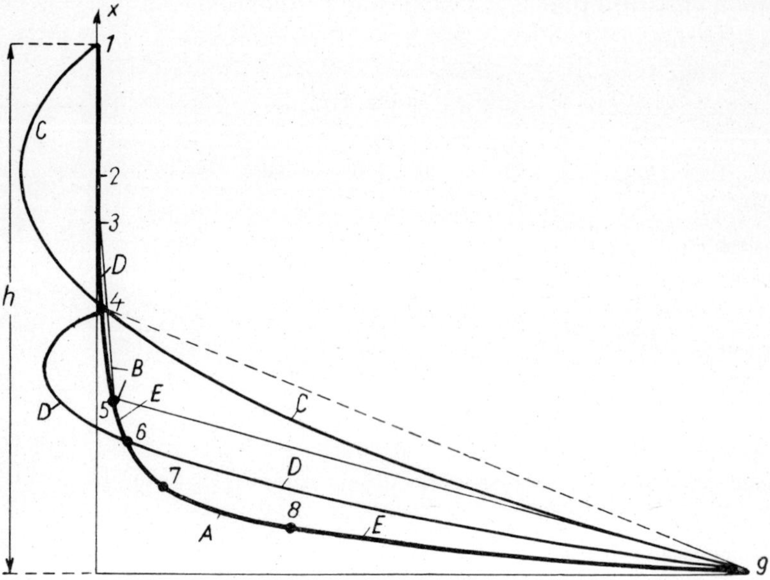

Fig. 1-3

strength grows at a less rapid rate in the range of large cross-sections than in the domain of small ones. This is illustrated by Fig. 1-3 in which curve A represents the actual distribution of field strength along the height of the body of Ex. 1, whereas the broken line B consisting of three rectilinear sections 1-3, 3-5 and 5-9 shows an approximation calculated with method B (the abscissae of curve B are computed at points 1, 3 and 5 with the usual method). The potential difference V is represented by the area between the line and the axes of the co-ordinate system. Hence it is evident that if curve A is substituted by the broken line, a potential difference greater than the actual is obtained.

The greater the discrepancy, the greater the magnetizing force and the changes in the cross-section along the height.

As to the coincidence of the results obtained by methods A and B, there is nothing surprising in it, nor is it by any means conclusive. Method A differs from method B in two respects. Method A relies not on four but on only three actual values of H_x (the abscissae of curve A in points 1, 4 and 9) which necessarily curtails accuracy, i.e. yields for V an even higher value if it is obtained as an area limited by the axes of the co-ordinate system of the two straight lines 1-4 and 4-9. On the other hand, method A approximates the field strength H_x between the said values closer than method B because the field strength is assumed to change not linearly but parabolically according to curve C. Owing to this, the result to be obtained will obviously be smaller. This explains why the values obtained with the methods A and B are in fair agreement, yet impermissibly high.

All this can readily be made evident by computing the above four magnetic bodies with methods more exact than A and B. This method, to be referred to as "method C", consists of the following: five values H_x shall be computed at heights 0, $h/4$, $h/2$, $3h/4$ and h, and for the determination of V the field strength H_x shall be substituted by two quadratic parabolas (i.e. by using Simpson's formula) within the ranges from 0 to $h/2$ and from $h/2$ to h. Obviously, method C is more accurate than method A because it relies on more actual values of H_x. It is also more exact than method B for the above reason, as well as because it uses a more exact approximation (a parabola instead of a straight line).

A collation of columns 6, 7 and 8 in Table 1-1 shows that the values obtained with methods A and B for the magnetic bodies in Exs. 1 and 2 are respectively 25 and 40 per cent higher than those obtainable with the more precise method C. For Exs. 3 and 4 these values are as high as respectively 70 and 90 per cent. This is shown also by Fig. 1-3 in which the quadratic parabola 1-2-4 of the broken line D constructed according to method C almost coincides with the actual curve A, while the co-ordinates of the quadratic parabola 4-6-9 are on the average substantially smaller than the section 5-9 of the broken line B.

In reality, however, the errors involved in the computation of the potential difference V with methods A and B are far greater. This will be more obvious if the exactness of the control method is increased until the error becomes manifest right at the outset. For this purpose let us calculate seven actual values H_x and approximate them in three different sections of the body, assuming that the field strength changes between each section parabolically (i.e. using Simpson's rule). The sections for which the actual H_x values will be computed shall be selected at heights 0, $h/12$, $h/6$, $h/3$, $h/2$, $3h/4$ and h, i.e. at distances diminishing with the decrease of the cross-section (increase of the saturation). This intricate method, to be referred to as method D, is obviously very precise, and the values V thus obtained may be regarded as the actual potential differences. As is evident from Fig. 1-3, with this method not only the parabolas 1-2-4 and 4-5-7 of the broken line E coincide with the actual curve A but also the parabola through points 7-8-9.

A comparison of columns 8 and 9 of Table 1-1 shows that, except for Ex. 1, the values obtained with method D are 14 per cent (Ex. 2), 23 per cent (Ex. 3) and 49 per cent (Ex. 4) lower than those obtained with method C. This means that the data yielded by methods A and B are excessively high. The error in Ex. 1 amounts to respectively 23 and 27 per cent; in Ex. 2 to respectively 61 and 67 per cent; in Ex. 3 to respectively 114 and 120 per cent, and in Ex. 4 to respectively 273 and 274 per cent.

We may conclude that the exact determination of the potential difference V at a given flux Φ requires the application of method D. It should, however, be realized that this method consists of the following operations. On dividing the body into three sections (in the general case into n sections), beside the two known cross-sections, another five (in the general case $2n - 1$) cross-sections should be determined and, beside the known value of the maximum induction, another six (in the general case $2n$) flux density values should be calculated for all intermediate sections. Then seven field strength values (in the general case $2n + 1$) should be found along the curve of magnetization or in Table 1-2. The next step is to compute, for each section of the body, the mean value H with Simpson's formula, i.e. to perform another three (in the general case n) calculations. Hence, all in all, twenty-two (in the general case $7n + 1$) operations are required to obtain the value V. Our examples clearly show that the exact determination of the potential difference V for a given flux Φ with method D is a very cumbersome procedure.

We are, however, often faced also with the necessity of solving the opposite problem: to determine the value of flux Φ belonging to a given potential difference V. The solution of such problems with the usual methods is even more cumbersome. In such cases the distribution of the field strength H_x along the height is unknown, which makes it impossible to find the corresponding values B_x and consequently also Φ. Hence any Φ belonging to some V can, with the usual methods, be determined only by means of successive approximation. An arbitrary value of flux Φ should be selected and the corresponding potential difference V determined by integration of the sections, as was done in the above examples. If the value V is obtained higher or lower than the given value, the computation should be repeated for some lower or higher value of V until the value V obtained coincides with the given value.

The following example shows the clumsiness of such computations.

Example 5. Let us determine the value of Φ for the body in Ex. 4 if $V = 1{,}000$ A.

The induction in the largest cross-section is assumed to be $B_0 = 14{,}700$ G. The twenty-two (in the general case $7n + 1$) operations yield $V = 435$ A.

Let us then assume B_0 to equal 16,700 G. After performing another seventeen operations (in the general case $5n + 2$, since $2n + 1$ cross-sections are known) V is obtained as 1,460 A. Assuming again that $B_0 = 15{,}400$ another seventeen operations yield $V = 710$ A. The quadratic curve $B = f(V)$ is now constructed through the three V values, and for $V = 1{,}000$ A we have $B_0 = 16{,}000$ G, i.e. $\Phi = 16{,}000 \cdot 1.152 = 18{,}430$ M.

Consequently, fifty-seven (in the general case $17n + 6$) operations have to be performed to find the exact value in the given case. Obviously, such an intricate procedure is not only a time-absorbing task but involves also a vast possibility of errors. What is more, an inexperienced person may assess the results to be expected incorrectly, which, of course, considerably increases the number of necessary operations to be performed for the successive approximations.

Even more cumbersome and more time-absorbing is the task of determining the relations between the values V and Φ and the geometrical form of the body.

The solution of such problems would be of considerable theoretical and practical importance. It would make it possible to enhance the exactness of the calculation of magnetic circuits almost to the level of the computation of electrical circuits, i.e. the dimensions and configuration of the magnetic bodies could be selected so as to obtain the desired magnetic conditions.

It follows from these considerations that the first task of the present work is to develop a nomographic method ensuring the possibility of quickly and exactly solving the following three theoretical problems concerning the reluctance of ferromagnetic bodies:

a) to determine the potential drop V caused by a given flux Φ,

b) to determine the flux Φ creating a given magnetic potential difference V,

c) to determine the form and dimensions of ferromagnetic bodies required for any given flux Φ to create any given magnetic potential difference V.

1-2. The Usual Methods for Determining the Reluctance of the Teeth and the Parallel-Connected Slots

Throughout the discussion of the problems hitherto dealt with we have relied on the simplifying assumption that the flux passing through a body has a constant value in every cross-section. In reality, however, the flux in electrical machines traverses not only the ferromagnetic bodies (teeth) but also the non-ferromagnetic spaces (slots) that are connected, magnetically, in parallel with the ferromagnetic bodies.

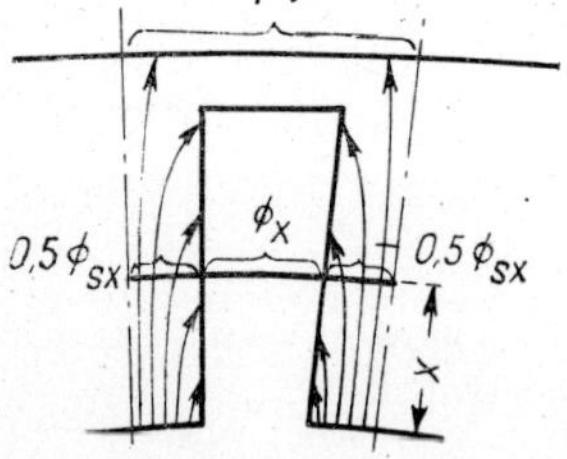

Fig. 1-4

Let us investigate this problem in connection with a case of rather common occurrence in practice, to wit, that of a wedge-shaped tooth and a slot having parallel walls.

Since the magnetic field strength in the tooth varies with height, the slot flux is of different magnitude in the different sections of the slot. Toward the bottom of the slot the flux is greater than near the air gap. If the flux traversing a space consisting of a tooth and the two halves of the adjacent slots (to be referred to in the following as the sphere of a tooth and parallel slots) is assumed to have a constant value Φ_τ at any height x, then the flux will be found to be distributed unequally along the height between the tooth and the slots (Fig. 1-4).

The slot flux at a height x may be presumed with fair approximation to be

$$\Phi_{sx} = 0.4\pi b' l H_x \tag{1-3}$$

where the effective width

$$b' = b + \frac{b_0 + b_2}{2}(1 - \gamma) \tag{1-4}$$

whilst b_0 and b_2 represent respectively the maximum and minimum width of the tooth.

In this equation b is the width of the slot to which the space

$$\frac{b_0 + b_2}{2}(1 - \gamma)\, l$$

filled with insulation material between the sheets should be added; l is the length of the tooth and H_x the field strength in the tooth at the same height. Denoting the flux crossing the tooth at a height x by Φ_x and the flux through the slot at the same height by Φ_{sx}, the equation $\Phi_x = \Phi_\tau - \Phi_{sx}$ or in another form

$$B_x b_x \gamma l = b_x \gamma l H_x \mu_x = \Phi_\tau - 0.4\pi b' l H_x \tag{1-5}$$

is obtained.

The latter equation reveals the reason why the solution of the problem is so cumbersome. In order to determine H_x at a height x, the flux density $B_x = \Phi_x / b_x \gamma l$ must be a known quantity, consequently part Φ_x of flux Φ_τ which traverses the tooth must also be known. On the other hand, Φ_{sx} depends, according to Eq. (1-3), upon the value of H_x required.

For the cases when the flux Φ_τ is known and the potential difference V along the tooth is to be determined, the following rather cumbersome method has been used.

The tooth and the slot are divided into several sections, the values of the corresponding cross-sections determined and the flux Φ_{x1} through the first cross-section of the tooth assessed. Now follows the determination of the flux density in this cross-section

$$B'_{x1} = \frac{\Phi_{x1}}{b_{x1} \gamma l}$$

and the computation of the corresponding H_{x1} with the aid of the magnetic characteristic. Then, using Eq. (1-3) we determine the parallel slot flux of the first section Φ_{sx1} and check whether the sum $\Phi_{x1} + \Phi_{sx1}$ equals the required quantity Φ_τ.

Should this sum be found to exceed or fall short of Φ_τ, the assessment of the starting value Φ_{x1} is sure to be incorrect. If so, the approach should be revised and the calculation repeated until the equation $\Phi_{x1} + \Phi_{sx1} = \Phi_\tau$ is satisfied. If the values Φ_{x1} and Φ_{sx1} are known, H_{x1} can be computed. Then Φ_x, Φ_{sx} and H_x can similarly be determined for the other cross-sections selected, whereupon departing from H_{x1}, H_{x2} etc. (as in Exs. 1 to 5) the value V is calculated. Obviously, the solution of this problem requires a considerable amount of work and time, as is shown also by the example below.

Example 6. The wedge-shaped tooth is 3 cm high, its effective length γl is 1 cm, its maximum width being 2.2 cm and its minimum width 1 cm. The effective width of the slot $b' = 1$ cm. Let us exactly determine V belonging to flux $\Phi_\tau = 23{,}350$ M. The tooth should be divided into three sections, each having a height $h/3$. To compute for each section the value of the mean field strength according to Simpson's rule (necessary also for the computation of V with the precise method D), H_x must be calculated not only for the four cross-sections limiting these three sections, but also for intermediate cross-sections at $h/6$, $3h/6$ and $5h/6$.

The next thing to do is to compute the slot factor belonging to the smallest tooth cross-section, which yields the following values for the field strength: 1,075, 240, 80, 25, 9, 8 and 8 A/cm. The application of Simpson's rule to the three sections, in turn, yields $V = 393$ A.

Thus the determination of V for a given value Φ_τ with the usual method requires the performance of twenty-nine operations.

Sometimes instead of the above-described complicated method another, rather simple method is used which will be referred to as the "simplified method". It consists of calculating the flux density in one cross-section only, at a height $x = h/3$ of the body. The flux is assumed to cross the tooth alone. The flux density value thus obtained is then used for the determination of field strength $H_{1/3}$ in this cross-section, which is regarded as the mean field strength of the tooth. Hence

$$V = H_{1/3}\, h \qquad (1\text{-}6)$$

Unfortunately, the principal assumption here adopted, according to which the field strength $H_{1/3}$ is the mean field strength of the tooth, is unfounded. It is owing to this that the simplified method can, generally speaking, yield no correct results for every case, as is obvious from the following considerations.

Since in this method the width of the slot is neglected, correct results ought to be obtained if the width of the slot is zero, i.e. if the whole flux affects the tooth alone. This would mean that in the teeth $ABCD$ and $A'B'C'D'$ (Fig. 1-5) there is a uniform potential drop V because the same flux prevails in both teeth and the cross-section GH at $h/3$ remains unchanged. This, however, can never be the case since with the further decrease of the cross-section $A'B'$ to zero the field strength in it would in reality increase infinitely.

Even if it is assumed that a slot of normal size is connected parallel to the tooth (Fig. 1-5), the value V for a tooth of the configuration $A'B'C'D'$ should be higher than for a tooth of the form $ABCD$. This can readily be demonstrated by the following example.

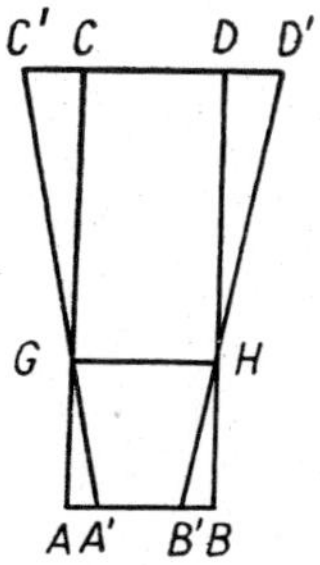

Fig. 1-5

Example 7. In a tooth with parallel walls the flux density is assumed to be 18,900 G which corresponds to a field strength $H = 206$ A/cm (constant along the whole length of the tooth).

If the height of the tooth is 3 cm, its effective length 1 cm and width 1 cm, while the effective width of the parallel-connected slot is 1 cm, then the slot flux $\Phi_{sx} = 250$ M according to Eq. (1-3).

Thus the total flux of the tooth and the slot is 19,150 M which creates a potential difference $V = 618$ A.

The tooth is now supposed to have a form $A'B'C'D'$ (Fig. 1-5), the slot and the cross-section GH to remain as they were in the first instance, and the minimum cross-section to have decreased to 0.6 cm.

According to Eq. (1-5) the flux density in the minimum cross-section increases to 25,300 G and the field strength to 3,200 A/cm, while the flux Φ_τ is divided into slot flux 3,950 M and tooth flux 15,200 M.

In the cross-section of 0.8 cm width lying in the middle between cross-sections $A'B'$ and GH the flux density will be 22,100 G, the field strength 1,185 A/cm while the flux will show the following values: 1,450 M for the slot and 17,700 M for the tooth.

On applying Simpson's rule the magnetic potential difference

$$V = \frac{205 + 4{,}740 + 3{,}200}{6} = 1{,}355 \text{ A}$$

is found to prevail along the lower third of the height alone. Consequently, the potential difference obtained for the lower third of the tooth exceeds itself twice the value V computed for the whole tooth with the simplified method.

To find out whether or not the simplified method has any practical foundation, the author has undertaken analytical calculations checking thereby the results obtained with the simplified method for six cases (cf. Exs. 8 to 13 in Table 1-3) differing from each other in the ratio of the maximum and minimum cross-sections of the tooth and in the varying degrees of the magnetizing force.

TABLE 1-3

No of Ex.	Ratio of max. and min. tooth cross-section	Flux in M	Max. field strength in A/cm	Value of V according to	
				method D	simplified method
1	2	3	4	5	6
8	1.6	23,350	1,075	729	720
9	2.2	23,350	1,075	381	240
10	3.4	23,350	1,075	198	27
11	1.6	26,440	2,110	1,860	2,175
12	2.2	26,440	2,110	968	570
13	3.4	26,440	2,110	493	84

In Exs. 9 and 12 a tooth and a slot having the same dimensions as in Ex. 6 are investigated. In Exs. 8, 10, 11 and 13 the height, the length and the width of the tooth are the same as in Ex. 6, and so are the dimensions of the slot. The maximum width of the tooth in Exs. 8 and 11 is 1.6 cm, while in Exs. 10 and 13 it is 3.4 cm. In Exs. 11 to 13 both the tooth and the slot are subject to a large magnetizing force (the maximum field strength being 2,110 A/cm), and in Exs. 8 to 10 to a small one (the maximum field strength being no more than 1,075 A/cm).

The exact value of V in Ex. 8 is determined in the same way as in Ex. 6, i.e. by computing the field strength in seven cross-sections at the following heights: 0, $h/6$, $h/3$, $h/2$, $2h/3$, $5h/6$ and h. Proceeding from the field strength values thus obtained (1,075, 480, 240, 135, 80, 41 and 25 A/cm), Simpson's rule is applied to three adjacent cross-sections at a time, and V is obtained as 729 A.

To obtain the exact value of V in Ex. 9 the tooth and the slot are divided into two sections, each equalling $h/2$. In the first range the width of the tooth varies from 1 cm to 1.6 cm, in the second from 1.6 to 2.2 cm. Since the character of the change in induction along the height in the first range is similar to that of the change in the induction of Ex. 8, the potential difference for this part is $V_{\text{I}} = 729/2 = 364.5$ A. In the second range $V_{\text{II}} = 16.5$ A is computed from the field strength values 25.8, 6 and 5 A/cm prevailing at $h/2$, $3h/4$ and h. Thus the mean value of the potential difference V for both ranges will be 381 A.

To compute the exact value of V in Ex. 10, the tooth and the slot are again divided into two parts each being $h/2$ high. In the first range the width of the tooth changes from 1 cm to 2.2 cm, in the second from 2.2 to 3.4 cm. The distribution of the magnetic flux density along the height of the tooth in the first range is analogous to the distribution of flux density in the tooth of Ex. 9. Consequently, for this range $V_{\text{I}} = 381/2 = 190$ A. For the second range $V_{\text{II}} = 7.5$ A is computed from the field strength values 6, 4.5 and 3 A/cm belonging to $h/2$, $3h/4$ and h. Thus the mean value for both ranges is obtained as $V = 198$ A. The exact values of V for the other examples in Table 1-3 are computed in the same way though the magnetizing force is different.

On comparing columns 5 and 6 of Table 1-3 it becomes evident that the simplified method yields exact results in Ex. 8 only, i.e. in case of a certain configuration of the tooth and a certain magnetizing force. With the same form of the tooth but with a somewhat altered flux (Ex. 11) the simplified method involves a 16 per cent error. If the form of the tooth is different and the flux is unchanged, the actual value of V in Ex. 9 will be found to be almost 60 per cent higher, and in Ex. 10 almost seven times higher than the values obtained with the simplified method. If both the flux and the ratio of the maximum and minimum width are increased, the actual value of V will turn out to be 70 per cent higher in Ex. 12, and six times higher in Ex. 13 than the value yielded by the simplified method.

As is evident from the examples in Table 1-3, the simplified method can claim no general application. It may yield correct results only in the case of certain definite relations between the maximum and minimum tooth cross-sections, the width of the slot and a definite degree of saturation of the teeth, as in Ex. 8. This may account for the wide-spread use of the simplified method in factories producing electrical machines in which the dimensions of the teeth and the slots are approximately analogous. Nevertheless it should also be realized that the detection of the errors that may be committed in using the simplified method requires a cumbersome scientific analysis and, failing to perform it, the errors often remain hidden.

If the simplified method is found unfit for such relatively simple cases as a ferromagnetic body and slots with straight walls, it is obvious that in instances where the shape of the non-ferromagnetic space is somewhat involved, such as a cylinder, for instance, one cannot even guess the height belonging to the mean field strength V/h.

Thus for the exact computation of the potential difference V corresponding to flux Φ_τ the usual method at our disposal requires a rather complicated and cumbersome procedure as expounded on p. 12.

As far as the inverse task, the determination of flux Φ_τ belonging to a given value of V is concerned, its solution with the usual methods is even more difficult. This consists in selecting an arbitrary value Φ_τ and in computing with the above-described cumbersome method the corresponding value V. Should this turn out to be higher or lower than the given value V, the computation is to be repeated with another assumed value of flux Φ_τ. It can readily be seen that this requires no less than $29 + 2\ (29 - 5 - 7) + 1 = 64$ operations.

We may then conclude that the usual methods can offer no satisfactory practical means for assessing the role of parallel non-ferromagnetic spaces occurring in the different parts of electrical machines. It is equally clear that this problem acquired added importance with the increase of magnetizing force in the ferromagnetic bodies. That is why the author has set himself the task to develop further the nomographic method for the determination of reluctance in a region consisting of a ferromagnetic body and a parallel-connected non-ferromagnetic space, a common arrangement to be referred to as the region of "the tooth and the parallel slot".

This new method is meant to ensure a rapid and exact solution of the following problems:

a) to determine the potential drop V created by the intersection of the region "tooth and parallel slot" by a given flux Φ_τ,

b) to determine the flux Φ_τ passing through the above region under the influence of a given potential difference V.

1-3. *Substituting Series-Connected Reluctances by a Single Resulting Reluctance*

While computing the magnetic circuits of electrical machines and devices we usually come across several reluctances, as for instance in the examples quoted in sections 1-1 and 1-2, which are series-connected to one another. Thus the tooth of the asynchronous machine of Fig. 1-6 can be divided into four parts along its height by the

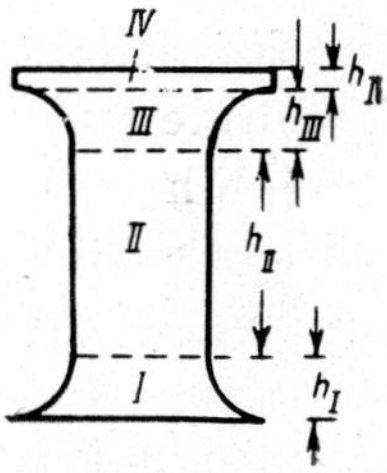

Fig. 1-6

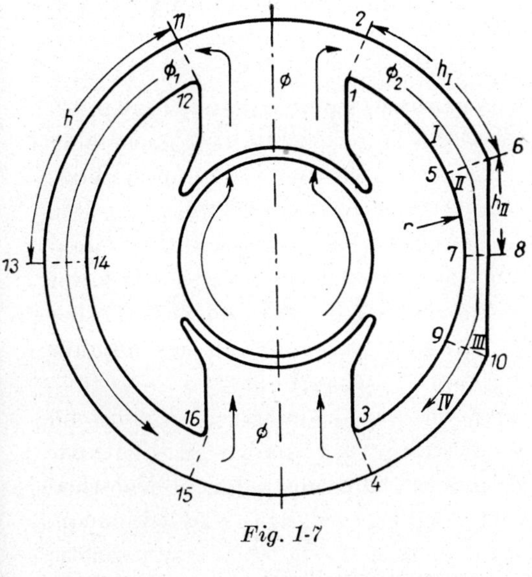

Fig. 1-7

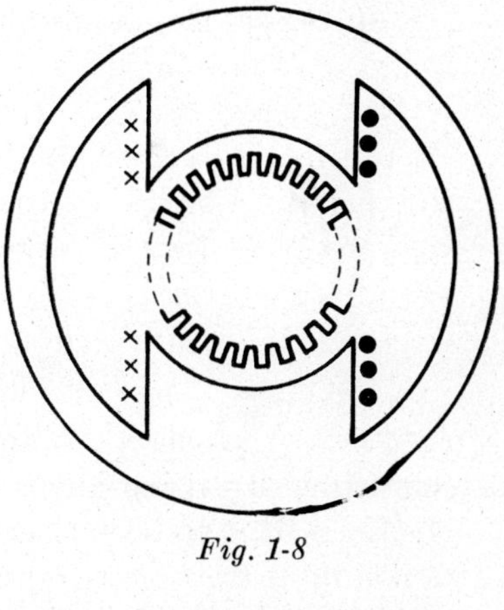

Fig. 1-8

cross-sections at h_{I}, h_{II}, h_{III} and h_{IV}, of which the first part and the third have the configuration shown in Fig. 1-1e, the second the configuration illustrated in Fig. 1-1b, and the fourth has the form shown in Fig. 1-1a. The tooth flux crosses all these parts successively.

Another example is the stator yoke of a d.c. traction motor. Part of its outer surface is cut off so as to bring the shaft of the motor closer to the axis of the wheel. In this case the right-hand half of the stator yoke consists of the series-connected bodies II and III shaped as shown in Fig. 1-1g, and of the bodies I and IV with a configuration of Fig. 1-1a. In all these cases, even if the reluctance V/Φ of each subsequent part were known, the relation between the flux and the sum ΣV of the individual potential differences V, i.e. the value of the over-all reluctance of the machine parts (tooth, yoke) consisting of the said elements, would still remain unknown.

There are cases when several bodies of different shape are connected in series magnetically without constituting a structural element as a whole. This applies, for instance, to the magnetic system of d.c. machines (Fig. 1-8) in which the flux crosses subsequently the armature yoke, the teeth, the poles and the stator yoke. In such cases what we are often concerned with is the over-all influence of all ferromagnetic bodies upon the value of the flux at a given magnetomotive force (mmf), i.e. the relation of the flux to the over-all magnetic potential drop V along each body, in other words, the sum of their reluctances.

Configurations are often met in which the magnetic flux successively crosses a number of spaces consisting of a ferromagnetic body and a non-ferromagnetic gap. This is the case on armatures* having graded teeth (Fig. 1-9a), as well as in the armatures with half-closed slots (Fig. 1-9b) where the slots connected in parallel to the teeth of rectangular shape or of the configuration shown in Fig. 1-6 are filled with non-ferromagnetic material.

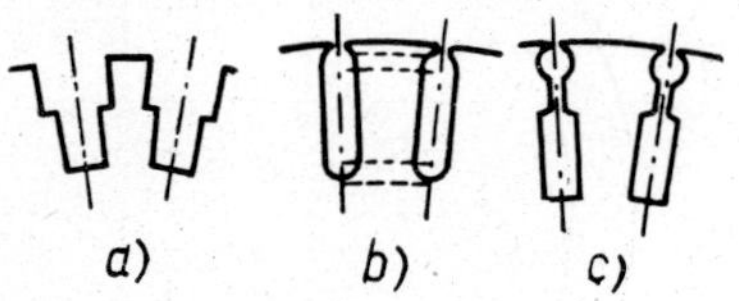

Fig. 1-9

An even more complicated example is shown in Fig. 1-9c occurring in asynchronous machines of the double squirrel-cage type. It can readily be seen that we have to deal with five series-connected fields of tooth and parallel slot.

The problem of determining the over-all reluctance of such series-connected fields by means of the usual methods has not even been raised owing to the considerable difficulties involved in its solution.

* The term "armature" will be understood as the revolving part of any electrical machine, consequently also that of the d. c. machines.

One might ask whether the usual methods of calculating electrical circuits could not be applied for computing series-connected ferromagnetic bodies, i.e. for determining from the dimensions and configuration of the reluctances R_{m1}, R_{m2} etc. the resultant reluctance $R_{mr\,s} = \Sigma R_{mn}$ which may yield the immediate relation between V and Φ for every possible value.

This task could be formulated in the following manner:

a) To replace series-connected ferromagnetic bodies, each having given dimensions and configuration, by a single body having the same dimensions and configuration so that any flux Φ in this resultant body should create the same potential difference ΣV as in all the series-connected bodies together.

b) To replace series-connected fields of tooth and parallel slot, in each of which both the tooth and the slot have given dimensions and form, by a single field of tooth and parallel slot. Thus the resultant tooth and the resultant slot must have such dimensions and form as to ensure that a value ΣV equalling the sum of the potential differences in the series-connected fields should correspond to any arbitrary flux Φ_τ.

The substitution of such reluctances of different dimensions and form by a single resultant is a problem that, on account of its complicatedness, has never been solved with the usual methods; and what is more, has, as far as we know, not even been formulated.

1-4. Difficulties Due to the Variation of the Air Gap and to the Demagnetizing Reaction of the Armature

It has hitherto been assumed that the magnetic flux traverses one or several series-connected regions each consisting of a ferromagnetic body with (or without) a parallel non-ferromagnetic space. In reality, however, series-connected to the reluctance of the region of tooth and parallel slot is, in all revolving electrical machines, the reluctance of that part of the air gap which corresponds to the given tooth distribution (Fig. 1-10).

In standard machines the resultant reluctance of the region tooth—slot—gap represents the major part of the reluctance of the whole machine. If the magnetomotive force of the field coil F_e is given and the flux of the machine is known, it is usually not difficult to determine the potential difference V_0 between the surface of the pole and the bottom of the slot; for instance between points 1 and 3 (Fig. 1-10) at no load. Nevertheless, the potential difference V along the tooth between points 2 and 3, and the potential difference (V_0—V) acting in the gap between points 1 and 2, remain unknown.

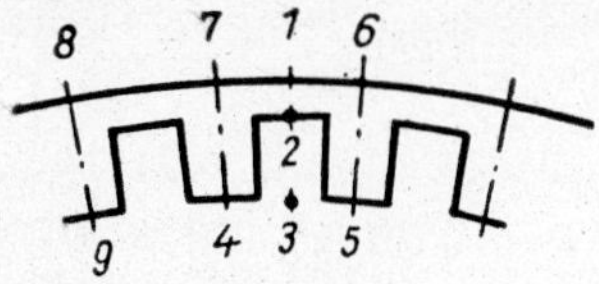

Fig. 1-10

If the value of Φ_τ in this region were known, for wedge-shaped teeth and slots with parallel walls, for instance, the method expounded in section 1-3 could be used and the potential difference V along the tooth, as well as the potential difference V_0—V acting in the air gap could thereby be determined. The latter could be computed with the following formula:

$$V_0 - V = \frac{\Phi_\tau}{\tau_s l \, 0.4 \pi} \delta k_c \tag{1-7}$$

where τ_s = the width of the slot
δ = the width of the air gap
k_c = Carter's gap coefficient.

The flux Φ_τ cannot be known beforehand unless the size of the air gap δ is constant and the potential difference V_0 is equal at any point in the gap. Under such conditions flux Φ_τ can be computed by dividing the total flux by the number of teeth to be found under the pole at any one moment. If, however, the values of either δ or V_0 are not equal throughout the air gap, the flux Φ_τ will no longer be constant and can therefore not be regarded as an *a priori* known quantity. If Φ_τ is not known at a given point in the air gap, the value of V acting along the teeth cannot be determined. Without knowing the value of V, the corresponding value Φ_τ cannot be found either, even by resorting to the extremely complicated and cumbersome method expounded in the previous section.

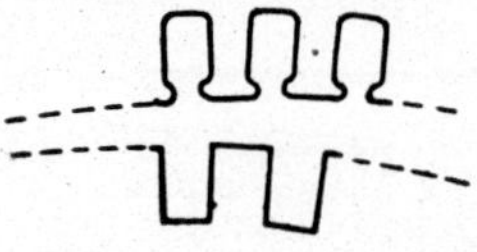
Fig. 1-11

This problem becomes particularly involved if the teeth and the slots are arranged along the two sides of the air gap (for instance, in commutator machines with pole-face-neutralizing windings, in synchronous machines with damping windings) and if the air gap varies along the circumference of the rotor (Fig. 1-11). Thus the distribution of the potential difference V_0 pertaining to the total active layer* of the machine, over the air gap and the two regions of tooth and parallel slot, is unknown and, in addition, the width of these regions and the magnitude of the fluxes traversing them may as well be quite different.

In all the above cases the usual methods lead up to a vicious circle and we are unable to determine the values of V and Φ_τ at a given point below the pole. Furthermore, if we realize that these values should be computed for each slot pitch under the pole, it becomes evident why it is so difficult to find, with the usual methods, the distribution of flux density along the armature periphery and, consequently, the distribution of electrical potentials along the commutator, if any.

The uneven distribution of δ and V_0 is not infrequent, on the contrary, it occurs rather often in high-powered up-to-date d.c. machines and synchronous machines.

Usually the air gap is made to increase gradually toward the edges of the poles in order to obtain an even change of flux density beneath them. The even change ensures in d.c. machines a decrement of losses and better commutation as against machines with sudden changes in flux density beneath the edges of the poles. In synchronous machines this ensures the sinusoidal wave form of the electromotive force.

As to the distribution of the potential difference V_0 it is known that, in any d.c. machine, when loaded, a value of $\pm Ay$ is added to the potential difference acting between the surface of the pole and the bottom of the slot at no load, where A is the specific electric loading and y is the distance from the centre of the pole to the point investigated on the armature periphery. Accordingly, the values of V_0 are distributed under the pole along the straight line 1′-3′ (Fig. 1-12a). (The distribution of V_0 beyond the limits of the pole is now neglected.) The flux density in the air gap, even if the gap is uniform, is distributed along the armature periphery according to curve 1-2-3-4.

In machines where the magnetomotive force of the armature is insignificant as compared to the potential difference V_{0m} under the centre of the pole, the demagnetizing reaction of the armature may sometimes be neglected without incurring the risk of great

* Air gap, teeth and slots will sometimes be referred to as the *active layer*.

errors. Yet in machines designed for operation with the possible weakening of the field (for instance, in traction motors) the magnetomotive force of the armature in relation to the excitation flux substantially increases and, consequently, the deformation of the curve of flux density distribution over the circumference of the rotor, as well as the danger of sparking, acquire added significance.

The curve representing the distribution of potential differences V_0 has a complicated form even in machines whose operation is based on the action of a transverse armature field as, for instance, in rotary amplifiers with cross fields, in generators for the lighting of railway carriages, in some types of single-phase commutator motors, etc..

These considerations have induced the author to develop a nomographical method for the simple and exact computation of the influence of the air gap, whatever its shape may be, at any distribution of the potential difference V_0 over the whole active layer even with teeth and slots arranged along both sides of the gap.

1-5. Difficulties Due to the Saturation in the Pole Shoe

In the previous section our starting assumption has been that the distribution of V_0 is known. This assumption, however, does not hold good in case of certain machine types. In practice, for instance in d.c. machines, the pole form shown in Fig. 8 seldom occurs. Poles with very different shoes can be found in most machines (Figs. 1-12a, 1-13-a, or 1-13b), which, for economical reasons, have very small cross-sections. Consequently, their steel is highly saturated.

The saturation of the pole shoes is not necessarily a harmful phenomenon and may even turn out to be favourable if it is made good use of. By increasing their saturation a more even distribution of flux density beneath the pole tips may be achieved, which is extremely useful in several respects (for instance, for the reduction of the iron losses).

In this case, with a weak flux, the pole shoes will not be saturated and the character of induction distribution (curve 1-2-3-4 in Fig. 1-12) will be determined mainly by the size of the air gap. On increasing the flux, the shoe soon becomes saturated and part of the potential difference V_0 is spent along the shoe between points 7-8 and 9-10. The decrement of the potential difference, left over for the sphere of the

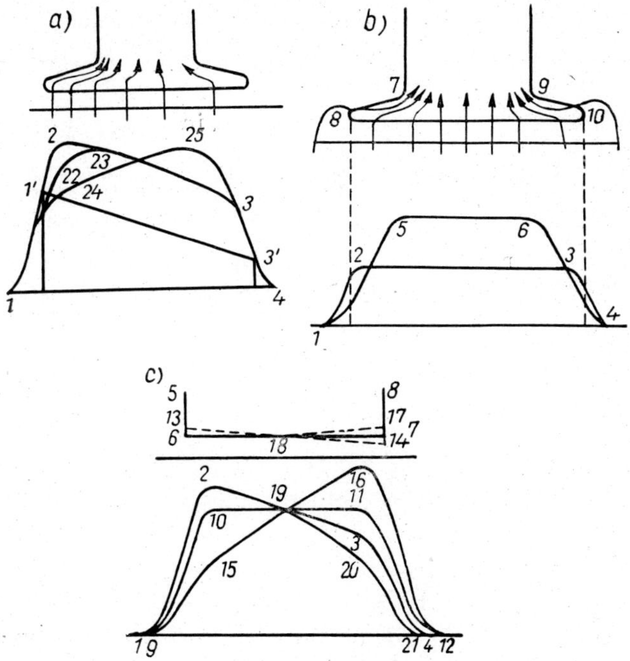

Fig. 1-12

air gap and the teeth, affects the distribution of flux density as a kind of useful increase of the air gap ensuring quite automatically a more even distribution in case of high flux densities (curve 1-5-6-4, in Fig. 1-12b).

If the air gap is uniform and the machine operates under load (cf. Fig. 1-12c), the curve of field strength distribution under one of the pole tips forms a peak (curve 1-2-3-4). In order to decrease the flux at the point where the peak is formed, the air gap under the corresponding tip should be increased. At the same time, the over-all decrease of the main flux could be prevented by reducing the air gap under the other shoe tip. Thus a non-symmetrical air gap would be obtained (a pole having a form 5-13-18-14-8). Such a gap would not be convenient for technical reasons, though it would substantially improve the form of the curve of flux density (9-10-11-12). If, however, the machine is reversible, such a gap would, in principle, be objectionable because the increase of the air gap on the one side and its decrease on the other would, in the case of inverse rotation, have a contrary effect. The point of the maximum potential difference would coincide with that of the smallest gap, whence the curve 9-10-11-12 would, in case of rotation in the opposite sense, change into curve 9-15-19-16-12 with a high peak under the right shoe.

If the air gap is made symmetrical, i.e. increased on the other side as well, then the curves for both senses of rotation are equal. Nevertheless, the shortcoming of this method is the decrease of the useful flux at a given excitation magnetomotive force owing to the increased reluctance in the region tooth—slot—gap (curve 9-10-19-20-21 corresponding to the symmetrical gap formed by the pole shaped 5-13-18-17-8).

Obviously, by changing the form of the air gap to improve the character of the curve of flux density distribution, one comes across certain difficulties and inconveniences. There is, however, an adequate method for obtaining the desired effect without these difficulties and shortcomings. This method consists in the reasonable saturation of the pole shoes. By applying this method under load one can achieve the saturation of the shoe in which the direction of the main flux and that of the armature reaction coincide. Thus the major part of the potential difference pertaining to the air gap and the pole shoe will be imparted to the latter, resulting in a substantial decrease of flux density in the air gap. In the other shoe the induction created by the main flux will considerably decrease owing to armature reaction; this pole shoe will therefore not be saturated, in general. It is thus possible to avoid the decrease of the flux set up by the symmetrical increase of the air gap under the shoes. When the rotor is revolving in the opposite sense the useful effect automatically appears on the other pole tip. Such a saturation of the shoe is equivalent to the automatic change of the air gap at a given point and to its transformation into a non-symmetrical gap. This position is shown in Fig. 1-12a where the curve of flux density distribution 1-2-3-4 corresponds to the saturated shoe, the curve 1-22-23-3-4 to the saturation of the left shoe and the curve 1-24-25-4 to the saturation of the right shoe if the sense of the armature reaction changes.

That is why in up-to-date electrical machines the saturation of the pole shoes is largely employed and the shoes have widely differing configurations. By changing the cross-section at different points of the shoe the designers intend to achieve different useful effects. One of the means of changing the section of the shoe is to apply steel plates stamped so as to impart to them different profiles (as 1-2-3-4-5-6 and 1-2-3-7-5-6 in Fig. 1-13b).

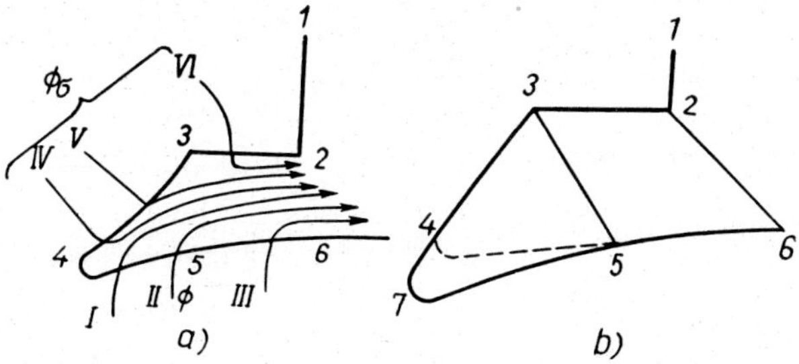

Fig. 1-13

All these circumstances exert different influences upon the reluctance of the active layer of the machine and render its computation extremely complicated.

In sections 1-1 to 1-4 we have shown the difficulties involved in the computation of the reluctance of the active layer. Yet in every case examined, at least the potential difference V_0 affecting the given reluctance was a known quantity. Now with the saturation of the pole shoe not even this assumption is available. Owing to saturation in the shoe, the potential difference between the surface of the shoe and the bottom of the slot decreases. This decrement depends upon the magnitude of the partial fluxes passing from the shoe to the different tooth pitches of the rotor; these, in turn, depend on the above-mentioned potential difference between the shoe and the bottom of the slot.

The extremely intricate interdependence between the leakage fluxes and the saturation makes this problem even more involved. Fig. 1-14 shows the distribution of the flux density due to the leakage fluxes of the field winding, with the usual simplified assumption that its magnetomotive force is evenly distributed over the pole surface in the form of an infinitely thin layer. The said leakage flux Φ_σ passes from the interpolar space into the pole shoe (see the lines of magnetic induction IV, V, VI in Fig. 1-13a) and crosses it together with part of the main flux Φ (see the lines I, II, III in Fig. 1-13a). In Fig. 1-14, the boundary between the main flux Φ and the leakage flux Φ_σ passes through point 6.

Should the shoe not be saturated, the above-mentioned two parts of the fluxes could be distinguished and the actual flux of the shoe be regarded as equalling their sum. Yet owing to the high saturation in the shoe, the potential drop in it will affect not only the magnitude of the main flux Φ but also flux Φ_σ. On the other hand, flux Φ_σ

when passing through the shoe has an opposite influence on the potential difference, resulting in an involved interrelation between Φ_σ and Φ. This phenomenon obviously complicates the computation of the reluctance of the active layer in the electrical machines.

Additional difficulties arise from the complicated configuration of the shoe and from the flux distribution between its parts. The pole shoes usually consist of several series-connected ferromagnetic bodies of different shape (as, for instance, part 1-2-6, part 2-6-5-3 and part 3-5-7 in Fig. 1-13b). When dealing with the problem of determining the reluctance of series-connected ferromagnetic bodies in section 1-3, the same flux was assumed to pass through all these parts.

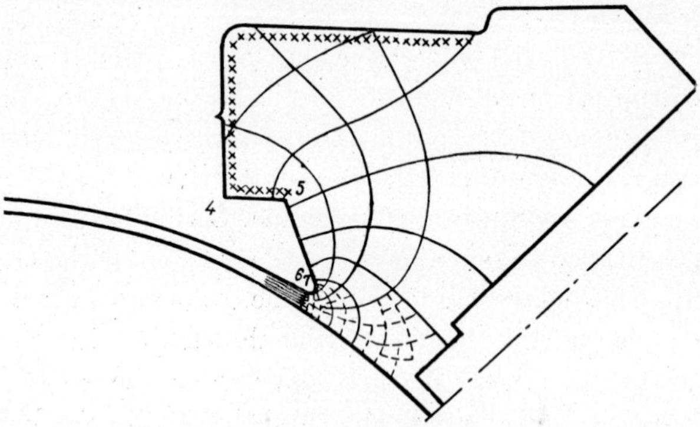

Fig. 1-14

In reality, however, the magnetic fluxes passing through the different parts of the shoe are different, which makes our problem an extremely intricate one. Thus, for instance, the entire magnetic fluxes Φ and Φ_σ pass through part 1-2-6 of the shoe (Fig. 1-13a). Part 2-3-5-6 is subject only to the lines of magnetic induction I, II, IV and V, but the part of Φ corresponding to line III, and the part of Φ_σ corresponding to line VI do not pass along the body 2-3-5-6 but enter it through the side walls 2-3 and 5-6. Finally, all force lines enter part 3-4-5 of the shoe through the side walls only.

Since the above questions arising from the saturation of the pole shoe are highly important for the computation of electrical machines, we have set ourselves the task of extending the nomographical method to include the solution of the following problems:

a) to determine the magnitude of leakage fluxes in the interpolar space with regard to the saturation in the iron;

b) to assess the influence of saturation in the shoe on the magnetic conditions in the active layer;

c) to compute the exact distribution of the resulting flux in the air gap and the surrounding iron at no-load and under load.

1-6. Leakage Fluxes in Shunt-Connected Saturated Magnetic Circuits

In saturated magnetic circuits we often come across problems reminiscent of the problem of determining leakage currents in electrical machines. Such is the case when a relatively small part of the magnetic flux passes across spaces surrounding the ferromagnetic bodies of the main magnetic paths, and shunting th-m magnetically. Examples of similar leakage fluxes which we have so far come across are the longitudinal flux passing through the parallel slot and the leakage fluxes of the pole shoes passing through the interpolar space.

In electrical circuits the analytical determination of leakage currents involve no difficulties because the voltage differences determining the said currents and the voltage drops called forth by them in the conductors are in linear relation to the currents. In the magnetic circuits, however, there is no linear relation between the corresponding fluxes and the magnetic potentials.

The said problem is even more intricate in parallel saturated circuits where the main flux passes through several branches while part of the flux passes through the air spaces separating the adjacent branches. If the ferromagnetic material of some particular branch is highly saturated, then the leakage flux penetrating the adjoining branch changes the magnetic conditions as well as the potential distribution there, which, in turn, may affect the magnitude of other leakage fluxes passing from the second branch into the third and so on. In such cases, owing to saturation, the application of the usual methods encounters exceptionally serious difficulties.

As an example of the problem of parallel magnetic circuits consisting of infinitely small links, let us determine the transverse slot fluxes due to the non-uniform saturation of adjoining teeth.

Let it be presumed, for instance, that teeth 1 and 2 (Fig. 1-15) travel along the pole shoe from right to left. When tooth 1 approaches the shoe and starts travelling underneath, the difference between the potential P_2 at the bottom of the slot and the potential P_1 at the top of the tooth rapidly increases to a definite value. During this time the subsequent tooth 2 has almost no flux, whence the magnetic potential P_2 in this tooth is practically equal at every point. Thus between the top parts of both teeth a potential difference $V = P_1 - P_2$ will

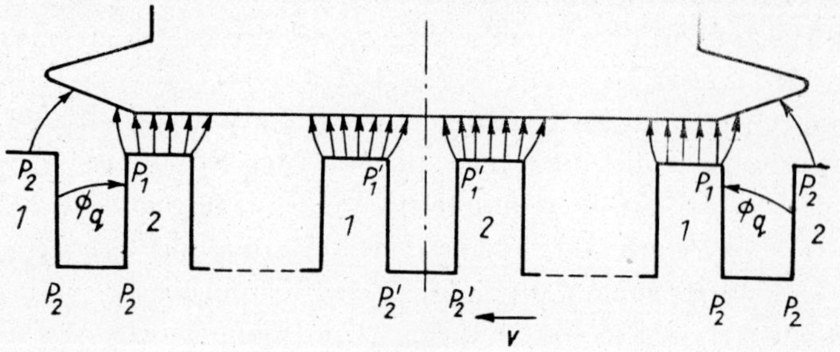

Fig. 1-15

prevail and a kind of equalizing transverse flux Φ_q will pass from one wall to the other.

When tooth 1 travels on, its flux and potential difference may further increase, depending on the shape of the air gap. But now the subsequent tooth 2 also begins to saturate and when the slot between these two teeth reaches the middle point of the pole, equal potential differences $V' = P'_1 - P'_2$ will prevail along both teeth at no load and in the case of a symmetrical air gap, whence the transverse flux vanishes.

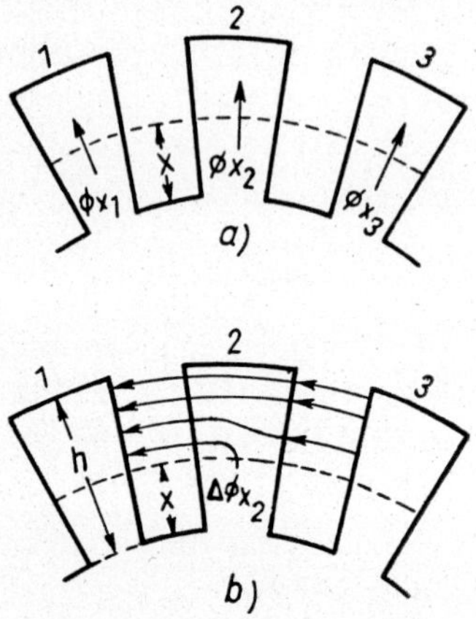

Fig. 1-16

It is easy to understand that at the opposite end of the pole shoe, depending on the increase of the air gap, a transverse slot flux will again appear, yet in the opposite sense. Obviously, the transverse flux changes, with the revolution of the rotor, at greater than fundamental frequency and increases the eddy currents induced in the conductors of the armature. Even if the flux density were distributed sinusoidally in the air gap, the potential differences would change according to a quite different curve having high peaks. If the curve of the flux density distribution in the gap is considerably distorted, these peaks will be particularly high.

The determination of the exact magnitudes of the transverse slot fluxes and the eddy currents induced by them is often an important item in calculating electrical machines. Their computation is, however, connected with considerable difficulties because the potential difference between the two adjacent teeth responsible for the transverse fluxes is not known *a priori*.

Even if we could overcome all the difficulties enumerated above and compute, in some way or other, the flux Φ_{xm} passing any mth tooth in any cross-section at a height x (Fig. 1-16a), as well as the pertaining field strength H_{xm} without considering the transverse slot fluxes, the above problem would still remain unsolved.

The transverse flux density B_{xq2-1} at a height x in the slot between teeth 1 and 2 can be determined from the expression

$$B_{xq2-1} = \frac{0.4\,\pi}{b} \int_0^x (H_{x1} - H_{x2})\,dx$$

where H_{x1} and H_{x2} are the field strength in teeth 1 and 2 respectively at a height x.

In the same manner, the density of the transverse flux in the slot between teeth 2 and 3 at x is

$$B_{xq3-2} = \frac{0.4\,\pi}{b} \int_0^x (H_{x2} - H_{x3})\,dx$$

where H_{x3} is the field strength in tooth 3 at a height x.

Relying on the inductions computed, part Φ_{xq2-1} of the transverse flux (Fig. 1-16b) passing from the second tooth into the first within the range from x to h

$$\Phi_{xq2-1} = \frac{0.4\,\pi l}{b} \int_x^h \left[\int_0^x (H_{x1} - H_{x2})\,dx \right] dx$$

and part of the transverse flux passing from the third tooth into the second within the same limits

$$\Phi_{xq3-2} = \frac{0.4\,\pi l}{b} \int_x^h \left[\int_0^x (H_{x2} - H_{x3})\,dx \right] dx$$

can be computed.

In general the transverse flux passing from a slot into the tooth is not equal to the flux leaving this same tooth and entering the subsequent slot, consequently the difference of the fluxes thus created

$$\Delta\Phi_{x2} = \frac{0.4\,\pi l}{b} \int_x^h \left[\int_0^x (H_{x1} - 2H_{x2} + H_{x3})\,dx \right] dx \qquad (1\text{-}8)$$

will have to pass through the second tooth longitudinally.

These longitudinal fluxes $\Delta\Phi_{xm}$ have so far been neglected in computing the fluxes Φ_{xm} (see Fig. 1-16a) which accounts for the corresponding error $\pm\Delta H_{xm}$ in the calculation of the field strengths H_{xm}.

Consequently, the computation of the transverse slot fluxes according to the above formulae contains the following errors:

$$\Delta\Phi_{xq2-1} = \frac{0.4\,\pi l}{b} \int_x^h \left[\int_0^x (\Delta H_{x1} - \Delta H_{x2})\,dx \right] dx$$

and

$$\Delta\Phi_{xq3-2} = \frac{0.4\,\pi l}{b} \int_x^h \left[\int_0^x (\Delta H_{x2} - \Delta H_{x3})\,dx \right] dx$$

To judge the magnitude of these errors, the following has to be considered.

The value $\Delta\Phi_{xm}$ compared to fluxes Φ_{xm} is not significant and can be neglected in many cases as, for instance, in computing the radial distribution of induction in the air gap. The ratio of the pertaining field strengths ΔH_{xm} and H_{xm} is a substantially higher value. In many cases as, for instance, in determining the potential drop V_m for the individual teeth, even this value may be neglected. Yet when we have to deal with the transverse slot fluxes themselves, the value of the errors incurred ΔH_{xn} can no longer be neglected.

If we take into account that the values V_m increase along the armature periphery from zero to a maximum and again decrease to zero, it becomes evident that on an average the differences between the two values V_m of the adjacent teeth responsible for the transverse slot fluxes are substantially lower than the values V_m. It follows that the magnitudes

$$\int_x^h dx \int_0^x \Delta H_{xm}\,dx$$

and the transverse slot fluxes are, on an average, also substantially greater than their corresponding differences. But if some value is obtained as the difference of two high values, then this difference may vary within a wide range and even alter its sign, even if the individual values change relatively slightly. Hence the desired results would not be obtained even by trying to correct, with the iterative method, the errors committed in computing the values of potential differences in the teeth and those of the transverse fluxes (which, besides, would be very laborious).

Now transverse slot fluxes of entirely different magnitude and direction would correspond to the new values of magnetic potential differences in the teeth, corrected with due regard to the values $\Delta\Phi_{xm}$, and even greater changes $\Delta\Phi_x$ (in magnitude and direction) would correspond to the former. As a result, the fundamental preconditions underlying the correction would prove incorrect. Thus the solution of the said problem leads into a vicious circle: not knowing the actual values H_{xm}, we are unable to compute the transverse slot fluxes, and not knowing these and the differences ΔH_{xm} of H_{xm} created thereby, we are unable to calculate the exact values H_{xm}. It is thus evident that the usual methods for computing magnetic circuits in electrical machines are unsuitable for the solution of this problem.

Attempts have been made in the past to solve this problem analytically. The German scientist Dreyfus posed this problem in a forty-page paper.* A thorough analysis of his paper, however, shows that the methods suggested by him are by no means suitable for this purpose. In order to express analytically the magnetic conditions created by saturation, Dreyfus resorts to simplifications of very doubtful value, and sometimes to inadmissible ones concerning the configuration of the teeth, the induction distribution of the transverse slot fluxes along the height of the slots, as well as concerning the form of the magnetic characteristic.

Beside the fact that the machine thus idealized had little in common with the real objects, Dreyfus had to make extremely complicated and cumbersome mathematical calculations which have eventually led to insignificant results. His inferences apply only to no-load operation and by no means to the most important regime, i.e. to operation under load. This can be accounted for by realizing that

* *Die Bestimmung der in den Ankern von Dynamos auftretenden Nuten-Querflüsse*, in *A. f. E.* 1917, vol. vi.

Dreyfus' fundamental assumption concerning the trapezoidal distribution, along the periphery of the rotor, of the potentials in the teeth (which is a poorly founded inference), proves, even in the case of a uniform air gap, with no saturation in the pole shoe and at no load, to be completely incorrect if the armature reaction strongly deforms the curve of flux density distribution along the periphery of the rotor. Dreyfus himself felt the necessity of admitting in his paper that he had failed "to reveal the secret of the additional losses under load" and that "...neither theory nor experiments had hitherto been able to shed light upon these difficult issues..., because under load the armature reaction distorts the field in the air gap and the picture varies according to the changes in load...".

Having realized that the complicated mathematical method advanced by Dreyfus could not be applied in practice even if it yielded better results, another German scientist Ollendorf* suggested a formula, a comparatively simple one, for the computation of transverse fluxes due to the saturation of the teeth:

$$\Phi_q \approx \Phi_p \frac{1}{2} \sin \frac{\pi}{\tau} x \times$$

$$\times \left\{ 1 - \frac{1}{\operatorname{ch} \frac{\pi}{\tau} \sqrt{\frac{(\mu b_s + \mu b_t)\left[(b_s + b_t) + (\mu - 1)\, b_t\, (\delta_w - \sigma)\right]}{(\mu b_s + b_t)(b_s + \mu b_t)}}} \right\} \qquad (1\text{-}9)$$

where Φ_q = transverse slot flux pertaining to the unit of machine length

Φ_p = main flux pertaining to the unit of machine length
τ = pole pitch
x = distance from the middle point of the pole
b_s = width of the slot
b_t = width of the tooth
d = depth of slot
δ = length of air gap under the middle point of the pole
δ_w = length of air gap with due regard to Carter's coefficient
μ = permeability of the tooth steel.

An accurate analysis of this formula and of the method by which it has been obtained shows the grave errors that can be committed

* *Potentialfelder in der Elektrotechnik.*

when in a purely analytical method very simplified and idealized assumptions are selected as a starting point. In order to differentiate the magnetic potential in the region of a tooth and a parallel slot along both the longitudinal and transverse directions, Ollendorf assumes that the permeability μ in all teeth is equal. In other words, he replaces the actual curve of magnetization by a straight line passing through the zero point. In addition to this, he assumes the teeth and the slots to have parallel walls, i.e. the permeability μ along the height of the tooth to be also constant.

Furthermore, he believes it possible to start from the fact that the radial component of the flux density due to the main flux is distributed cosinusoidally over the periphery of the rotor. Finally, he fails to consider or, possibly, to notice the inverse effect of the transverse fluxes upon the magnetic conditions in the teeth.

It is easy to understand that, with such assumptions, no mathematical difficulties arise in the computation of the longitudinal and transverse flux densities. Yet this is only the consequence of the insufficiently founded method by which the above formula has been developed.

By assuming the magnetic permeability μ to be constant, i.e. by discarding the basis from which the problem of the distribution of transverse slot fluxes over the periphery of the rotor has been derived, Ollendorf decides the question *a priori*. From the conditions assumed by him it can, for instance, be established that the value Φ_q should always be distributed sinusoidally if the flux Φ_p is distributed cosinusoidally.

Such considerations, by which the actual conditions are highly idealized, yield results far from reflecting the real facts. Obviously, the computation of Φ_q requires the knowledge of the value μ which Ollendorf suggests to determine the actual magnetic characteristic. Ollendorf, however, failed to show in his book and, naturally, was unable to reveal how to find — among the infinitely many possible permeabilities μ pertaining to the different flux densities according to the magnetizing curves — the very value of μ that is supposed to solve the problem. What is more, Ollendorf's formula clearly shows that no universal μ can exist for the solution of this problem.

Obviously, the potential drops V_m along the teeth with increasing distance from the middle point of the pole must decrease more rapidly than the decrement of flux density, in consequence of which the values

V_m cannot change according to the same law if the induction is distributed cosinusoidally. It follows that the values Φ_q, being proportional to the differences between values V_m of two adjacent teeth, as has been pointed out, cannot vary according to the sine law. This shows that Ollendorf's essential assumptions are not sufficiently founded and consequently his results cannot be correct either.

Unlike the methods developed by Dreyfus and Ollendorf who have failed to take into account the complicated actual conditions in the electrical machines, the author's nomographic method relies on the actual form of the steel and the true magnetizing characteristics taking exactly into account also the effect of all kinds of load. An attempt is therefore made in this book to extend the system of these methods to the shunt-connected saturated magnetic circuits with a view to determining the fluxes crossing them as well as the pertaining potential differences.

As an example we shall examine the question of transverse slot fluxes due to saturation in the teeth. The results thus obtained, with due regard to the real conditions, will be checked in practice so as to make them exactly comparable to the above results obtained by the purely analytical methods.

1-7. Difficulties Involved in the Exact Determination of Iron Losses

In heavily saturated high-speed machines the specific rôle of the iron losses markedly increases. By reducing these losses a considerable reduction in the rise of temperature may sometimes be achieved and the power of the machine may thus be increased.

The computation of eddy current losses in the iron seems, at first glance, to be quite clear in the light of the usually applied methods. The formulae used for determining these losses are quite simple and rely partly on known factors (for instance, on the frequency of magnetic reversal) and partly on inaccurately calculated values (for instance, flux density in the air gap). If, in addition to this, we consider that the reaction of the eddy currents in the laminar steel can in most cases be neglected, the calculation method of these losses may seem to be scientifically well founded.

This conclusion, unfortunately, does not agree with reality. The formulae, for instance, determining the losses in the teeth of the rotor of a d.c. machine, have been developed with the usual method from the assumption that the distribution of flux density over the armature periphery is sinusoidal. This assumption, however, does not seem to hold for the case of no-load operation, nor is it of any use for full-load operation because the curve of flux density distribution is considerably distorted and there is a marked increase of losses in the steel. This explains the peculiar fact that, following the exact determination of the iron losses undertaken with the usual methods, the result is invariably increased by 50 or 100 per cent in order to obtain the "additional iron losses" under load.

This criticism of the formulae applied in the usual method may be objected to by saying that it is not worth while computing the losses with such precision because, for technical reasons (e.g. filing off the steel etc.), the actual losses in the steel will anyway be greater than the values obtained by more accurate computation.

Such an approach to the problem does not seem to be quite correct even if the sole purpose of the computation formulae and methods were the determination of the losses to be expected. The main purpose of these methods, however, is to find the ways and means of decreasing and correctly distributing the losses, which requires computation to show exactly and clearly on what the values of the partial losses depend and to reveal the influence of all pertaining factors. On investigating, for instance, the effect of flux density distribution over the armature periphery upon the iron losses in the steel, it becomes evident that the losses under load will be greater than at no load, independently of whether the steel is filed off or not.

Thus having developed methods permitting the determination of magnetic relations in any part of a machine, we shall endeavour to develop simple formulae for the computation of iron losses both at no load under load of any magnitude.

1-8. Difficulties of Computing Eddy Currents in Copper Conductors

An important problem in constructing electrical machines is the exact determination of losses due to eddy currents in copper conductors as, for instance, the eddy currents created by the transverse slot fluxes dealt with in section 1-6.

This problem is more complicated than any of the previous ones because, for the computation of these eddy currents, it is not enough to know the distribution of the transverse slot fluxes at every point under the pole, though their determination alone is an insolvable task with the usual methods, as has been pointed out in section 1-6.

The distribution of transverse slot fluxes, as obtained on the basis of the exact distribution of the potential differences in the teeth over the periphery of the rotor, will not correspond to reality because the eddy currents themselves, due to the transverse slot fluxes, create a magnetomotive force acting across the slot and having an adverse effect on the magnitude of the slot fluxes inducing them.

It should be remembered that for the case of a sinusoidal change in the flux passing through the conductor relatively simple formulae have been developed by several investigators. They are suitable for computing the eddy currents, and also the losses due to them with regard to the damping effect of the rotor conductors. In reality, however, the transverse slot fluxes do not change sinusoidally but according to a curve with very pronounced peaks.

It is quite true that the distribution curve of the primary slot fluxes can be analyzed into its harmonics, and the above formulae can be used to calculate the losses due to the individual harmonics. This, in fact, was done by Dreyfus who devoted a long paper* to the problem of the harmonic analysis of the curve, showing the distribution of the transverse slot fluxes.

Unfortunately, the application of the harmonic analysis yields no satisfactory results in the practical work of the factory engineer, because it requires a considerable amount of time to be performed. The more time it consumes, the greater the departure of the curve to be analyzed from the sinusoidal form, i.e. the greater the losses to be expected. Consequently, the difficulties involved in the harmonic analysis are the greatest exactly in those cases when its application would seem to be the most important. In addition to this, on account of the many algebraic and graphic operations required, its accuracy is markedly jeopardized, i.e. the more complicated the form of the curve to be analyzed, the less probable is the correctness of the outcome.

Another important shortcoming of the harmonic analysis is that the results are not perspicuous. Let us assume, for instance, that an exact distribution of the transverse slot fluxes has been found in the machine and the losses to be expected have been computed by the harmonic analysis of this curve. If these losses turn out to be too

* *Wirbelstromverluste in massiven Ankerleitern bei Leerlauf*, in *A. f. E.* 1918, vol. vi.

great and we wish to change the dimensions and the form of the corresponding parts of the machine to obtain a better condition as far as losses are concerned, we encounter considerable difficulties.

The point is that every change in the distribution curve of the transverse slot fluxes at any place, immediately changes the amplitude and the phase of all harmonics, without exception. In order to assess, at least approximately, the decrease of losses by changing the form of the distribution curve, the whole process of harmonic analysis should be repeated for the new form of the curve. The main shortcoming of the harmonic analysis then consists in the impossibility of immediately obtaining the relation between the local distribution of eddy currents and the configuration of the magnetic system.

One of the main reasons why the usual methods have confined themselves to the application of the extremely complicated and cumbersome procedure of harmonic analysis has obviously been the complexity and the difficulty of finding the induction curve itself.

If the determination of the transverse slot fluxes is in itself a time-consuming process, and the computation of the losses due to them is of paramount importance, it is indispensable to resort to the involved procedure of harmonic analysis for the determination of the losses.

Should we succeed in finding a simple method for the solution of the problems enumerated above, the necessity arises of materially simplifying also the computation of the damping phenomena. Thus we shall endeavour to develop a method ensuring a quick and accurate computation of losses due to eddy currents in copper conductors, and the exact determination of their values over the periphery of the armature. The latter will enable us to reveal the effect of the configuration of the magnetic system upon these losses and, by changing the configuration of the individual parts, to achieve their maximum reduction.

CHAPTER TWO

PRINCIPLES UNDERLYING THE NOMOGRAPHIC DETERMINATION OF MAGNETIC RELATIONS IN FERROMAGNETIC BODIES WITH CONTINUOUSLY CHANGING CROSS-SECTION

2-1. *Theoretical Approach to the Solution of the Problem*

Let it be assumed that a magnetic flux Φ passes through a body (Fig. 2-1a) with a constant profile $ABCD$ throughout its length γl, and that no fluxes leave or enter the side walls.* The body in question has a base AB parallel to the cover CD while the walls AC and BD are represented by portions of a parabola of second order.

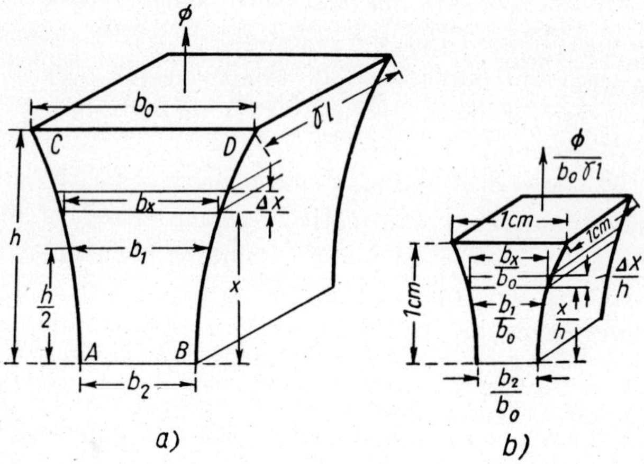

Fig. 2-1

In chapter 1 we have found a relation between the values V and Φ for the wedge-shaped body in the form of equation (1-2b). The same formula applies, obviously, to this case too, yet the function

$$f\left(\frac{\Phi}{b_x \gamma l}\right)$$

* The side line of the profile, the projection of its lateral surface, will henceforward be referred to by the term side "wall".

will depend on the form of curves AC and BD which can be expressed analytically as

$$b_x = b_0 f'\left(\frac{x}{h}\right)^*$$

where b_0 = the maximum width of the body
h = the height of the body
b_x = the width at a height x.

Thus Eq. (1-2b) assumes the following form:

$$\frac{V}{\Phi} = \frac{1}{\Phi} \int_{x=0}^{x=h} f\left(\frac{\Phi}{b_0 \gamma l f'\left(\frac{x}{h}\right)}\right) dx$$

In chapter 1 it has been stated that this equation does not enable us to compute exactly the relation between V and Φ even for the simplest case of a wedge-shaped body, and that the approximate computation of this relation for the individual parts of the body does not ensure the accuracy required or else takes up too much time to be performed. A theoretically different approach is, therefore, made to determine the reluctance of the above-mentioned body. The interdependence between V and Φ is tentatively represented by a curve or set of curves whose ordinates will indicate V and the abcissae Φ.

In this case, for each value of Φ we shall be able to find immediately the corresponding value of V and, inversely, for each value of V, the corresponding value of Φ will be determinable. In other words, it will be possible to find the actual reluctance of the ferromagnetic body for any magnetic demand, i.e. to solve the problems enumerated in section 1-1.

The construction of such curves, however, involves the following difficulties. To obtain only one set of similar curves, it is indispensable that the potential difference should depend on one other value only beside flux Φ.

In fact, however, as shown by the above form of Eq. (1-2b), the value of V depends, beside Φ, also on the values of b_0, γl, h and $f'(x/h)$, i.e. on four parameters which may have any magnitude. This

* $f'(x/h)$ does not represent a derivative, nor will f' stand for any derivative in the following. For differentiation df/dx will be used.

difficulty may be overcome by introducing the concept of the "unit body".

Let us imagine a body (Fig. 2-1b) 1 cm high, 1 cm long, with a maximum width of 1 cm, having a cross-section changing along height according to the same rules as in the actual body (Fig. 2-1a) through which passes a magnetic flux equal to $\Phi/b_0\gamma l$. Such a body will be referred to as the "unit body". Obviously, the width of the unit body at a height x/h equals b_x/b_0, while the minimum width is b_2/b_0 where b_0 is the maximum width of the actual body, b_2 its minimum width and b_x its width at a height x. In all cross-sections of the unit body of Fig. 2-1b the same values of flux density and field strength prevail as in the corresponding cross-sections of the actual body of Fig. 2-1a. Let us cut a Δx parallelepiped from the actual body at a height x and a corresponding parallelepiped of $\Delta x/h$ height from the unit body at a height x/h. In this case the potential difference along the height $\Delta x/h$ of the parallelepiped of the unit body will equal $H_x \Delta x/h$ and along the height Δx of the parallelepiped of the actual body it will be $H_x \Delta x$. Since the number of such parallelepipeds in both bodies of Fig. 2-1 is equal $(h/\Delta x)$, the potential difference along the whole height of the unit body created by flux $\Phi/b_0\,\gamma l$ will be V/h.

The introduction of the concept "unit body" has thus enabled us to avoid considerable difficulties. Instead of trying to find graphically the relation between V and Φ for the actual body to which such values belong as h, b_0 and γl, we can now substitute the latter by a corresponding unit body and obtain graphically the relation between V/h and $\Phi/b_0\gamma l$ in the form of the ordinates and abscissae of some kind of curve. The actual potential difference is obtained by multiplying the ordinates of this curve by h, and the actual flux by multiplying the abscissae of the curve by $b_0\gamma l$. Thus, if each curve corresponds to a certain form of the unit body, i.e. to a certain function $f'(x/h)$, it will be possible to determine the magnetic relations in bodies of different shape by using only one set of such curves.

Nevertheless, for the construction of a similar set of curves, the following difficulties must be overcome. When introducing the concept of the "unit body" it has been assumed that the width of the body (Fig. 2-1) changes along height according to a quadratic parabola, consequently, at any given value of b_0 the function $f'(x/h)$ can be determined by the aid of at least two values b_x pertaining to two arbitrary heights x, for instance, to the minimum width b_2 and the width b_1 at $x = h/2$. Hence, to characterize the form of any theoretical unit body, two parameters must be known, to wit, the ratios b_0/b_2 and b_0/b_1.

In this case, for each possible ratio b_0/b_1 a corresponding set of curves should be obtained, and each curve should correspond to a definite value of b_0/b_2. Obviously, in order to cover all possible relations of b_0/b_1 and b_0/b_2, a vast number of such sets should be constructed, which would make this method hardly applicable in practice.

Before trying to find the general solution of this problem, let us investigate a particular and simpler case, that of the wedge-shaped body. In such bodies the mean width b_1 can easily be determined by the aid of the known values b_0 and b_2, consequently, the magnetic relations for all possible forms of wedge-shaped unit bodies may be represented as a single set of the above-mentioned curves pertaining to different ratios b_0/b_2.

2-2. Theoretical Considerations Underlying the Nomographic Determination of the Magnetic Relations in Wedge-Shaped Ferromagnetic Bodies

Let the minimum width and the maximum width of a wedge-shaped body be b_2, b_0 respectively and their ratio $b_2/b_0 = a$. Let this body be substituted by the wedge-shaped unit body (Fig. 2-2a), and the inductions $\Phi/b_x\gamma l$ prevailing in the widths 1, a and $(1 + a)/2$ be marked B_0, B_2 and B_1.

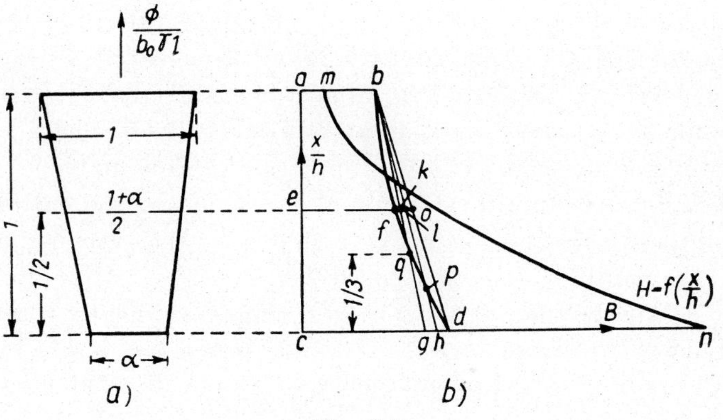

Fig. 2-2

These inductions correspond to the sections *ab*, *cd* and *ef* in Fig. 2-2b. No great error is committed by assuming induction B_x to change between these sections according to a quadratic parabola* through points *b*, *f* and *d*. This induction distribution corresponds to the distribution of field strength H_x shown by any curve *mn*. The area *amnc* (Fig. 2-2b) is represented by the integral

$$\frac{V}{h} \int_0^1 H_x d\left(\frac{x}{h}\right) \tag{2-1}$$

Let us imagine that the flux density along the height of the unit body, owing to the change in its form, is distributed according to another rule $B'_x = f'(x/h)$, for instance, not as shown by the curve *bfd*, but linearly along the straight line *bh* from B_0 (portion *ab*) to some ϱB_0 (portion *ch*).

The straight line *bh* can have a position in which the area V/h remains unaltered in spite of the change in the distribution of H_x along the height x/h. This is made possible by the fact that in one part of the body the induction and the field strength increase, while in the other they decrease.

If then the flux through the body is assumed to increase, both the flux density, i.e. the abscissae of curve *bfd*, and the field strength, i.e. the abscissae of curve *mn*, as well as the value V/h will grow. The new curve *bfd* can also be substituted by a new straight line *bh*, and the latter will again have a position in which a new value V/h corresponds to the field strength distribution according to the new straight line *bh*. In the general case the magnitude of ϱ pertaining to the position of the new curve *bfd* will somewhat differ from the value of ϱ pertaining to the position of the previous curve *bfd*. These values of ϱ can, however, be proved to differ but slightly from one another because for any value of the flux and for any value a, characterizing the form of the tooth, they lie within rather narrow limits.

The above two limit values of ϱ correspond to the extreme positions of the straight line *bh* in Fig. 2-2b. One of the extreme positions can be obtained by connecting points *b* and *d*, i.e. by assuming that the flux density in the body of Fig. 2-2a increases linearly from B_0 to

* This rather exact assumption referring to the distribution of inductions must not be mixed up with Richter's inaccurate assumption concerning the parabolic distribution of the field strength.

B_2. The potential difference V''/h thus obtained will, obviously, be greater than the actual magnitude of V/h because in the sections having widths b_0 and b_2 the flux density and therefore also the field strength remain unchanged while in all other sections the new values of induction B''_x will be higher than the actual values B_x. It follows that the required value of the maximum flux density ϱB_0 must undoubtedly be less than B_2. The other extreme position of the straight line *bh* is obtained by assuming that the flux density increases linearly along another straight line *bg*, for which the area of the trapezium *abgc* coincides with the area *abfdc*. In this case, as is known, the parabola *bfd* and the straight line *bg* intersect at the height $x/h = 1/3$ (point *q*), whence the equality of the areas *abgc* and *abfdc* can be expressed analytically by the formula

$$\int_0^{1/3} (B_x - B'''_x)\, d\left(\frac{x}{h}\right) - \int_{1/3}^{1} (B'''_x - B_x)\, d\left(\frac{x}{h}\right) = 0 \qquad (2\text{-}2)$$

where B'''_x represent the abscissae of the straight line *bg* and B_x those of curve *bfd*.

A new field strength distribution H'''_x pertains to the new induction distribution B'''_x of curve *bg*. Since in the region of small flux densities the changes of induction create smaller changes in the field strength than in the region of great flux densities, the relation

$$\frac{H_x - H'''_x}{B_x - B'''_x}$$

within the range $0 < x/h < 1/3$ will show higher values than in the range of $1/3 < x/h < 1$. Consequently, by substituting $H_x - H'''_x$ for $B_x - B'''_x$ in Eq. (2-2), the left side will be greater than zero. This can be expressed in the following form:

$$\int_0^h H_x\, dx > \int_0^h H'''_x\, dx \qquad (2\text{-}2a)$$

showing that V'''/h pertaining to the flux density distribution of the straight line *bg* is always less than the actual potential difference V/h.

Thus it has been established that the required straight line *bh* along which the flux density B'_x must be distributed, in order to obtain a potential difference equal to the actual value V/h, lies within the extreme straight lines *bd* and *bg*. By denoting the relation of the sections *kl* and *ko* by ε, i.e. if

$$\frac{\overline{kl}}{\overline{kx}} = \varepsilon \tag{2-3}$$

the result obtained may be formulated as follows: the factor ε must have a value lying between the limits $0 < \varepsilon < 1$.

The position of the straight line *bh* between the limits *bd* and *bg*, determined by the value ε, can be assessed by the following considerations.

Let us assume that the values ϱ and ε for the given ratio B_2/B_0 have been determined correctly and the exact position of the straight line *bh* has been found which intersects the curve *bfd* of the actual flux density at some point *p*. In this case the actual flux densities between points *h* and *p* will be substituted by somewhat lower values and between points *p* and *b* by somewhat higher values. Thus, in the section *hp* the magnitude of H_x slightly decreases owing to the decrease of the flux density, while in the section *pb* it increases owing to the increment of the flux density.

Let us find now the values of ϱ and ε for a greater ratio B_2/B_0. If the factor ε is assumed to remain unaltered, then point *p* will correspond to the previous height x/h. Yet on account of the increase in magnetic demand, substantially greater field strength differences will correspond to the above-mentioned differences of flux density in the range between points *h* and *p*.

On the other hand, in the range between points *p* and *b* the changes in the field strength will be essentially smaller than between points *h* and *p*, in spite of the fact that the flux densities increase also in the range between points *p* and *b*, because the absolute values of the flux density in the section *bp* are relatively low. It follows that in computing V/h a certain error has been committed, i.e. a smaller value obtained if it is assumed that the same value of ε belongs also to greater ratios B_2/B_0. This error may be eliminated by bringing the straight line *bh* somewhat closer to the limit *bd*, i.e. by selecting the value of ε somewhat higher for the high values of B_2/B_0 than for its smaller values. Since ϱ also increases with the increment of B_2/B_0, the factor ε should be increased according to the increment of ϱ.

The set of curves $V/h = f(\Phi/b_0\gamma l)$ in which each curve corresponds to a definite form of a ferromagnetic body characterized by ϱ, should, in fact, be constructed for all theoretically possible values of ϱ. Nevertheless, as it will be shown later, for all cases occurring in practice it is sufficient to construct curves for values of ϱ lying between $\varrho = 1$ and $\varrho = 2.6$.

The control computations for the different values of B_0 and of ϱ have revealed the following assumption to be fairly accurate: the value of ε within the said limits is proportional to the value of ϱ, and for the mean value of ϱ, i.e. $\varrho = 1.8$, it has the mean value 0.5, i.e.

$$\varepsilon = \frac{\varrho}{3.6} \tag{2-4}$$

On the other hand, the area of the trapezium is

$$abgc = \overline{ek}\,\overline{ac} = \overline{ac}\,(\overline{ef} + \overline{fk}) = \overline{ac}\,(B_1 + \overline{fk})$$

while the area *abfdc*, according to Simpson's formula equals

$$\overline{ac}\,\frac{\overline{ab} + 4\overline{ef} + \overline{cd}}{6} = \frac{B_0 + 4B_1 + B_2}{6}\,\overline{ac}$$

These two areas are equal, i.e.

$$B_1 + \overline{fk} = \frac{B_0 + 4B_1 + B_2}{6}$$

It also follows that

$$\overline{eo} = \overline{ef} + \overline{fk} + \overline{ko} = \frac{\overline{ab} + \overline{cd}}{2}$$

i.e.

$$B_1 + \overline{fk} + \overline{ko} = \frac{B_0 + B_2}{2}$$

and

$$\overline{el} = \overline{ef} + \overline{fk} + \overline{kl} = \frac{\overline{ab} + \overline{ch}}{2}$$

i.e.

$$B_1 + \overline{fk} + \overline{kl} = \frac{B_0 + \varrho B_0}{2}$$

By solving these two equations with due regard to Eqs. (2-3) and (2-4), we have

$$\varrho = 1.8\,\frac{B_2 + 4B_1 - 2B_0}{-B_2 + 2B_1 + 4.4B_0} \tag{2-5}$$

Considering that

$$\frac{B_0}{B_2} = \frac{b_2}{b_0} = a$$

and that

$$\frac{B_1}{B_2} = \frac{b_2}{b_1} = \frac{2a}{1+a}$$

the final formula is

$$\varrho = 1.8 \frac{1 + 7a - 2a^2}{-1 + 7.4a + 4.4a^2} \tag{2-6}$$

In computations requiring no high accuracy a simpler formula may be used:

$$\varrho = \frac{2}{3}\left(\frac{1}{a} + \frac{2}{1+a}\right) - \frac{1}{3} \tag{2-7}$$

This is obtained by presuming that ε has the same mean value for any magnitude of ϱ as for $\varrho = 1.8$. It can readily be proved that the magnitudes of ϱ computed with Eqs. (2-6) and (2-7) are identical for $a = 1$ (i.e. $\varrho = 1$). The same identity holds for the case of $\varrho = 1.8$ (i.e. $a = 0.528$). The control computations have shown that the deviations of other a and ϱ values are extremely small.

The interrelations of the values as deduced above have a paramount importance for the solution of our problem. We have succeeded in transforming the wedge-shaped unit body into an equivalent body whose height, effective length and maximum width are 1 cm (because B_0 has been assumed to remain unaltered), but which has a different minimum width, $1/\varrho$, and a different form ensuring the linear distribution of the flux density along its height. If the same flux $\Phi/b_0\gamma l$ passes through the two bodies, the distribution of the potential drop is also identical V/h, i.e. they have equivalent reluctances.

It follows that the reluctance of all possible wedge-shaped unit bodies can be represented by a single set of curves in which each curve pertains to a definite value ϱ.

2-3. *The Construction of the Set of Curves*

We shall now proceed to construct the set of curves yielding the relations between V/h and $\Phi/b_0\gamma l$ for different ϱ values.

According to our assumption the flux density B'_x is distributed along the height of the equivalent unit body according to the rule

$$B'_x = B_0\left[1 + (\varrho - 1)\frac{h - x}{h}\right] \quad (2\text{-}8)$$

changing from B_0 to ϱB_0. By differentiating Eq. (2-8) according to x, we obtain

$$\frac{dB'_x}{dx} h = - B_0 (\varrho - 1)$$

By expressing from this equation the value dx/h and substituting it into Eq. (2-1), the following function is obtained:

$$\frac{V}{h} = \frac{1}{B_0 (\varrho - 1)} \int_{B_0}^{\varrho B_0} H_x \, dB'_x \quad (2\text{-}9)$$

By drawing the magnetic characteristic $H = f(B)$ in Fig 2-3 (curve OAB) and assuming that the abscissa $OD = B_0$ corresponds to the ordinate AD, and the abscissa $OC = \varrho B_0$ to the ordinate BC, the area $ABCD$ is obtained as

$$S = \int_{B_0}^{\varrho B_0} H_x \, dB'_x$$

and the section $\overline{DC}$ to be

$$m = (\varrho - 1) B_0$$

Thus Eq. (2-9) can be written in the form

$$\frac{V}{h} = \frac{S}{m} \quad (2\text{-}10)$$

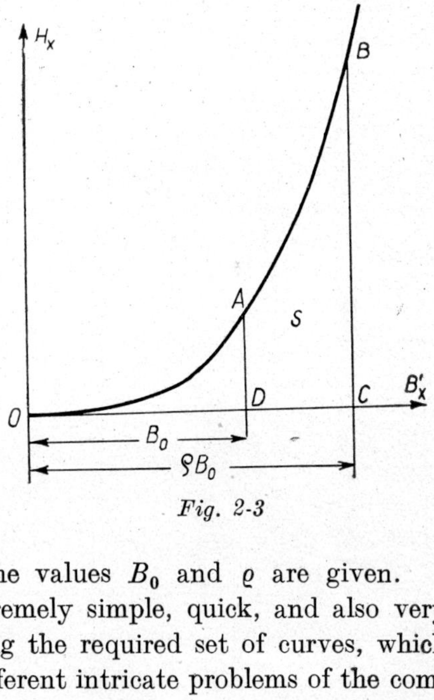

Fig. 2-3

from which the value V/h can exactly be computed in case the values B_0 and ϱ are given.

This relation yields an extremely simple, quick, and also very accurate method for constructing the required set of curves, which enables us to solve easily the different intricate problems of the computation of magnetic circuits.

Let us draw the ordinate pertaining to a definite abscissa k (for instance to 10,000 G) on the magnetic characteristic of the steel

$H = f(B)$ (curve OAB in Fig. 2-4a). Subject to the accuracy required, let us select some value ϱ (e.g. $\varrho = 1.13$) and draw the next ordinate pertaining to the abscissa $1.13\,k$, then the second to $1.13^2\,k$, the third to $1.13^3\,k$, and so on.

Thus we obtain the elementary areas of approximately trapezoidal form (e.g. $ABCD$) whose bases m_1, m_2, m_3, etc. increase from left to right according to the ratios $1 : 1.13 : 1.13^2$, etc..

The construction should be continued up to the maximum flux densities occurring in practice. Thus such areas as S_1, S_2, etc. are obtained.

By dividing all these areas by their own bases, we have the series S_1/m_1, S_2/m_2, etc..

Here S_1/m_1 represents the mean ordinate corresponding to m_1, i.e. the mean value of field strength if the flux density increases linearly from k until $1.13\,k$. In other words, the ratio S_1/m_1 equals the value V/h prevailing in the equivalent unit body in case of $B_0 = k$ and $\varrho = 1.13$. Similarly the ratio S_2/m_2 is equal to V/h prevailing in the same equivalent body if $B_0 = 1.13\,k$. If follows that in order to construct curve OE (Fig. 2-4a), characterizing the dependence of the potential difference V/h on the flux $\Phi/b_0\gamma l$ of the given equivalent unit

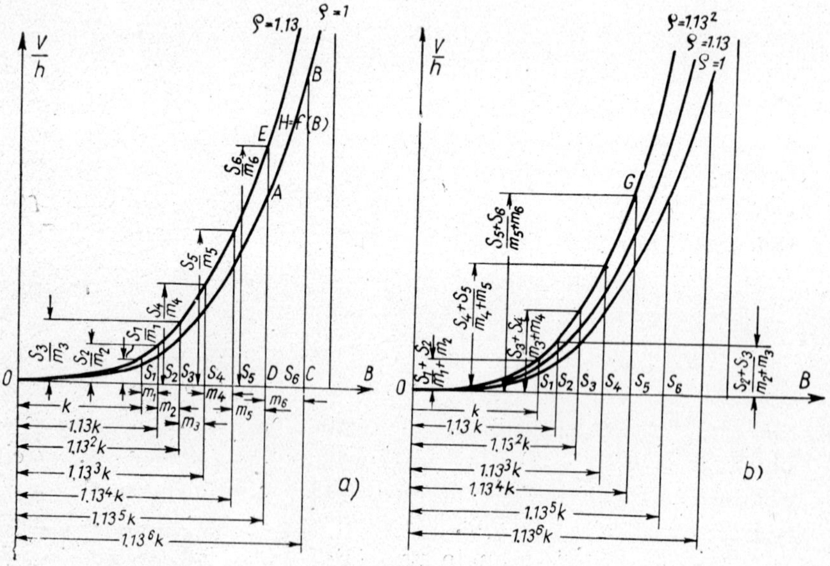

Fig. 2-4

body with the factor $\varrho = 1.13$ (i.e. its reluctance), only such points should be plotted whose ordinates correspond to S_1/m_1, S_2/m_2, S_3/m_3, etc. and whose abscissae belong to k, $1.13\,k$, $1.13^2\,k$, etc..

By computing in a similar way the values

$$\frac{S_1 + S_2}{m_1 + m_2}, \quad \frac{S_2 + S_3}{m_2 + m_3} \quad \text{etc.}$$

and plotting them as ordinates pertaining to the same abscissae k, $1.13\,k$, $1.13^2\,k$, etc., a second curve OG is obtained (Fig. 2-4b) showing the reluctance of another equivalent unit body with the factor $\varrho = 1.13^2$, i.e. the dependence of V/h on the flux $\Phi/b_0\gamma l$. Similarly, the values

$$\frac{S_1 + S_2 + S_3}{m_1 + m_2 + m_3} \quad \text{etc.}$$

yield a third curve for the equivalent unit body with $\varrho = 1.13^3$, etc..

By continuing this construction until, for instance, $\varrho = 2.66$, eight curves are obtained for the following values of ϱ: 1.13, 1.28, 1.44, 1.63, 1.84, 2.08, 2.35, 2.66.

As is shown by practice, beside the above eight basic curves, any required number of intermediate curves may be obtained with fair accuracy by the aid of simple approximation. For instance, in the case shown in Figs. 2-3 and 2-4, four intermediate curves between the first and the second can be obtained by dividing by five, for each ordinate, the horizontal distance between these basic curves. It may then be assumed that the four points belonging to the intermediate curves pertain to the following parameters:

$$\varrho = 1.13^{1/5} \approx 1.025 \qquad \varrho = 1.13^{2/5} \approx 1.05$$

$$\varrho = 1.13^{3/5} \approx 1.075 \qquad \varrho = 1.13^{4/5} \approx 1.10$$

By dividing similarly the horizontal distances between the curves obtained for $\varrho = 1.13$ and for $\varrho = 1.13^2$, intermediate curves are obtained for the following values $\varrho = 1.13^{6/5} \approx 1.16$ and $\varrho = 1.13^{7/5} \approx \approx 1.19$, etc..

The curves obtained by the said simple and rapid method enable us to determine the exact relation between any value $B_0 = \Phi/b_0\gamma l$, V/h

and ϱ, i.e. between the values of the flux, the potential difference and the form of any wedge-shaped ferromagnetic body.

Our set of curves shows the interrelation of three basic parameters, B_0, V/h and ϱ of the magnetic circuits and, with the nomographic method, enables the problems enumerated in section 1-1 to be solved. Since nomographic methods will be applied also in the following to the solution of the problems mentioned in chapter 1, the method for the computation of magnetic circuits, developed by the author, will be termed nomographic and the set of curves obtained will be referred to as a nomogram.

A nomogram constructed on the magnetizing curve of a definite kind of electrical steel* will be used to solve the tasks here dealt with. (See Supplement I.)

The curves of the nomogram cover the range from $\varrho = 1$ to $\varrho = 2.66$. The greatest ordinate corresponds to a field strength of 3,000 A/cm, the greatest abscissa to a flux density of 30,000 G. The meaning of the straight line to the left of the ordinate axis will be explained later.

The nomograms pertaining to the different kinds of steel can readily be constructed with the help of the afore-mentioned method. In order to enable the reader to use ready-made nomograms, we enclose nomograms also for another kind of electrical steel** (Supplement II) and for cast iron (Supplement III).

In applying the nomographic method one also comes across such wedge-shaped bodies whose factor a is smaller than 0.4.

If we consider that the highest flux density occurring in electrical machines and devices is about 25,000 G, then in case of $a < 0.4$ the flux density prevailing in the maximum cross-section of the body will be less than 10,000 G, i.e. the pertaining field strength will be extremely small in the neighbourhood of the maximum cross-section as compared to the highest field strengths. It follows that for practical purposes it is sufficient to take into account that part h' of the height within which the flux density is greater than 40 per cent of the maximum induction. The remaining part of the height, i.e. $h - h'$ may be neglected altogether.

* The thickness of the electrical steel sheet is 0.5 mm, the specific loss $p_{10,000} = 3.3$ W/kg. The data of the magnetizing curve are given in Table 1-2.

** The thickness of the electrical steel sheet is 0.5 mm, the specific loss $p_{10,000} = 1.8$ W/kg.

2-4. Approach to the Practical Determination of the Magnetic Relations in the Wedge-Shaped Ferromagnetic Bodies

The theoretical proofs formulated in section 2-2 yield the following approach to the practical determination of the magnetic relations in the wedge-shaped ferromagnetic bodies.

A) The determination of V for a given Φ

This task will be solved in the following order of succession.

1. The relation $a = b_2/b_0$ is to be determined.

If a is smaller than 0.4, it is assumed that $a = 0.4$ and the distance h' from the minimum cross-section to the width $b_x = 2.5\ b_2$ is determined.

2. The magnitude of ϱ is determined with the formula (2-7) or, if a high degree of accuracy is required, with formula (2-6).

3. The flux density $B_0 = \Phi/b_0\gamma l$ is determined in the maximum cross-section.

4. By using the nomogram, point C pertaining to the abscissa $\overline{LC} = B_0$ should be found on the curve for the computed value ϱ. (See Fig. 2-5.)

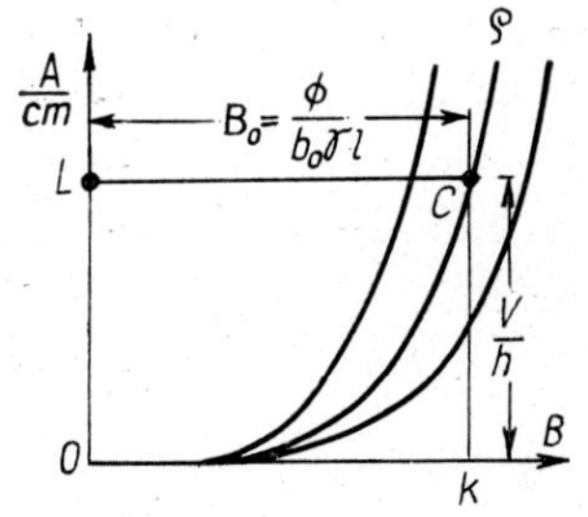

Fig. 2-5

5. The ordinate $\overline{CK}$ of point C is multiplied by the height of the body h if $a \geq 0.4$, or by h' if $a < 0.4$, whence the potential drop V is obtained.

B) The determination of Φ for a given V

This task will be solved in the following order of succession.

1. The value a and ϱ are computed as in *A)*.

2. The ordinate $\overline{CK}$ is determined by dividing V by h if $a \geq 0.4$, or by h' if $a \leq 0.4$.

3. By using the nomogram, point C pertaining to the computed ordinate $\overline{CK}$ should be found on the curve for the computed value ϱ (Fig. 2-5). The abscissa $\overline{LC}$ of this point yields the value of B_0 which, after being multiplied by $b_0\gamma l$ yields Φ.

C) The determination of the geometrical form of the ferromagnetic body if Φ and V are known

With a given width b_0 this task is solved in the following order of succession.

1. Determine in the nomogram point C (Fig. 2-5) whose abscissa $\overline{LC} = \Phi/b_0\gamma l$ and ordinate $\overline{CK} = V/h$.

2. Determine on which curve this point lies, i.e. find the corresponding value ϱ.

3. Compute with Eqs. (2-6) or (2-7) the factor a pertaining to the obtained value ϱ.

4. The value b_2 corresponding to the given value b_0 is determined with the help of a.

If b_0 is not given, we have an infinite number of solutions whose geometrical place is the straight line LC running parallel to the abscissa axis at a distance of V/h from it. In this case the task can be solved in the following order of succession.

1. Any arbitrary point C is selected on this straight line and the value B_0 is obtained as the length LC.

2. B_0 is used to compute the maximum width

$$b_0 = \frac{\Phi}{B_0 \gamma l}$$

3. Determine the curve on which the selected point C lies, i.e. find the pertaining value ϱ.

4. Compute the factor a with the value obtained for ϱ and thus the minimum width b_2.

The parameters b_0 and b_2 depend upon the selected position of point C.

A few examples will be quoted to show how simple the nomographic method renders the solution of the tasks that seem extremely intricate when tackled with the usual methods.

Table 2-1 contains parameters for the determination of the potential differences in two ferromagnetic bodies with dimensions identical with those of the bodies in Exs. 1 and 3 of Table 1-1.

On comparing columns 8 and 9 of Table 2-1 we find that the value V computed with Eq. (2-6), which can readily be obtained with the nomographic method, coincides fairly well with the value V obtained by using the exact method D requiring the performance of twenty-two operations.

TABLE 2-1

No. of Ex.	Geometric form of the body	Flux M	Flux density in max. cross-section	α	ϱ acc. to Eq. (2-6)	Mean field strength V/h A/cm	Potential diff. V A	
							Nomographic method	Method D
1	2	3	4	5	6	7	8	9
14	As in Ex. 1	19,250	16,700	0.666	1.46	780	2,340	2,310
15	As in Ex. 3	19,250	10,000	0.4	2.34	290	870	840

TABLE 2-2

No. of Ex.	Geometric form of the body	Given value of V A	V/h A/cm	α	ϱ acc. to Eq. (2-6)	Flux density B_0 nomographically G	Flux Φ M	
							Nomographic method	Method D
1	2	3	4	5	6	7	8	9
16	As in Ex. 1	681	227	0.666	1.46	14,700	17,000	17,000
17	As in Ex. 3	543	181	0.4	2.34	9,550	18,350	18,400

Table 2-2 contains two examples of determining the value of Φ for a given magnitude of V. The examples refer to the same ferromagnetic bodies as in Exs. 1 and 3 of Table 1-1. A comparison of columns 8 and 9 of Table 2-2 shows that the values Φ obtained with Eq. (2-6) coincide with the values obtained by using the usual method D requiring the performance of 57 operations.

Two examples will be quoted below showing the solution of the task of determining the geometrical form of a ferromagnetic body for given values of Φ and V. This task which cannot be solved with the usual method will here be disposed of within a few minutes. At the same time Ex. 19 yields an infinite number of solutions.

Example 18. A flux $\Phi = 19{,}250$ M passes through a wedge-shaped body having the following dimensions: height $h = 3$ cm, length $\gamma l = 1$ cm and maximum width $b_0 = 1.152$ cm. Determine the value of the ratio $b_2/b_0 = a$ for a potential drop $V = 2{,}340$ A in the body.

By using the nomogram we find the point of intersection of the ordinate $\overline{CK} = V/h = 780$ A/cm and of the abscissa $\overline{LC} = 19{,}250/1.152 = 16{,}700$ G to lie on the curve $\varrho = 1.46$. The formula (2-6) yields $a = 2/3$, i.e. $b_2 = 0.768$ cm.

Example 19. Let us assume that in Ex. 18 there is no restriction such as $b_0 = 1.152$ cm, i.e. that the magnitude of b_0 can be chosen arbitrarily. If so, an infinite number of points of the nomogram pertain to the ordinate $\overline{CK} = V/h = 780$ A/cm. All of them lie at the intersection of a curve ϱ and of a vertical straight line pertaining to a given abscissa; in other words, through all these points a relation is created between some definite value of ϱ and some value of B_0 determined thereby. Thus, for instance, the flux densities $B_0 = 21{,}400$, 18,800, 16,200, 14,300, 12,700, 11,600, 10,400 G belong to such values of ϱ as 1, 1.25, 1.52, 1.76, 2.03, 2.24, 2.53. It follows that $b_0 = 0.9$, 1.02, 1.19, 1.34, 1.52, 1.66, 1.85 cm. The corresponding values b_2 can be computed from b_0 and ϱ.

2-5. Theoretical Considerations Underlying the Nomographic Determination of Magnetic Relations in Ferromagnetic Bodies with Convex Parabolic Walls

Let us investigate the unit bodies with cross-sections changing according to the rule of quadratic parabola (Fig. 2-6).

The only restriction imposed is that the width of the body changes in a definite direction along its height. Our task consists in finding a *single* set of curves representing the reluctances of all such bodies in spite of the geometrical form of the body being determined by two parameters.

The method of determining the magnetic relations in wedge-shaped bodies, developed in section 2-2, was based on the assumption that the actual distribution of the magnetic flux density along the height of the unit body can be substituted by a parabolic distribution. Thus, if the flux density in the body (Fig. 2-6a) is also distributed according to some quadratic parabola, the same method could be applied to this body. In other words, by reducing the unit body (Fig. 2-6a) to a wedge-shaped unit body, the above-mentioned set of curves could be constructed for this "reduced unit body" and the above nomographic method could be applied to it.

For this purpose the following operations will be performed.

The unit body *ACDB* (Fig. 2-6a) is substituted by a wedge-shaped body *AGEFHB* limited by the tangents *EGA* and *FHB* constructed to the parabolas *AKC* and *BLD* in points *A* and *B*. Let us assume that the flux density B_x corresponding to flux $\Phi/b_0\gamma l$ is in this case distributed according to the parabolic curve *bed* (Fig. 2-6b). A comparison of these two bodies shows that they have identical maximum field strengths and that the width of the body *AGEFHB*

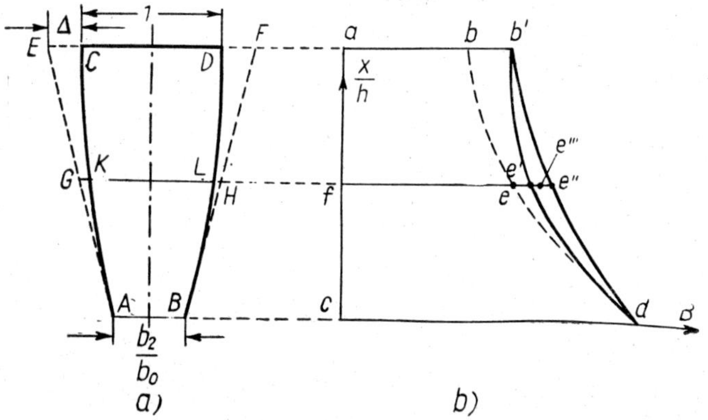

Fig. 2-6

in the neighbourhood of the smallest cross-section differs but slightly from the width of the body *AKCDLB*. Therefore in this range the difference of the flux density of the two bodies, and consequently also of their field strengths, is negligible.

Thus we are entitled to assume that the abscissae of the parabola *bed* in the range close to point *d* correspond to the distribution of flux density in the body *AKCDLB*. The same applies to any other parabola running through point *d* and having a derivative in this point identical to that of the parabola *bed*. By choosing from among all these possible parabolas parabola *b'e'd'*, whose abscissa in point $x/h = 1$ equals the actual flux density in the cross-section *CD*, it may be said that the abscissae of parabola *b'e'd* represent very accurately the actual distribution of the flux density both near the maximum and near the minimum cross-section.

In the general case, however, the actual flux density $\overline{fe''}$ in the middle cross-section KL will deviate slightly from the abscissa $\overline{fe'}$ of the parabola $b'e'd$, because the curve of the actual distribution of the flux density (not shown in Fig. 2-6b) is not an exact parabola. If it is assumed that $\overline{fe''} > \overline{fe}$, the value V/h corresponding to the flux density distribution of the curve $b'e'd$ will be somewhat smaller than the actual value.

Should the parabola $b'e'd$ be replaced by the parabola $b'e''d$, the abscissae of the latter in the range of point $x/h = 1/2$ would represent the actual distribution of flux density, yet the values obtained in the range of points $x/h = 0$ and $x/h = 1$ would be too high. Consequently, the value V/h computed according to the parabola $b'e''d$ would be somewhat higher than the actual one.

Thus two limit values have been found for V/h and we may say that its most exact value will be yielded by the parabola $b'e'''d$ (not shown in Fig. 2-6b) lying between the limit parabolas $b'e'd$ and $b'e''d$. For the assessment of the position of point e''' we may rely on the following considerations. Near point $x/h = 0$ the abscissae of the parabola $b'e'''d$ are somewhat greater than those of $b'e'd$ which corresponds to the actual distribution of the flux density. Near point $x/h = 1/2$ the abscissae of the parabola $b'e'''d$ will be somewhat smaller than those of the parabola $b'e''d$ corresponding to the actual distribution of flux density in the given range. The error committed in the computation of flux density in the range close to point $x/h = 0$, owing to the transition to the parabola $b'e'''d$, affects the resultant value of V/h more than the one committed near point $x/h = 1/2$, because the permeability of the ferromagnetic body for great flux densities is small. Hence point e''' must lie closer to point e' than to point e''. It will be assumed in the following that point e''' divides the segment $\overline{e'e''}$ in the ratio of 1/2, i.e. that $\overline{e'e'''} = 0.5\ \overline{e''e'''}$.

Thus it has been proved that the actual distribution of the flux density in the body $AKCDLB$ with parabolic walls can be replaced by the distribution of flux density according to the parabola $b'e'''d$. In other words, the actual "unit body" can be reduced to a "reduced unit body" in which the flux density is distributed along its height according to the said parabola. At a height $x/h = 1$ the "reduced unit body" has a flux density of $\overline{ab'} = \Phi/b_0\gamma l$, at $x/h = 0$, a flux density of $\overline{cd} = \Phi/b_2\gamma l$, at $x/h = 1/2$ a flux density of $\overline{fe'''} = \beta\,\overline{cd} = \beta\Phi/b_2\gamma l$, where the factor β can readily be determined on the basis of the above considerations.

In order to make the parabolas AC and BD (Fig. 2-6b) fulfil the conditions

$$\left(\frac{b_x}{b_0}\right)_{x/h=1} = 1; \quad \left(\frac{b_x}{b_0}\right)_{x/h=1/2} = \frac{b_1}{b_0}$$

and

$$\left(\frac{b_x}{b_0}\right)_{x/h=0} = \frac{b_2}{b_0}$$

the width b_x/b_0 of the body $AKCDLB$ should change according to the rule

$$\frac{b_x}{b_0} = 1 + \left(1 - \frac{x}{h}\right)\left(-3 + 4\frac{b_1}{b_0} - \frac{b_2}{b_0}\right) + \left(1 - \frac{x}{h}\right)^2 \left(2 - 4\frac{b_1}{b_0} + 2\frac{b_2}{b_0}\right)$$

In order to make the straight lines EA and FB satisfy the conditions

$$\left(\frac{b'_x}{b_0}\right)_{x/h=0} = \frac{b_2}{b_0}$$

and

$$\left(\frac{d\,\dfrac{b'_x}{b_0}}{dx}\right)_{x/h=0} = \left(\frac{d\,\dfrac{b_x}{b_0}}{dx}\right)_{x/h=0}$$

the width b_x'/b_0 of the body $AGEFHB$ should change according to the rule

$$\frac{b'_x}{b_0} = -1 + 4\frac{b_2}{b_0} - 2\frac{b_2}{b_0} - \left(1 - \frac{x}{h}\right)\left(-1 + 4\frac{b_1}{b_0} - 3\frac{b_2}{b_0}\right)$$

It follows that the width EF should be determined by the equation

$$\left(\frac{b'_x}{b_0}\right)_{x/h=1} = 1 + 2\Delta = -1 + 4\frac{b_1}{b_0} - 2\frac{b_2}{b_0}$$

and the width GH by the equation

$$\frac{b'_x}{b_0}_{x/h=1/2} = -\frac{1}{2} + 2\frac{b_1}{b_0} - \frac{b_2}{2b_0}$$

whence the induction

$$\overline{ab} = \frac{\Phi}{\gamma l(-b_0 + 4b_1 - 2b_2)}$$

and

$$\overline{fe} = \frac{2\Phi}{\gamma l(-b_0 + 4b_1 - b_2)}$$

proceeding from the values of flux density $\overline{ab}$, $\overline{fe}$ and $\overline{cd}$, the following formula is obtained for the changes in flux density B_x

$$B_x = \frac{\Phi}{\gamma l}\left[\frac{1}{-b_0 + 4b_1 - 2b_2} + \frac{h-x}{h}\left(-\frac{3}{-b_0 - 4b_1 - 2b_2} + \right.\right.$$
$$\left. + \frac{8}{-b_0 + 4b_1 - b_2} - \frac{1}{b_2}\right) +$$
$$\left. + \left(\frac{h-x}{h}\right)^2 \left(\frac{2}{-b_0 + 4b_1 - 2b_2} - \frac{8}{-b_0 + 4b_1 - b_2} + \frac{2}{b_2}\right)\right] \qquad (2\text{-}11)$$

In order to make the curve $b'e'd$ and its tangent (first derivative) coincide at point d in accordance with the curve bed and its tangent, the parabola $b'e'd$ should change according to the rule

$$B'_x = \frac{\Phi}{\gamma l}\left[\frac{1}{b_0} + \frac{h-x}{h}\left(-\frac{1}{-b_0 + 4b_1 - 2b_2} + \frac{8}{-b_0 + 4b_1 - b_2} - \right.\right.$$
$$\left. - \frac{1}{b_2} - \frac{2}{b_0}\right) + \left(\frac{h-x}{h}\right)^2 \left(\frac{1}{-b_0 + 4b_1 - 2b_2} - \frac{8}{-b_0 + 4b_1 - b_2} + \right.$$
$$\left.\left. + \frac{2}{b_2} + \frac{1}{b_0}\right)\right] \qquad (2\text{-}12)$$

By substituting $x/h = 1/2$ into Eq. (2-12), we have

$$\overline{fe'} = \frac{\Phi}{\gamma l}\left[\frac{1}{4b_0} + \frac{2}{-b_0 + 4b_1 - b_2} - \frac{1}{4(-b_0 + 4b_1 - 2b_2)}\right]$$

Since the flux density $\overline{fe''} = \Phi/b_1\gamma l$, the segment

$$\overline{fe'''} = \overline{fe''} - \frac{2}{3}(\overline{fe''} - \overline{fe'}) = \frac{2}{3}\overline{fe'} + \frac{1}{3}\overline{fe'} =$$

$$= \frac{\Phi}{3\gamma l}\left[\frac{1}{2b_0} + \frac{4}{-b_0 + 4b_1 - b_2} - \frac{1}{2(-b_0 + 4b_1 - 2b_2)} + \frac{1}{b_1}\right]$$

By introducing the factor $\beta = \overline{fe'''}/\overline{cd}$ we have

$$\beta = \frac{b_2}{3}\left[\frac{4}{-b_0+4b_1-b_2} - \frac{1}{2(-b_0+4b_1-2b_2)} + \frac{1}{2b_0} + \frac{1}{b_1}\right] \quad (2\text{-}13)$$

The same result would, obviously, have been obtained by proceeding from the condition $\overline{fe''} < \overline{fe'}$. Hence this formula (2-13) is of general validity.

In section 2-2 it has been shown that the parabolic distribution of flux density may be replaced by an arbitrary linear distribution characterized by the factor ϱ. By substituting into the general formula (2-5) valid for ϱ the values B_0, B_2 and B_1, i.e. in this case $B_0 = \overline{ab'}$, $B_2 = \overline{cd}$ and $B_1 = \overline{fe'''} = \beta\ \overline{cd} = \beta\ B_2$, and considering that $a = \overline{ab'}/\overline{cd}$, we have

$$\varrho = 1.8\frac{1-2a+4\beta}{-1+4.4a+2\beta} \quad (2\text{-}14)$$

For less exact calculations a simpler formula, similar to Eq. (2-7),

$$\varrho = \frac{2}{3}\frac{1}{a}(1+\beta) - \frac{1}{3} \quad (2\text{-}15)$$

may be obtained.

The formulae (2-14) and (2-15) thus deduced enable us to apply the set of curves constructed in section 2-3, and the nomographic method developed so far, to bodies having convex parabolic walls.

If $a < 0.4$, the treatment can be the same as for the wedge-shaped bodies, i.e. the part of the body in which the cross-section is more than 2.5 times the minimum cross-section can be neglected.

2-6. Approach to the Practical Determination of the Magnetic Relations in Ferromagnetic Bodies with Convex Parabolic Walls

On the strength of the theoretical proofs expounded in section 2-5, the magnetic relations in ferromagnetic bodies with convex parabolic walls can be determined in the same way as those in wedge-shaped bodies, with due regard to the following differences:

1. Beside a, the factor β should be determined also, with Eq. (2-13).

If $a < 0.4$, it is assumed to be 0.4 and the distance h' from the minimum cross-section to the cross-section $2.5\,b_2$ is determined.

The height of the body is denoted by h' and the width of the cross-section at $h'/2$ is taken as b_1.

2. The value ϱ is determined with Eq. (2-14) for exact calculations and with Eq. (2-15) in computations requiring less accuracy.

Let us check by practical examples the degree of accuracy of the results obtained with the above-mentioned method.

TABLE 2-3

No. of Ex.	Geometric form of the body	Flux Φ M	Induction B_0 in largest cross-section G	α	β according to Eq. (2-13)	ϱ according to Eq. (2-14)	Mean field strength V/h nomograph. meth. A/cm	Potential difference A nomograph. meth.	Potential difference meth. D
1	2	3	4	5	6	7	8	9	10
20	As in Ex. 2	17,000	14,750	0.666	0.713	1.35	140	420	420
21	As in Ex. 4	19,400	10,100	0.4	0.459	2.18	150	450	440

Table 2-3 contains the data for the determination of the potential differences in ferromagnetic bodies having dimensions similar to those of the bodies in Exs. 2 and 4. A comparison of columns

TABLE 2-4

No. of Ex.	Geometric form of the body	Given value V A	V/h A/cm	α	β according to Eq. (2-13)	ϱ according to Eq. (2-14)	Induction B_0 nomograph. method G	Magnetic flux Φ M according to nomograph. method	Magnetic flux Φ M according to method D
1	2	3	4	5	6	7	8	9	10
22	As in Ex. 2	1,460	487	0.666	0.713	1.35	16,900	19,500	19,250
23	As in Ex. 4	306	102	0.4	0.459	2.18	9,600	18,400	18,400

9 and 10 of Table 2-3 shows that the values V computed with Eqs. (2-14) and (2-13) differ but slightly from those obtained with the usual accurate method D.

The data in Table 2-4 refer to the determination of Φ if the values V are given for the same bodies. It will be seen that the value Φ in one case is identical with the value obtained with the usual exact method D requiring 57 operations, and in the other the difference is not more than 1.3 per cent.

2-7. *Theoretical Considerations Underlying the Nomographic Determination of the Magnetic Relations in Ferromagnetic Bodies with Concave Parabolic Walls*

If the walls AC and BD of a ferromagnetic body are not convex but concave parabolas (Fig. 2-7a), it may again be substituted by a reduced unit body in which the distribution of flux density shows

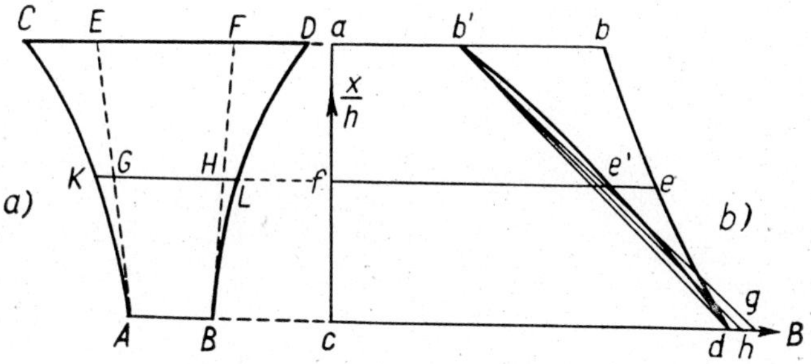

Fig. 2-7

a parabolic curve $b'e'''d$. Nevertheless the flux density of the body in Fig. 2-7a near the cross-section AB falls comparatively more slowly with the increase of the cross-section than in the body of Fig. 2-6a, whence, when substituting the parabola $b'e'''d$ for the curve *bed*, the abscissae of the former must be closer to the actual values of flux density, especially in the lower part of the body. Bearing this in mind, for the curve $b'e'''d$ we select curve $b'e'd$ obtained on the strength of the same considerations as for Fig. 2-6b. Therefore, with regard to Eq. (2-12),

$$\overline{fe'''} = \overline{fe'} = \frac{\Phi}{\gamma l}\left[\frac{1}{4b_0} + \frac{2}{-b_0 + 4b_1 - b_2} - \frac{1}{4(-b_0 + 4b_1 - 2b_2)}\right]$$

and

$$\beta = \frac{\overline{fe'''}}{\overline{cd}} = \frac{\overline{fe'}}{\overline{cd}} = b_2 \left[\frac{1}{4b_0} + \frac{2}{-b_0 + 4b_1 - b_2} - \frac{1}{4(-b_0 + 4b_1 - b_2)} \right] \tag{2-16}$$

The investigation of bodies with concave parabolic walls also raises the question of how to determine the limiting values of ϱ, since curve $b'e'd$ in Fig. 2-7b, unlike the curve $b'e'''d$ in Fig. 2-6b, may not have a concave form only but also a convex one. If the flux density in the body of Fig. 2-7a is distributed according to the straight line $b'd$, which is similar to the straight line bd in Fig. 2-2b, then the potential drop V/h created will be smaller than the actual one on the strength of the same considerations.

If the flux density is distributed along the straight line $b'g$, obtained in the same manner as the straight line bg in Fig. 2-2b, then the condition expressed in Eq. (2-2) will prevail, with the difference that the first member of this equation will be negative, the second positive. Consequently, the left side of Eq. (2-2a) assumes a higher value than the right side, i.e. V'''/h pertaining to the flux density distribution according to the straight line $b'g$ will be greater than the actual value $V/h = V'/h$.

It follows that the value ϱ will necessarily remain also in the case of the body of Fig. 2-7a between two limits, corresponding to the limits obtained for the wedge-shaped body. Similarly, the higher the value ϱ, the closer is the straight line $b'h$ to the straight line $b'd$. Thus the factor ε can, in this case too, be regarded as equalling $\varrho/3.6$, whence ϱ can invariably be determined with Eqs. (2-14) and (2-15).

2-8. *Approach to the Practical Determination of the Magnetic Relations in Ferromagnetic Bodies with Concave Parabolic Walls*

It follows from the theoretical proofs expounded in section 2-7 that the magnetic relations in steel bodies with concave parabolic walls can be determined in the same manner as those in bodies with convex parabolic walls, with the sole difference that factor β is determined with Eq. (2-16) and not with Eq. (2-13).

Let us check the exactness of our results by the aid of two examples referring to bodies with concave parabolic walls. The potential differences, as determined for these two bodies and the pertaining data, are given in Table 2-5. In Ex. 24 the width of the body changes according to the rule $b_x = 0.768 + 0.384\ (x/h)^2$, and in Ex. 25, according to $b_x = 0.768 + 1.152\ (x/h)^2$. The height of both bodies $h = 3$ cm, and their length $\gamma l = 1$ cm. Since the body in Ex. 25 has the factor $\varrho > 2.66$ with a pertaining value of $a = 0.4$, it can be replaced by a body having the following parameters: $a = 0.5$; $b_0 = 2b_2 = 1.536$ cm; $h' = 2.445$ cm and $b_1 = 0.96$ cm.

TABLE 2-5

No. of Ex.	Geometric form of the body	Magn. flux Φ M	Flux density in max. cross-section B_0 G	a	β according to Eq. (2-16)	ϱ according to Eq. (2-14)	Mean field strength V/h A/cm	Potential difference V, A according to	
								nomographic method	method D
1	2	3	4	5	6	7	8	9	10
24		19,250	16,700	0.666	0.913	1.59	1,360	4,080	4,100
25		19,400	12,650	0.5	0.875	2.13	1,040	2,540	2,500

A comparison of columns 9 and 10 of Table 2-5 shows that the values V obtained with Eqs. (2-14) and (2-16) are identical with those obtained by means of method D.

TABLE 2-6

No. of Ex.	Geometric form of the body	Given value V A	V/h A/cm	a	β according to Eq. (2-16)	ϱ according to Eq. (2-14)	Flux density acc. to nomographic method G	Flux Φ M according to	
								nomographic method	method D
1	2	3	4	5	6	7	8	9	10
26	As in Ex. 24	1,300	430	0.666	0.913	1.59	14,700	17,000	17,000
27	As in Ex. 25	1,650	675	0.5	0.875	2.13	11,900	18,300	18,400

In Table 2-6 we have the results of the determination of the values Φ for the given values V of these bodies. A comparison of columns 9 and 10 shows that the values obtained with Eqs. (2-14) and (2-16) and those obtained with the method D are almost identical.

The Determination of the Geometrical Form of a Body if the Values of Φ and V are Given

The nomographic method developed by the author greatly simplifies the determination of the geometric configuration of the body with given magnetic parameters, and yields at the same time an infinite number of solutions. Depending on the magnitude of the minimum cross-section selected, this body may be wedge-shaped, or may have convex or concave walls, respectively.

In the case of given values of V and Φ, the geometrical form of ferromagnetic bodies with parabolic walls is determined in the following order of succession:

1. According to the method explained in section 2-4, item C: 1, 2 and 3, the values ϱ and a belonging to a wedge-shaped body should be found. Let this value be a_k.

2. The required value b_2 is assumed and the pertaining value a computed. If $a = a_k$, the body is wedge-shaped and we have

$$b_1 = \frac{b_0 + b_2}{2}$$

If $a < a_k$, the body has convex parabolic walls, if $a > a_k$, it has concave ones. In the latter case the computation is continued as follows:

3. With Eq. (2-14) the factor β is computed for a and ϱ.

4. The value b_1 is computed on the basis of β, b_0 and b_2. Eq. (2-13) or (2-16) is used for the cases when a is smaller, or greater than a_k, respectively.

Example 28. Flux $\Phi = 19{,}250$ M passes through a body with parabolic walls, 3 cm high, 1 cm long and having a maximum width of 1.152 cm. Let us determine the geometrical form pertaining to a potential difference $V = 2{,}340$ A.

The use of the nomogram, as in Ex. 18, yields $\varrho = 1.46$. With Eq. (2-7) we obtain from ϱ the value $a = 2/3 = a_k$. However, in a wedge-shaped body only one magnitude a and one corresponding b_2

belong to this value ϱ according to Eqs. (2-6) and (2-7), yet if the most different values a and b_2 are assumed, the pertaining values can be determined with Eqs. (2-14) and (2-15).

If, for instance, $b_2 = 0.768$, then $a = 2/3$. Since for this case $a = a_k$, a wedge-shaped body is obtained for which $b_1 = 0.96$ cm.

On choosing, for instance, $b_2 = 0.8064$, we have $a = b_2/b_0 = 0.7 > a_k$. In this case the body has concave walls. With Eq. (2-15) from ϱ and a we have $\beta = 0.88$. On the basis of Eq. (2-16), b_0, b_2 and β yield $b_1 = 0.93$ cm. If, for instance, b_2 is chosen to be 0.691 cm, then $a = 0.6 < a_k$. In this case the body has convex walls. With Eq. (2-15) $\beta = 0.645$ is obtained.

Eq. (2-13) yields $b_1 = 1.045$ cm.

2-9. Theoretical Considerations Underlying the Nomographic Determination of the Magnetic Relations in Ferromagnetic Bodies of Particular Form

Even if the curves AC and BD are not exactly parabolic, they can, in most cases, be regarded as such and the corresponding values of β and ϱ determined from Eqs. (2-13) or (2-16) and (2-14) or (2-15), respectively.

Forms limited by circular arcs (i.e. parts of cylindrical areas) can often be found in electrical machines as, for instance, in the case of half-closed slots or if ventilation ducts are present in the rotor and the stator.

Bodies of such forms (Fig. 2-8) can also be substituted by a reduced unit body (to be referred to in the following as "secondary reduced unit bodies"). For this purpose the circular arcs AC and BD are replaced by parabolas of the second order AC' and BD' whose tangents in the region of greatest flux densities, i.e. between the points A and B, coincide with the tangents of the circular arcs.

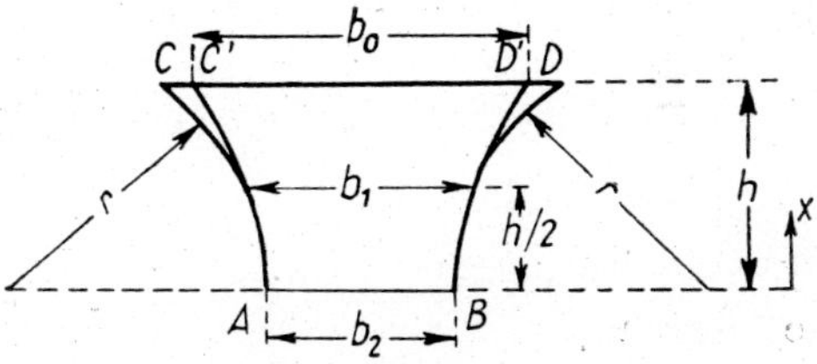

Fig. 2-8

Since there is an infinite number of such parabolas, the restriction should be imposed that parabolas and the circular arcs should intersect at $x = h/2$. Thus the magnetic conditions in the cross-section of width b_1, where a comparatively high flux density prevails, remain still unchanged.

The parabolas satisfying all these conditions can be expressed by the equation

$$b_x = b_2 + 4(b_1 - b_2)\left(\frac{x}{h}\right)^2$$

In this case

$$b_1 = b_2 + 2r - 2\sqrt{r^2 - \left(\frac{h}{2}\right)^2} \tag{2-17}$$

$$b_0 = 4b_1 - 3b_2 \tag{2-18}$$

Thus the body of Fig. 2-8 is reduced to the case of the body examined having parabolic walls $ABD'C'$. By substituting into Eq. (2-13) the value of b_0 from Eq. (2-18), a formula is obtained from which the factor β can be determined

$$\beta = 0.5 + \frac{b_2}{6b_0} + \frac{4\frac{b_2}{b_0}}{3 + 9\frac{b_2}{b_0}} \tag{2-19}$$

If $b_0 > 2.5\, b_2$, we proceed as for $\alpha < 0.4$, i.e. substitute for b_0 the value $b_x = 2.5\, b_2$ pertaining to the height h'. This is obviously obtained by the aid of the formula

$$\frac{h'}{h} = \sqrt{\frac{3b_2}{8(b_1 - b_2)}} \tag{2-20}$$

By substituting into Eq. (2-19) the value $2.5\, b_2$ instead of b_0, we obtain $\beta = 0.85$. For α we have in this case 0.4. Eq. (2-14) yields for the values α and β the magnitude $\varrho = 2.63$.

It has throughout been assumed so far that ferromagnetic bodies have symmetrical forms. This, however, is not a necessary condition and is in no way made necessary by the results obtained. The magnetic relations of the bodies in Fig. 2-9, for instance, can readily be determined with the method given in section 2-10.

There are cases when (Fig. 2-10) part $k\Phi_2$ of flux Φ_2 passing through the minimum cross-section of the wedge-shaped body enters or leaves the side wall and is evenly distributed along the height of the body. In this case the flux density in the minimum cross-section will be

$$B_2 = \frac{\Phi_2}{b_0 \gamma l a}$$

whilst in the cross-section of width b_1

$$B_1 = \frac{\Phi_2 \cdot 2(1-k)}{b_0 \gamma l (1+a)}$$

and in the maximum cross-section

$$B_0 = \frac{\Phi_2 (1-2k)}{b_0 \gamma l}$$

The actual distribution of flux density in the body investigated can, without considerable error, be replaced by a linear distribution characterized by some value ϱ which can be obtained by substituting the above values B_0, B_1 and B_2 into Eq. (2-5). This new body, crossed by a constant flux, will now be magnetically equivalent to the given body and have the following parameters: height h, maximum cross-section $b_0 \gamma l$ and

$$\varrho = 1.8 \frac{\dfrac{1}{a(1-2k)} + 8\dfrac{(1-k)}{(1+a)(1-2k)} - 2}{\dfrac{1}{-a(1-2k)} + 4\dfrac{(1-k)}{(1+a)(1-2k)} + 4.4} \tag{2-21}$$

The term "equivalent magnetic bodies" is often used in this and the subsequent chapters. In this connection, the following concepts should be made clear:

Equations (2-6), (2-14), (2-13), (2-16), (2-19) and (2-21) express the *analytic relations* between ferromagnetic bodies which have different geometric configurations and flux density distribution, yet can be reduced to one another to be equivalent in respect of the relation between the values B_0 and V/h, i.e. to have identical ϱ values.

At the same time the nomogram expresses the *graphical relation* between such bodies as have *different ϱ factors*, yet may be equivalent as far as the values B_0 and V/h are concerned. Take as an example a horizontal straight line passing an through arbitrary point C (Fig. 2-5). This line represents the geometrical place of the solutions pertaining to a definite value V/h. It shows how the changes in B_0 (i.e. $b_0 \gamma l$) are compensated by the changes in factor ϱ characterizing the form of the body and vice versa, so as to maintain all such variants concerning the values of V/h equivalent.

These two types of equivalence will be widely used in the following chapters: the analytical reduction of the form of the body or of the flux distribution to another equivalent configuration or another equivalent flux distribution, as well as the graphical determination of the geometrical places of the possible equivalent solutions.

2-10. Approach to the Practical Determination of Magnetic Relations in Ferromagnetic Bodies of Particular Form

A) Bodies bounded by cylindrical walls

If the configuration of the body corresponds to the form shown in Fig. 2-8, V is determined for a given Φ, and Φ for a given V, in the same manner as for bodies with concave parabolic walls. Here b_1 is computed with Eq. (2-17), b_0 with Eq. (2-18) and β with Eq. (2-19). If β is found to be smaller than 0.85, the computation should be undertaken for body having a maximum width 2.5 b_2, $\varrho = 2.63$, height h' calculated with Eq. (2-20).

Let us check the computation method developed against practical examples. Table 2-7 shows the results

TABLE 2-7

No. of Ex.	Geometric form of body	Given magnetic parameter	b_1 according to Eq. (2-17) cm	b_0 according to Eq. (2-18) cm	α	β according to Eq. (2-19) cm	ϱ according to Eq. (2-14) cm	Magnetic parameter required according to the nomographic method	Magnetic parameter required according to the method D
29		$\Phi = 50{,}400$ M	2.27	3.08	0.65	0.912	1.635	$\frac{V}{h} = 1{,}360$ A/cm	$\frac{V}{h} = 1{,}360$ A/cm
30		$\frac{V}{h} = 395$ A/cm	2.27	3.08	0.65	0.912	1.635	$B_0 = 14{,}150$ G	$B_0 = 14{,}200$ G

of magnetic calculations for a body with walls of a quadrantal form if $b_2 = 2$ cm, $\gamma l = 1$ cm and $r = h = 1$ cm.

Ex. 29 shows that V/h, computed for a given flux Φ with Eqs. (2-19) and (2-14), is exactly the same as the values obtained with method D requiring 22 operations. The determination of B_0 (in Ex. 30) for a given mean field strength with Eqs. (2-19) and (2-14), also yields a result identical with the one obtained with method D requiring 57 operations.

Example 31. A ferromagnetic body has the form of the one shown in Ex. 29 and the following parameters: $b_2 = 0.8$ cm, $\gamma l = 10$ cm, $h = 0.5$ cm, $r = 0.5$ cm. Determine the potential drop V created

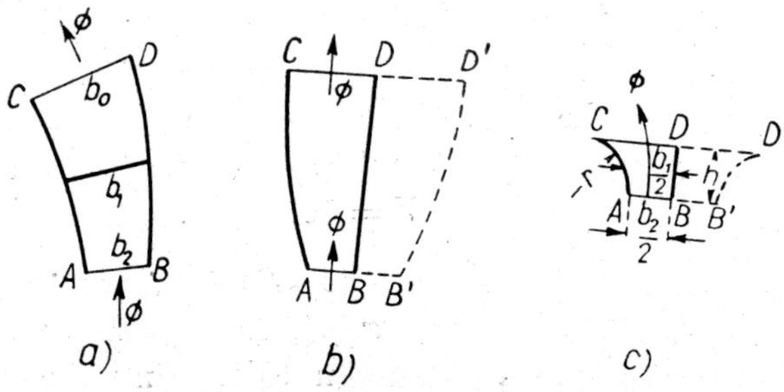

Fig. 2-9

by flux $\Phi = 2 \cdot 10^5$ M. Let the actual body be replaced by an equivalent magnetic body. By using Eqs. (2-17), (2-18), (2-19) and (2-14) we have: $b_1 = 0.935$ cm, $b_0 = 1.34$ cm, $\beta = 0.899$, $a = 0.597$, $\varrho = 1.79$.

Determine ordinate $\overline{CK} = 1160$ A/cm pertaining to abscissa $\overline{LC} = 14{,}900$ G on the curve corresponding to $\varrho = 1.79$. By multiplying the ordinate by $h = 0.5$ cm we obtain $V = 580$ A.

B) Bodies bounded by concave and convex walls

In computing the body of Fig. 2-9a, bounded by a concave wall and a convex one, we can proceed from the values b_2, b_1 and b_0 as if the body had symmetrical parabolic walls.

C) Bodies bounded by curved and straight walls

The bodies of Fig. 2-9b and Fig. 2-9c are bounded by a curvilinear and a rectilinear wall. To such a body, one of a similar shape should be added to obtain a symmetrical body, with the symmetry axis along the rectilinear side.

The computation will then follow the same pattern as for bodies of symmetrical walls (see sections 2-6 and 2-8) with the flux taken as 2Φ.

Example 32. The ferromagnetic body 5-6-7-8 or 9-10-8-7 of Fig. 1-7 is part of the stator yoke of a d.c. machine. Its parameters are: $r = 40$ cm, $h = 18$ cm, $\gamma l = 29.5$ cm and $b_2/2 = 6$ cm. Determine the potential drop V created by flux $\Phi = 4.3 \cdot 10^6$ M.

Substitute this body by a reduced body equivalent to it magnetically. Since the examined part of the yoke is the half of the body of Fig. 2-9c, the respective formulae yield the following values:

$$\frac{b_1}{2} = 7 \text{ cm}\,; \quad \frac{b_0}{2} = 10 \text{ cm}\,; \quad \beta = 0.9\,; \quad \alpha = 0.6\,; \quad \varrho = 1.78$$

Determine ordinate $\overline{CK} = 900$ A/cm pertaining to abscissa $\overline{LC} = 14{,}500$ G on the curve corresponding to $\varrho = 1.78$. After multiplying by $h = 18$ cm we obtain $V = 16{,}200$ A.

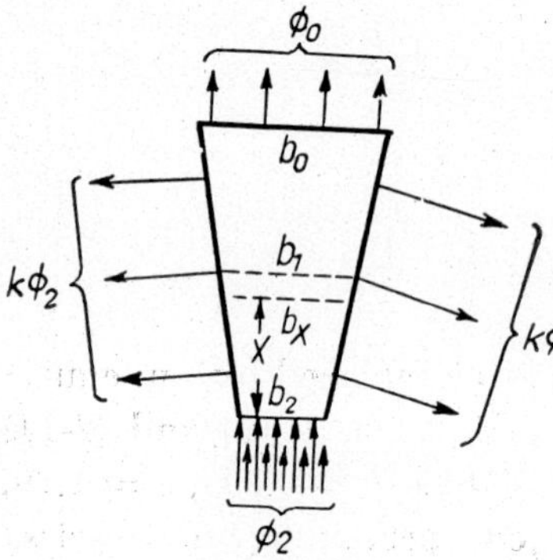

Fig. 2-10

D) Bodies in which part of the flux passes through the side walls

In calculating the body (Fig. 2-10) we proceed from the given values α and k and compute the value of ϱ with Eq.(2-21).

The remaining steps in the computation are the same as for the usual wedge-shaped body (cf. section 2-4).

Example 33. Determine the flux Φ at a given V $= 3{,}840$ A for the wedge-shaped body of Fig. 2-10 having the following parameters: $b_2 = 1$ cm, $b_0 = 2$ cm, $h = 3$ cm, $\gamma l = 1$ cm and $k = 0.083$.

Compute factors α and $\alpha : \varrho = 0.5$ and $\varrho = 2.28$.

Abscissa $\overline{LC} = B_0 = 12{,}300$ G is determined nomographically for ordinate $\overline{CK} = V/h = 1{,}280$ A/cm with the curve $\varrho = 2.28$. This yields $\Phi_0 = 24{,}000$ M.

CHAPTER THREE

THE NOMOGRAPHIC DETERMINATION OF THE RESULTANT RELUCTANCE IN SERIES-CONNECTED FERROMAGNETIC BODIES

3-1. The Statement of the Problem and an Approach to its Solution

It has been pointed out in chapter 2 that the reluctance of ferromagnetic bodies of a certain shape, i.e. the ratio of the potential difference V to the flux Φ can be expressed with factor ϱ and the maximum cross-section $b_0 \gamma l$. Consequently, the problem of determining the resultant reluctance of series-connected ferromagnetic bodies can be worded as follows. The series-connected bodies characterized by heights $h_{\mathrm{I}}, h_{\mathrm{II}}, \ldots, h_k$, by maximum cross-sections $b_{0\mathrm{I}} \gamma l$, $b_{0\mathrm{II}} \gamma l, \ldots, b_{0k} \gamma l$ and by the factors $\varrho_{\mathrm{I}}, \varrho_{\mathrm{II}}, \ldots, \varrho_k$, should be replaced by a single body of a height $h_{\mathrm{rs}} = \Sigma h$. This body should have a maximum cross-section $b_{0\mathrm{res}} \gamma l$ and a factor ϱ_{res} so that any flux Φ would create a potential difference ΣV in it, as great as in all the series-connected bodies together.

A thorough analysis of the nomogram in Supplement I will reveal a connection between the individual curves characteristic of the different factors ϱ. This relation is reflected in the fact that the ratio of the abscissae of any two curves is constant, with fair accuracy, for all values of the ordinates (the degree of accuracy will be dealt with in detail later). In other words, the relation of the abscissa B_0 of point C on curve ϱ (Fig. 3-1) to the abscissa B'_0 of point C' on curve ϱ' (having both equal ordinates V/h) is the same as the relation of abscissa kB'_0 of point C_k on curve ϱ to the abcissa kB'_0 of point C'_k on curve ϱ' (points C_k and C'_k belonging to another ordinate V'/h).

This rule permits the principle of the equivalence of bodies having different configurations to be considerably extended.

As stated in section 2-9, a ferromagnetic body characterized by the factor ϱ and the maximum width b_0 can be replaced by another body with another factor ϱ' and another maximum width b'_0 yielding, for a definite value of flux Φ, the same mean field strength V/h in both bodies. A body with a flux density distribution from B_0

to ϱB_0 (Fig. 3-2), in which the magnetic relations are characterized by point C (Fig. 3-1), can be substituted, for instance, by a body with a flux density distribution from B_0' to $\varrho' B_0'$, in which the magnetic relations correspond to point C'. The values b_0' and ϱ' permit an infinite number of such combinations which correspond to the points of intersection of the straight line running through point C (parallel to the abscissa axis) and of the curves of different parameters ϱ.

By increasing the flux Φ to $k\Phi$ we obtain the flux density distribution in one body from kB_0 to ϱkB_0 and in another from kB_0' to

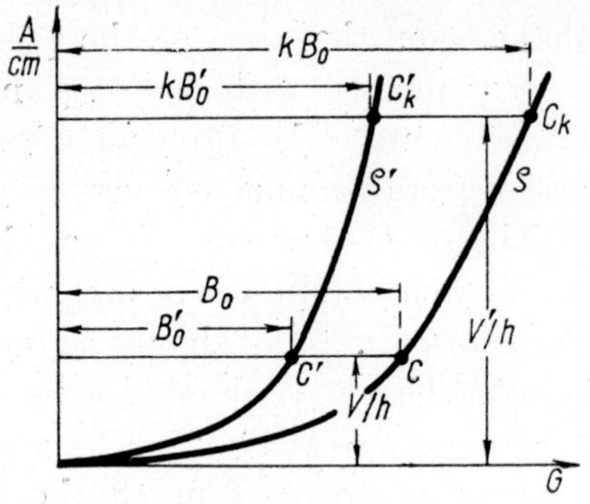

Fig. 3-1

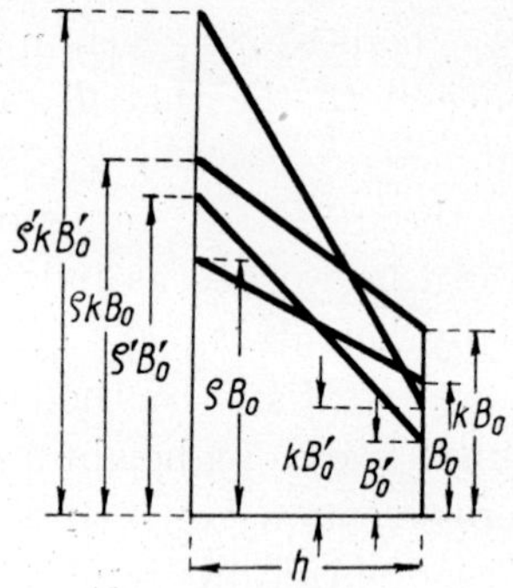

Fig. 3-2

$\varrho k B_0'$. Thus the magnetic relations in the first body will correspond to point C_k (Fig. 3-1), while in the second to C_k'.

A new flux density distribution corresponds to a new induction distribution in both bodies, which may be entirely different from the one applying to the former. Yet, as is obvious from the above relation of the different curves of the nomogram, the mean field strength in both bodies will again have the same magnitude V'/h.

Thus any body characterized by b_0 and ϱ may be substituted by another, magnetically equivalent body characterized by other values b_0' and ϱ'. These bodies will be equivalent (practically have indentical field strength in case of the same flux) not only for a certain flux but for all possible values of flux Φ.

To begin with, let us examine two series-connected bodies subject to the same flux Φ. Let the first body be characterized by $b_{0\text{I}}$, ϱ_{I} and h_{I}, the other by $b_{0\text{II}}$, ϱ_{II} and h_{II}. In the first body there is an equivalent flux density distribution according to the trapezoid *abcd* (Fig. 3-3) extending from $B_{0\mathrm{I}} = \Phi/b_{0\mathrm{I}}\gamma l$ to $\varrho_\mathrm{I} B_{0\mathrm{I}}$, and in the other body according to the trapezoid *defg* from $B_{0\mathrm{II}} = \Phi/b_{0\mathrm{II}}\gamma l$ to $\varrho_\mathrm{II} B_{0\mathrm{II}}$. In the first body point C_I (Fig. 3-4) on curve ϱ with abscissa $B_{0\mathrm{I}}$ and ordinate $V_\mathrm{I}/h_\mathrm{I}$ corresponds to the said magnetic demand and in the other body the corresponding point is C_II on curve ϱ_II with abscissa $B_{0\mathrm{II}}$ and ordinate $V_\mathrm{II}/h_\mathrm{II}$.

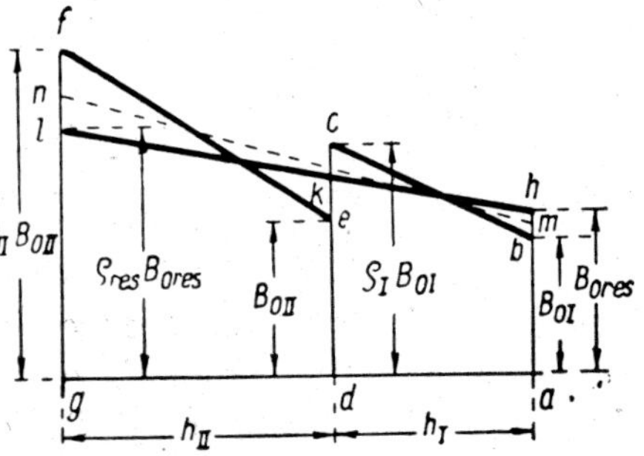

Fig. 3-3

Hence, the flux density distribution in the first body can be substituted by some other equivalent distribution, for instance, according to the trapezoid *ahkd* (Fig. 3-3), while in the other body it can be expressed as an equivalent distribution in accordance with the trapezoid *dklg*.

Of the infinite amount of straight lines *hk* and *kl*, in each body there is one coinciding in direction and forming thus the straight line *hkl*. The induction grows linearly along both bodies from any value $B_{0\mathrm{res}}$ (section *ah*) to the value $\varrho_\mathrm{res} B_{0\mathrm{res}}$ (section *gl*). Since the induction distribution according to the trapezoid *ahkd* creates the potential difference V_I and the induction distribution along the trapezoid *dkgl* produces the potential difference V_II, the flux density growing from $B_{0\mathrm{res}}$ to $\varrho_\mathrm{res}\ B_{0\mathrm{res}}$ creates the potential difference $V_\mathrm{I} + V_\mathrm{II}$. Consequently, the two bodies with the parameters h_I, $b_{0\mathrm{I}}$, ϱ_I, and h_II, $b_{0\mathrm{II}}$, $\varrho_{0\mathrm{II}}$ respectively, have been replaced by a body of height $h_\mathrm{I} + h_\mathrm{II}$, a maximum width $b_{0\mathrm{res}} = \Phi/B_{0\mathrm{res}}\,\gamma l$, having a factor ϱ_res. The new body is equivalent to the ensemble of the two actual bodies because, with the same flux, the resulting quantity $V_\mathrm{I} + V_\mathrm{II}$ is acting through both bodies.

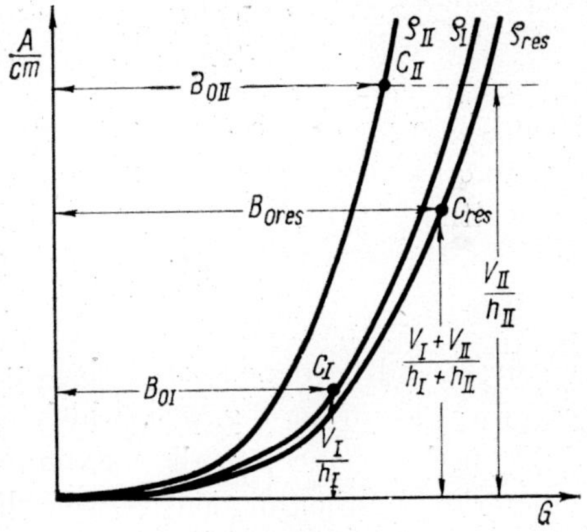

Fig. 3-4

Thus we have found a theoretical approach to the solution of replacing two series-connected reluctances by a single resultant reluctance.

3-2. *Simplified Method of Replacing Series-Connected Ferromagnetic Bodies by a Single Resultant*

Having found the theoretical solution of substituting two series-connected reluctances by a single resultant, we may turn to the problem of determining the values B_{0res} and ϱ_{res}.

At first glance it may seem that ϱ_{res} must be computed in a complicated manner from the trapezoid *ahlg*. This, however, is not necessary because, relying on the above-demonstrated possibility of the equivalence of different trapezoids, the trapezoid *ahlg* may be substituted by another, for instance, by *amng* (Fig. 3-3) having other values B_{0res} and ϱ_{res}. The solution of this task yields an infinite amount of trapezoids because there are innumerable points C_{res} (Fig. 3-4). These points C_{res} lie parallel to the abscissa axis and have the ordinate

$$\frac{V_{I}+V_{II}}{h_{I}+h_{II}}=\frac{h_{I}\left(\frac{V_{I}}{h_{I}}\right)+h_{II}\left(\frac{V_{II}}{h_{II}}\right)}{h_{I}+h_{II}} \tag{3-1}$$

From these points we may select any one magnitude ϱ_{res}, satisfying the practical requirements, and obtain a corresponding value B_{0res}, i.e. width

$$b_{0res}=\frac{\Phi}{B_{0res}\gamma l} \tag{3-2}$$

It should be remembered that in the conclusion deduced above we proceeded from Fig. 3-1, which is not entirely accurate. Let us check in this connection the maximum error that may be committed in determining the flux density with the help of this method, if several curves of the nomogram are substituted by the curve $\varrho = 1.44$, whose value ϱ lies somewhere in the middle of the region used in practice.

Should the above rule be entirely accurate, the following equation would be valid:

$$\frac{B_{0\varrho,V/h}}{B_{0\varrho',V/h}}=\frac{B_{0\varrho,V'/h}}{B_{0\varrho',V'/h}} \tag{3-3}$$

where $B_{0\varrho, V/h}$ = abscissa of the point having an ordinate V/h on curve ϱ,

$B_{0\varrho', V/h}$ = abscissa of the point having an ordinate V/h on curve ϱ',

$B_{0\varrho', V'/h}$ = abscissa of the point having an ordinate V'/h on curve ϱ.

$B_{0\varrho', V'/h}$ = abscissa of the point having an ordinate V'/h on curve ϱ'.

If ϱ' is chosen to be 1.44 and V'/h to be 1,300 A/cm, then the formula assumes the form

$$\frac{B_{0\varrho, V/h}}{B_{0\,1.44, V/h}} = \frac{B_{0\varrho, 1,300}}{B_{0\,1.44, 1,300}} \tag{3-4}$$

The error ΔB_0 committed in computing the flux density for the different values ϱ and V/h can be determined with the following equation

$$\frac{B_{0\varrho, V/h} + \Delta B_{0\varrho, V/h}}{B_{0\,1.44, V/h}} = \frac{B_{0\varrho, 1,300}}{B_{0\,1.44, 1,300}}. \tag{3-5}$$

This error will be the less, the more ϱ approximates 1.44 and the closer the ordinate of V/h lies to the ordinate 1,300 A/cm. Thus, in order to determine the greatest possible error, the extreme curves $\varrho = 1$ and $\varrho = 2.66$, and the extreme field strengths $V/h = 3,000$ A/cm and $V/h = 300$ A/cm, should be selected. The computation of the possible greatest errors $\Delta B_{0\varrho, V/h}$ yields the results given in Table 3-1.

TABLE 3-1

V/h A/cm	B_0 for different ϱ and V/h G			Error for different values of ϱ and V/h G		
	$\varrho=2.66$	$\varrho=1.44$	$\varrho=1$	$\varrho=2.66$	$\varrho=1.44$	$\varrho=1$
3,000	12,650	20,350	25,000	— 400	0	+ 450
1,300	10,750	17,850	22,420	0	0	0
300	8,950	15,300	19,750	+ 250	0	— 450

A comparison of the errors with the corresponding values of flux density $B_{0\varrho, V/h}$ permits the conclusion that the greatest possible errors do not exceed 3 per cent if all the curves ϱ are replaced by the curve $\varrho = 1.44$.

Nevertheless a small error in computing flux density produces a much greater one in determining the value V/h. It should, however, be remembered that the resultant potential difference $\Sigma V = V_{\mathrm{I}} + V_{\mathrm{II}}, \ldots + V_k$ pertaining to a given flux Φ may readily be determined even without replacing the series-connected bodies by a resultant body because, according to the method described in chapter 2, the corresponding value V may readily be calculated for each body. The method here explained can best be applied to the opposite task, a more difficult one, when the flux Φ is to be determined on the basis of a given potential difference ΣV. By using in such cases the middle curve $\varrho = 1.44$, the error incurred in computing the flux Φ will be negligibly small.

In the case of several series-connected ferromagnetic bodies, the maximum cross-section $b_{0\mathrm{res}}\gamma l$ of the resultant body may be obtained by determining on the curve for $\varrho = 1.44$ a point whose ordinate equals

$$\frac{\Sigma V}{\Sigma h} = \frac{V_{\mathrm{I}} + V_{\mathrm{II}} + \ldots + V_k}{h_{\mathrm{I}} + h_{\mathrm{II}} + \ldots + h_k} = \frac{h_{\mathrm{I}}\left(\frac{V_{\mathrm{I}}}{h_{\mathrm{I}}}\right) + h_{\mathrm{II}}\left(\frac{V_{\mathrm{II}}}{h_{\mathrm{II}}}\right) + \ldots + h_k\left(\frac{V_k}{h_k}\right)}{h_{\mathrm{I}} + h_{\mathrm{II}} + \ldots + h_k} \tag{3-6}$$

3-3. Approach to the Practical Application of the Simplified Method of Replacing Series-Connected Ferromagnetic Bodies by a Resultant

A) Replacing two series-connected bodies

According to the theory expounded in section 3-2, the resultant reluctance of two series-connected ferromagnetic bodies can be determined in the following order of succession:

1. Factors ϱ_{I} and ϱ_{II} are computed.
2. An arbitary flux Φ is chosen.
3. The ordinate $V_{\mathrm{I}}/h_{\mathrm{I}}$ of point C_{I} lying on curve ϱ_{I} and having an abscissa $B_{0\mathrm{I}} = \Phi/b_{0\mathrm{I}}\gamma l$ is determined (Fig. 3-4).
4. The ordinate $V_{\mathrm{II}}/h_{\mathrm{II}}$ of point C_{II} lying on curve ϱ_{II} and having an abscissa $B_{0\mathrm{II}} = \Phi/b_{0\mathrm{II}}\gamma l$ is determined.

5. The value

$$\frac{V_{\mathrm{I}} + V_{\mathrm{II}}}{h_{\mathrm{I}} + h_{\mathrm{II}}}$$

is determined with the help of Eq. (3-1).

6. The next step is to determine the abscissa B_{ores} of the resultant point C_{res} lying on curve $\varrho = 1.44$ and having an ordinate

$$\frac{V_{\mathrm{I}} + V_{\mathrm{II}}}{h_{\mathrm{I}} + h_{\mathrm{II}}}$$

7. The value b_{ores} is computed with the formula (3-2).

Thus we obtain an equivalent body characterized by $\varrho = 1.44$, $b_0 = b_{\mathrm{ores}}$ and $h = h_{\mathrm{I}} + h_{\mathrm{II}}$. The magnetic relations of this body for any flux or any potential difference can be determined by using the nomographic method expounded in chapter 2.

Table 3-2 shows the results obtained by replacing two ferromagnetic bodies by a resultant one for different geometric forms (Exs. 34 to 36).

Table 3-3 contains the magnetic relations in the resultant bodies obtained from the examples of Table 3-2.

B) Replacing several series-connected bodies

1. The values of ϱ_n are computed for all bodies.

2. An arbitrary flux Φ is selected.

TABLE 3-2

No. of Ex.	Geometric parameters						Assumed flux			Ordinate			Abscissa	
	Body I			Body II										
	h_{I} cm	$b_{0\mathrm{I}}\gamma l$ cm²	ϱ_{I}	h_{II} cm	$h_{0\mathrm{II}}\gamma l$ cm²	ϱ_{II}	Φ M	$B_{0\mathrm{I}}$ G	$B_{0\mathrm{II}}$ G	$\frac{V_{\mathrm{I}}}{h_{\mathrm{I}}}$ A/cm	$\frac{V_{\mathrm{II}}}{h_{\mathrm{II}}}$ A/cm	$\frac{V_{\mathrm{I}}+V_{\mathrm{II}}}{h_{\mathrm{I}}+h_{\mathrm{II}}}$ A/cm	B_{ores} on curve $\varrho = 1.44$ G	$b_{\mathrm{ores}}\gamma l$ cm²
1	2	3	4	5	6	7	8	9	10	11	12	13	14	15
34	4	2.54	1	2	4.95	2.66	57,500	22,600	11,600	1,400	2,000	1,600	18,400	3.12
35	2	2.72	1	5	3	1	60,900	22,400	20,300	1,300	400	660	16,550	3.68
36	3	2.7	2.08	4	2.29	1.63	37,800	14,000	16,500	1,750	1,420	1,560	18,300	2.06

TABLE 3-3

No. of Ex.	Geometric parameters of series-connected bodies	Resultant equivalent values computed according to Table 3-2			Given $V_I + V_{II}$ A	Abscissa B_{0res} pertaining to ordinate $\frac{V_I + V_{II}}{h_I + h_{II}}$ on curve $\varrho_{res} = 1.44$	Flux $\Phi = B_{0res} \cdot b_{0res}\gamma l$ M
		ϱ_{res}	$h_I + h_{II}$ cm	$b_{0res}\gamma l$ cm²			
1	2	3	4	5	6	7	8
37	Acc. to Ex. 34	1.44	6	3.12	16,200	20,000	62,400
38	Acc. to Ex. 34	1.44	6	3.12	2,820	16,000	49,920
39	Acc. to Ex. 35	1.44	7	3.68	13,000	18,800	69,200
40	Acc. to Ex. 35	1.44	7	3.68	1,360	14,700	54,100
41	Acc. to Ex. 36	1.44	7	2.06	19,500	20,100	41,400
42	Acc. to Ex. 36	1.44	7	2.06	3,300	16,000	33,000

3. For all bodies the ordinates V_n/h_n of such points are determined as lie on curve ϱ_n and have abscissae $B_{0n} = \Phi/b_{0n}\gamma l$.

4. $\Sigma V/\Sigma h$ is calculated with Eq. (3-6).

5. We determine the abscissa B_{0res} of a point lying on curve $\varrho = 1.44$ and having an ordinate $\Sigma V/\Sigma h$.

6. b_{0res} is computed with Eq. (3-2).

The subsequent steps are the same as in the case of a single body with parameters $\varrho = 1.44$, $b_0 = b_{0res}$ and $h = \Sigma h$.

Example 43. The tooth of the rotor in an asynchronous machine (Fig. 1-6) consists of three parts, I, II and III (part IV may be neglected since it is negligibly short and wide). Part II is characterized by the following parameters: $b_0 = 0.8$ cm, $\varrho_{II} = 1$, $h_{II} = 1$ cm and $\gamma l = 10$ cm. The corresponding values of parts I and III are: $b_{2II} = b_{2III} = 0.8$ cm, $h_I = h_{III} = 0.5$ cm and $\gamma l = 10$ cm.

In Ex. 31 the potential drop was obtained as $V_I = V_{III} = 580$ A for parts I and III, with the above characteristics and for the flux $\Phi = 200{,}000$ M.

As to part II, we likewise obtain in the case of a flux density of

$$\frac{200{,}000}{0.8 \cdot 10} = 25{,}000 \text{ G},$$

the ordinate $V_{II}/h_{II} = 3{,}000$ A/cm on curve $\varrho = 1$. The mean field strength is then

$$\frac{V_I + V_{II} + V_{III}}{h_I + h_{II} + h_{III}} = \frac{580 + 3{,}000 + 580}{0.5 + 1 + 0.5} = 2{,}080 \text{ A/cm}$$

which corresponds to the abscissa $B_{0res} = 19{,}100$ G on the curve $\varrho = 1.44$. Hence we have $b_{0res} = 1.045$ cm.

Thus the tooth in Fig. 1-6 can be substituted by a body characterized by $h = 2$, $b_{0res} = 1.045$, $\gamma l = 10$ and $\varrho = 1.44$.

Let us check the accuracy of the simplified method with examples taken from practice. In Table 3-3 we find the magnetic fluxes corresponding to different values $V_I + V_{II}$ affecting the resultant bodies, obtained by replacing the two series-connected bodies of Exs. 34 to 36. Should the simplified method be an accurate one, the crossing of the same fluxes through the same series-connected bodies separately (without their being replaced by a resultant one) would create the same sum of the potential differences, i.e. $V_I + V_{II}$.

If there is any inaccuracy involved in the simplified method, the above potential difference $V_I + V_{II}$ would be created by somewhat different magnetic fluxes.

Table 3-4 shows the fluxes creating the values $V_I + V_{II}$ corresponding to Table 3-3, when these fluxes pass through each of the two series-connected bodies of Table 3-2 (Exs. 44 to 49) separately.

On comparing column 8 of Table 3-3 with the same column of Table 3-4 the accuracy of the simplified method can be established. The results of these examples, covering a vast range of the values ϱ, h, and $b_0\gamma l$, are found in fifty per cent of the cases to be identical (Exs. 37 and 44, 38 and 45, 40 and 47). In the other cases the deviation does not exceed 1.8 per cent.

The examples clearly show that the flux densities and the flux for a given magnetic potential difference itself can simply and readily be computed in magnetic circuits composed of several series-connected ferromagnetic bodies.

Table 3-5 contains examples of the application of the above method for determining the magnetic relations in ferromagnetic bodies of complicated form. In Ex. 51 the air gap is not taken into account.

TABLE 3-4

No. of Ex.	Geometric parameters						Flux Φ M	B_{0I} G	B_{0II} G	Ordinate V_I/h_I A/cm	Ordinate V_{II}/h_{II} A/cm	Resultant potential difference $V_I + V_{II}$ A
	Body I			Body II								
	h_I cm	$b_{0I}\gamma l$ cm²	ϱ_I	h_{II} cm	$b_{0II}\gamma l$ cm²	ϱ_{II}						
1	2	3	4	5	6	7	8	9	10	11	12	13
44	4	2.54	1	2	4.95	2.66	62,300	24,450	12,550	2,600	2,900	16,200
45	4	2.54	1	2	4.95	2.66	49,900	19,650	10,100	280	850	2,820
46	2	2.72	1	5	3	1.0	68,000	25,000	22,650	3,000	1,400	13,000
47	2	2.72	1	5	3	1.0	54,000	19,850	18,000	315	145	1,360
48	3	2.7	2.08	4	2.29	1.63	41,800	15,500	18,250	2,950	2,640	19,400
49	3	2.7	2.08	4	2.29	1.63	32,400	12,000	14,150	590	380	3,300

TABLE 3-5

No. of Ex.	Configuration	Geometric parameters								Factors ϱ		Flux M	Ordinate V/h for A/cm		$\frac{V_I + V_{II}}{h_I + h_{II}}$ A/cm	*	$(b_0\gamma l)$ res cm²
		Body I				Body II											
		h_I cm	b_{0I} cm	b_{2I} cm	$(\gamma l)_I$ cm	h_{II} cm	b_{0II} cm	b_{2II} cm	$(\gamma l)_{II}$ cm	ϱ_I	ϱ_{II}		Body I	Body II			
1	2	3	4	5	6	7	8	9	10	11	12	13	14	15	16	17	18
50		1.2	1.5	1	1	1.8	1.8	0.8	1	1.465	2.12	26,000	1,120	2,250	1,800	18,700	1.39
51		5.79	2.005	1.365	29	0.3	1.75	1.75	29.6	1.43	1	1,000,000	900	250	870	17,050	58.7

* Abscissa B_{0res} G corresponding to ordinate $\frac{V_I + V_{II}}{h_I + h_{II}}$ on curve $\varrho = 1.44$.

3-4. The Exact Method of Replacing Several Series-Connected Ferromagnetic Bodies by One Resultant

It follows from section 3-3 that accuracy of the simplified method is sufficient for the computation of magnetic circuits in electrical machines.

Nevertheless, it will not be superfluous to develop a method with which even the above-mentioned small errors can be avoided, for cases when particularly great accuracy is required.

On examining the deviation of curves ϱ from the method expounded in section 3-1, the author has found the curves of the nomogram to be subject to the following method with great accuracy.

Let it be assumed that on curve $\varrho = 1.44$ the abscissa 17,850 G belongs to the ordinate 1,300 A/cm and that on any curve $\varrho = \varrho_a$ lying to the left of curve $\varrho = 1.44$ the abscissa B_{0a} pertains to this ordinate. On increasing both abscissae k times (Fig. 3-5), the ordinate V/h is found to pertain to the abscissa 17,850 k on curve $\varrho = 1.44$ and the ordinate

$$\frac{V}{h} - \left(\Delta\frac{V}{h}\right)_a$$

to belong to the abscissa kB_{0a} on curve ϱ_a where

$$\left(\Delta\frac{V}{h}\right)_a = C_a\left(\frac{V}{h} - 1{,}300\right) \qquad (3\text{-}7)$$

For curve ϱ_a, the value C_a is constant, depending on the distance between curves $\varrho = 1.44$ and $\varrho = \varrho_a$, while $(\Delta V/h)_a$ is an error due to the use of the simplified method for the computation of V/h.

If V/h is less than 1,300 A/cm, we obtain on curve ϱ_a the ordinate $V/h + (\Delta V/h)_a$ instead of the ordinate V/h.

If the curve examined lies to the right of curve $\varrho = 1.44$ (curve ϱ_b in Fig. 3-5) and the ordinate 1,300 A/cm on this curve belongs to the abscissa B_{0b}, then by increasing k times the abscissae 17,850 and B_{0b}, the ordinate belonging to the abscissa kB_{0b} on curve ϱ_b will again not be V/h but

$$\frac{V}{h} + \left(\Delta\frac{V}{h}\right)_b$$

where

$$\left(\Delta\frac{V}{h}\right)_b = C_b\left(\frac{V}{h} - 1{,}300\right) \qquad (3\text{-}8)$$

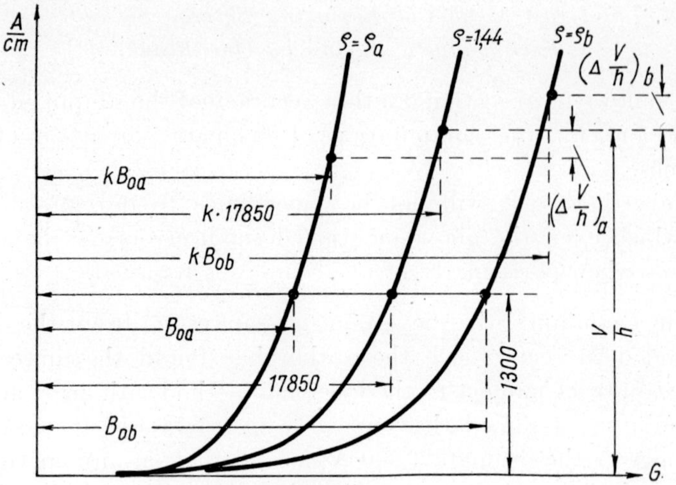

Fig. 3-5

The values C_a and C_b are the greatest for curves $\varrho = 2.66$ and $\varrho = 1$, respectively, while both values of C are the less, the closer curve ϱ_a or curve ϱ_b lies to curve $\varrho = 1.44$. If $\varrho_a = \varrho_b = 1.44$, both C_a and C_b are zero. Tnus it has been established that there is an almost linear relationship between the slight error made by using the simplified method and the value V/h.

If in Fig. 3-3 the flux density distribution along the straight line bc is substituted by the distribution along hk, a small error is committed for the following reason. If the mean field intensity belonging to the change in the flux density B_{0I} according to the trapezoid $abcd$ and to the change in the flux density B_{0res} according to the trapezoid $ahkd$ equals V_I/h_I, then the value pertaining to the change in the flux density kB_{0res} according to the trapezoid $ahkd$ (with a new ordinate value) will not be V'_I/h_I (obtained with the change in the flux density kB_{0I} according to the trapezoid $abcd$ with the same new scale), but a value of mean field intensity differing from the former by

$$\pm \triangle \frac{V'_I}{h_I}$$

A similar error of

$$\pm \triangle \frac{V'_{II}}{h_{II}}$$

is made if the trapezoid *defg* is replaced by the trapezoid *dklg*. If the field strength is distributed as in Fig. 3-3, this error has the same sign as $\Delta V'_{\mathrm{I}}/h_{\mathrm{I}}$, though in general it may have the opposite sign. Since the substitution of *ahkd* and *dklg* by *ahlg* involves no error, the error, if the flux density distribution in the resultant body is assumed according to the trapezoid *ahlg*, will be

$$\pm \triangle \frac{V'_{\mathrm{I}}}{h_{\mathrm{I}}} \pm \triangle \frac{V'_{\mathrm{II}}}{h_{\mathrm{II}}}$$

Nevertheless the replacement of the trapezoid *ahlg* by the final trapezoid *amng* again leads to an error whose sign and magnitude depend only on the sign and magnitude of the corresponding factors C_a or C_b according to Eqs. (3-7) and (3-8).

Hence among the infinite number of possible trapezoids *amng* there is one (i.e. among the possible values ϱ_{res}, there is one ϱ_{res}) to which the transition from *ahlg* involves the same error as is made by substituting *abcd* and *defg* by *ahlg*, though with the opposite sign. This means that on choosing the above-mentioned factor ϱ_{res}, the error

$$\triangle \frac{V'_{\mathrm{I}}}{h_{\mathrm{I}}} \pm \triangle \frac{V'_{\mathrm{II}}}{h_{\mathrm{II}}}$$

disappears in the result.

Should the flux $k\Phi$ undergo further change, the values V'_{I} and V'_{II} are increased or decreased accordingly. Consequently, according to Eqs. (3-7) and (3-8), the errors involved in the substitution of *abcd* and *defg* by *ahlg* will also increase or decrease linearly. On the other hand, a corresponding increment or decrement of the value

$$\frac{V'_{\mathrm{I}} + V'_{\mathrm{II}}}{h_{\mathrm{I}} + h_{\mathrm{II}}}$$

will be obtained, whence the opposite error made by replacing the trapezoid *ahlg* by the trapezoid *amng* also increases or decreases linearly. It follows that by choosing curve ϱ_{res} to yield correct results for the fluxes Φ and $k\Phi$, it will give correct results for any other flux as well. The corresponding curve ϱ_{res} can be determined on the basis of the following considerations.

We must find the curve ϱ_{res} on which the point pertaining to the abscissa $B_{0\mathrm{res}}$ is C_{res} with the ordinate $\Sigma V/\Sigma h$, and the point pertaining to the abscissa $kB_{0\rm res}$ is $C'_{\rm res}$ with the ordinate $\Sigma V'/\Sigma h$ (Fig. 3-6) where ΣV is the sum of the potential differences obtained if flux Φ crosses both series-connected bodies, and $\Sigma V'$ is the resultant potential difference created by $k\Phi$. Consequently, if $\Sigma V/\Sigma h$ is determined with the formula (3-1) and

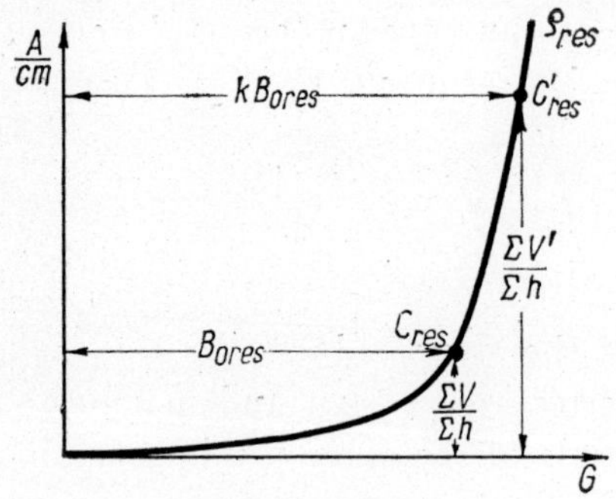

Fig. 3-6

$$\frac{V'+V'_{\rm II}}{h_{\rm I}+h_{\rm II}}=\frac{h_{\rm I}\left(\frac{V'_{\rm I}}{h_{\rm I}}\right)+h_{\rm II}\left(\frac{V'_{\rm II}}{h_{\rm II}}\right)}{h_{\rm I}+h_{\rm II}} \tag{3-9}$$

is computed, all that remains is to find the curve whose abscissae, pertaining to the above-mentioned ordinates, are related to one another as $1:k$.

3-5. An Approach to the Practical Application of the Exact Method of Replacing Series-Connected Ferromagnetic Bodies by a Resultant One

A) Replacing two series-connected bodies

The theory given in section 3-4 yields the following exact method for replacing two series-connected bodies by one resultant:

1. Factors $\varrho_{\rm I}$ and $\varrho_{\rm II}$ are calculated.
2. Some value of flux Φ and of $k\Phi$ is selected, respectively.
3. We determine the ordinates $V_{\rm I}/h_{\rm I}$ and $V_{\rm I}/h_{\rm I}$ of points $C_{\rm I}$ and $C'_{\rm I}$ (Fig. 3-7) lying on curve $\varrho_{\rm I}$ and having the abscissae $B_{0\rm I}=\Phi/b_{0\rm I}\gamma l$ and $kB_{0\rm I}$.
4. We determine the ordinates $V_{\rm II}/h_{\rm II}$ and $V'_{\rm II}/h_{\rm II}$ of points $C_{\rm II}$ and $C'_{\rm II}$ lying on curve $\varrho_{\rm II}$ and having the abscissae $B_{0\rm II}=\Phi/b_{0\rm II}\gamma l$ and $kB_{0\rm II}$.
5. The values

$$\frac{\Sigma V}{\Sigma h}=\frac{V_{\rm I}+V_{\rm II}}{h_{\rm I}+h_{\rm II}} \quad \text{and} \quad \frac{\Sigma V'}{\Sigma h}=\frac{V'_{\rm I}+V'_{\rm II}}{h_{\rm I}+h_{\rm II}}$$

are then computed with Eqs. (3-1) and (3-9), respectively.

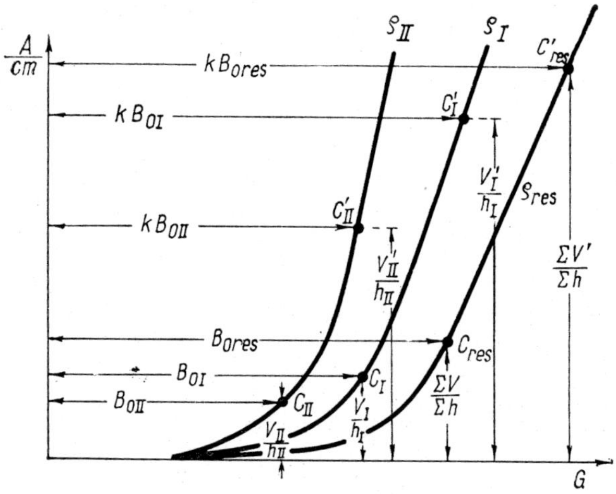

Fig. 3-7

6. We find the curve ϱ_{res} for which the abscissae B_{0res} and kB_{0res} pertaining to the ordinates $\Sigma V/\Sigma h$ and $\Sigma V'/\Sigma h$ are related to one another as $1 : k$.

7. The next step is to compute

$$b_{0res} = \frac{\Phi}{B_{0res}\gamma l} = \frac{k\Phi}{kB_{0res}\gamma l}$$

For any arbitrary values ΣV and Φ the magnetic relations are computed in the same manner as for one body characterized by $h = h_{I} + h_{II} = h_{res}$, $b_0 = b_{0res}$ and $\varrho = \varrho_{res}$.

Table 3-6 contains the resultant reluctance (i.e. the values ϱ_{res} and $b_{0res}\gamma l$) for some pairs of series-connected bodies as determined with the above-described exact method.

B) Replacing several series-connected bodies

If several series-connected bodies are to be replaced the following procedure is to be resorted to, similar to the simplified method:

1. Compute for all bodies the pertaining value ϱ_n.
2. Choose any value of flux Φ and flux $k\Phi$.
3. Determine for each body the ordinates V_n/h_n and V_n'/h_n of the points on the corresponding curves ϱ_n, with the abscissae B_{0n} and kB_{0n}.
4. Compute $\Sigma V_n/\Sigma h_n$ and $\Sigma V_n'/\Sigma h_n$.

TABLE

No. of Ex.	Geometric parameters						Assumed fluxes M		$B_{0I} = \frac{\Phi}{b_{0I}\gamma l}$	$kB_{0I} = \frac{k\Phi}{b_{0I}\gamma l}$	$B_{0II} = \frac{\Phi}{b_{0II}\gamma l}$
	Body I			Body II							
	h_I cm	$b_{0I}\gamma l$ cm²	ϱ_I	h_{II} cm	$b_{0II}\gamma l$ cm²	ϱ_{II}	Φ	$k\Phi$	G	G	G
1	2	3	4	5	6	7	8	9	10	11	12
52	4	2.54	1	2	4.95	2.66	49,920	57,500	19,650	22,600	10,100
53	2	2.72	1	5	3	1	54,100	60,900	19,850	22,400	18,000
54	3	2.7	2.08	4	2.29	1.63	33,000	37,800	12,200	14,000	14,400

5. Determine curve ϱ_{res} for which the abscissae B_{0res} and kB_{0res} pertaining to the ordinates $\Sigma V_n/\Sigma h_n$ and $\Sigma V_n/\Sigma h'_n$ are related to one another as $1 : k$.

6. Compute

$$b_{0res} = \frac{\Phi}{B_{0res}\gamma l} = \frac{\Phi}{kB_{0res}\gamma l}$$

Here is an example to illustrate the above procedure.

Example 55. Use the exact method for determining the parameters of the resultant body which is equivalent to the rotor tooth in the synchronous motor of Ex. 43.

Assuming the flux $\Phi = 200{,}000$ M, we have $B_{0I} = B_{0III} = 14{,}900$ G (see Ex. 31) and $B_{0II} = 25{,}000$ G (see Ex. 43).

From curve $\varrho = 1.79$ we have the ordinate $V_I/h_I = V_{III}/h_{III} = 1{,}160$ A/cm, from curve $\varrho = 1$ the ordinate $V_{II}/h_{II} = 3{,}000$ A/cm, which yields

$$\frac{\Sigma V}{\Sigma h} = 2{,}080 \text{ A/cm}$$

Decrease the flux to $k\Phi = 184{,}000$ M and compute $kB_{0I} = kB_{0III} = 13{,}700$ G and $kB_{0II} = 23{,}000$ G. From curve $\varrho = 1.79$ determine the ordinate $V'_I/h_I = V'_{III}/h_{III} = 590$ A/cm, from curve $\varrho = 1$ the ordinate $V'_{II}/h_{II} = 1{,}600$ A/cm and $\Sigma V'/\Sigma h = 1{,}100$ A/cm.

Determine nomographically a curve whose abscissae for the ordinates 2,080 and 1,100 A/cm are related to one another as $1 : k$.

3-6

$kB_{0II}=$ $=\frac{k\Phi}{b_{0II}\gamma l}$	Ordinates of points C_I and C'_{II} on curve ϱ_I		Ordinates of points C_{II} and C_{II} on curve ϱ'_{II}		Ordinates of points C'_{res} and C_{res}		ϱ_{res}	Abscissae of points C_{res} and C'_{res}		$b_{0res}\gamma l=$ $=\frac{\Phi}{B_{0res}}$
G	V_I/h_I A/cm	V_I/h_I A/cm	V_{II}/h_{II} Acm	V_{II}/h_{II} A/cm	$\frac{V_I+V_{II}}{h_I+h_{II}}$ A/cm	$\frac{V_I+V_{II}}{h_I+h_{II}}$ A/cm		B_{0res} G	kB_{0res} G	cm²
13	14	15	16	17	18	19	20	21	22	23
11,600	280	1,400	850	2,000	470	1,600	1.44	16,000	18,400	3.12
20,300	315	1,300	145	400	195	660	1.22	16,600	18,750	3.24
16,500	680	1,750	450	1,420	550	1,650	1.85	13,200	15,150	2.495

This condition is satisfied by the curve $\varrho_{res} = 1.31$, and the corresponding abscissae will be 20,400 and 18,800 G.

Thus the resultant body has a maximum cross section of $b_{0res}\,\gamma l = 9.8$ cm².

Let us check the accuracy of this method by examples taken from practice. For this purpose compute the magnitudes V_I and V_{II} pertaining to some flux Φ for each of the Exs. 52 to 54 separately, then compare the sum obtained $V_I + V_{II}$ with $\Sigma V = V_I + V_{II}$ computed with the same flux for the resultant body.

The results of this checking are compiled in Table 3-7. As is shown by the comparison of columns 16 and 19, the exact method of replacing series-connected reluctances by a resultant yields results of high degree of accuracy, though it should be noted that the degree of accuracy obtained by the simplified method is amply sufficient for practice.

3-6. The Application of the Method of Replacing Individual Bodies by a Resultant in the Case of Compound-Connected Ferromagnetic Bodies

The methods developed in chapter 2 can be used for solving even more involved tasks, such as the determination of magnetic relations of several parallel-connected magnetic circuits each of which consists of several series-connected ferromagnetic bodies.

TABLI

No. of Ex.	Geometric parameters: Body I h_I cm	$b_{0I}\gamma l$ cm²	ϱ_I	Body II h_{II} cm	$b_{0II}\gamma l$ cm²	ϱ_{II}	Resulting body $h_I +$ $+ h_{II}$ cm	$b_{0res}\gamma l$ cm²	ϱ_{res}	Assumed flux Φ M	B_{0I} G	B_{0II} G
1	2	3	4	5	6	7	8	9	10	11	12	13
56	4	2.54	1	2	4.95	2.66	6	3.12	1.44	62,400	24,500	12,60(
57	2	2.72	1	5	3	1	7	3.24	1.22	69,200	25,400	23,00(
58	3	2.7	2.08	4	2.29	1.63	7	2.495	1.85	41,500	15,350	18,10(

Let us investigate, for instance, the magnetic circuit of a two-pole d.c. machine (Fig. 1-7) whose flux crosses both poles and goes through both parallel branches of the stator yoke.

Since one of the branches is partly cut away, the reluctances in the parallel-connected branches will not be identical and the flux Φ will be divided into two different parts Φ_1 and Φ_2. In such cases it is very difficult to determine the individual component of the flux because neither the potential difference between points 1 and 3 (or 12 and 16) nor the reluctance of each branch of the yoke is known. As long as the value of the partial fluxes is unknown, the field strength in no part of the iron can be determined. This being unknown, the potential difference cannot be found either, nor can the partial fluxes be determined. Consequently, in this case the usual method runs up against insurmountable difficulties.

The method developed in this book, however, offers a simple solution of the problem. For this purpose let us divide the incised half of the yoke into several series-connected sections. Thus it will be found sufficient to examine no more than the two sections I and II since they are identical with the sections III and IV. Having determined the maximum cross-section $b_0\gamma l$ and the value ϱ for these parts, they can be replaced by a resultant body characterized by $b_{0res}\gamma l$, ϱ_{res} and $h = h_I + h_{II}$.

The other half of the yoke consists usually of two series-connected parts which correspond to a resultant body with the parameters b'_{0res}, ϱ'_{res} and h.

Thus we have reduced the solution of this complicated task to the case of two parallel-connected reluctances characterized by

3-7

Ordinate V_I/h_I A/cm	Ordinate V_{II}/h_{II} A/cm	V_I+V_{II} computed as the sum V_I+V_{II} from columns 14 and 15	B_0res G	Ordinate $\frac{V_I+V_{II}}{h_I+h_{II}}$ pertaining to the abscissa B_{0res} A/cm	$\Sigma V=V_I+V_{II}$ computed nomograhically for the resultant body
14	15	16	17	18	61
2,600	2,900	16,200	20,000	2,700	16,200
3,300	1,600	14,600	21,300	2,085	14,600
2,820	2,500	18,460	16,600	2,640	18,480

identical height h and by the parameters

$$b_{0res}\gamma l,\ \varrho_{res},\ b'_{0res}\gamma l,\ \varrho'_{res}$$

Such a task can readily be solved with the nomographic method. Since the potential difference V as well as the values h and V/h are identical for both halves of the yoke, the point C (Fig. 3-8) on curve ϱ_{res} and point C' on curve ϱ'_{res} should be determined so as to find identical ordinates for them and so as to make the product of the abscissa $\overline{LC}$ and the value $b_{0res}\gamma l$ (flux Φ_2) and that of the abscissa $\overline{LC'}$ and the value $b'_{0res}\gamma l$ (flux Φ_1) yield flux Φ when added. Since the ordinate of points C and C' thus determined is multiplied by $2h$, it gives the potential difference along the yoke between the two poles.

Example 59. The left half of the yoke 11-12-14-13 of the machine in Fig. 1-7 has the following parameters: $h = 56$ cm, $b_0 = \overline{11-12} = 10.4$ cm, $\gamma l = 29.5$ cm, $b_2 = \overline{13-14} = 10.4$ cm and $\varrho'_{res} = 1$.

The body 1-2-5-6 is characterized by the parameters $h_I = 38$ cm, $b_{0I} = \overline{1-2} = 10.4$ cm, $\gamma, l = 29.5$ cm, $b_{2I} = \overline{5-6} = 10.4$ cm, i.e. $\varrho_I = 1$, while the body 5-6-8-7 by $h_{II} = 18$ cm, $b_2/2 = b_{2II} = \overline{7-8} = 6$ cm, $\gamma l = 29.5$ cm and $r = 40$ cm.

On this basis, by using Eqs. (2-17) to (2-20), the following values can be computed: $b_1/2 = b_{III} = 7$ cm, $b_0/2 = b_{0II} = 10$ cm, $\beta = 0.9$, $a = 0.6$ and $\varrho_{II} = 1.78$ (see Ex. 32).

We want to find Φ_1 and Φ_2, parts of $\Phi = 11.75 \cdot 10^6$ M crossing the poles.

To begin with, let the bodies I and II be replaced by a resultant body according to the simplified method.

By assuming flux $\Phi_2 = 4.3 \cdot 10^6$ M we obtain $B_{0I} = 14{,}000$ G and $B_{0II} = 14{,}000$ G. On curve $\varrho = 1$ we find the ordinate $V_I/h_I = 25$ A/cm ($V_I = 950$ A) pertaining to the abscissa B_{0I}, and on curve $\varrho = 1.78$ we find the ordinate $V_{II}/h_{II} = 900$ A/cm ($V = 16{,}200$ A) pertaining to the abscissa B_{0II}. For the ordinate $\Sigma V/\Sigma h = 307$ A/cm and the curve $\varrho_{res} = 1.44$ we obtain $B_{0res} = 15{,}300$ G, i.e. $b_{0res} = 9.5$ cm.

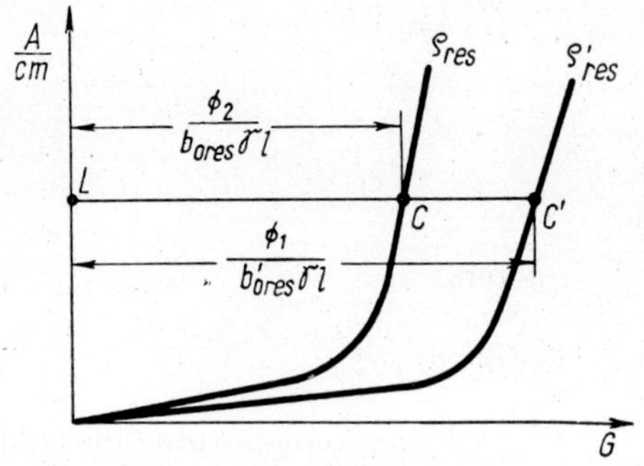

Fig. 3-8

Thus, considering the symmetry of the upper and lower half of the machine, we have two parallel-connected bodies, one of them characterized by the parameters $h = 112$ cm, $\varrho = 1$ and $b_0\gamma l = 307$ cm², the other by $h = 112$ cm, $\varrho = 1.44$ and $b_0\gamma l = 280$ cm².

Then the common ordinate of points C and C' (Fig. 3-8) is determined for which the sum is $307\,\overline{LC}' + 280\,\overline{LC} = 11{,}750{,}000$ M. Here $\overline{LC}'$ is the abscissa of the unknown point C' on curve $\varrho = 1$, while $\overline{LC}'$ is the abscissa of the other unknown point C' on curve $\varrho = 1.44$. The values 307 cm² and 280 cm² are the cross-sections $b_{0res}\,\gamma l$ of the two resultant bodies.

The nomogram shows that the ordinate of both C and C' is 1,180 A/cm, and the components of the fluxes

$$\Phi_1 = 307\overline{LC}' = 307 \cdot 22{,}200 = 6{,}810{,}000 \text{ M},$$
$$\Phi_2 = 280\overline{LC} = 280 \cdot 17{,}600 = 4{,}940{,}000 \text{ M}.$$

This example can alsobe solved by replacing the two parallel branches of the stator yoke by one resultant body. This means the further development of the above-mentioned principle concerning the equivalence of ferromagnetic bodies.

The body characterized by the parameters $h = 112$ cm, $\varrho = 1$ and $b_0\,\gamma l = 307$ cm², can be replaced by another equivalent body if, instead of point C, another point is chosen which has the same ordinate 1,180 A/cm yet lies on another curve running approximately in the middle between the curves $\varrho = 1$ and $\varrho = 1.44$. On curve

$\varrho = 1.19$, for instance, a point with the abscissa $B_0 = 20{,}200$ G is obtained, whence $B_0 \gamma l = 337$ cm². Similarly, a body characterized by $h = 112$ cm, $\varrho = 1.44$ and $b_0 \gamma l = 280$ cm² can be substituted by an equivalent body, for which the abscissa $B_0 = 20{,}200$ G pertains to the ordinate 1,180 A/cm on curve $\varrho = 1.19$, whence $b_0 \gamma l = 244$ cm².

Since the flux density in both parallel-connected bodies is now distributed identically, they can be replaced by a single body which is crossed by a resultant flux $\Phi_1 + \Phi_2$ producing the same distribution of flux density from 20,200 G to 1.19 · 20,200 G. This body must have the following cross-section and factor ϱ:

$$b_0 \gamma l = 337 + 244 = 581 \text{ cm}^2 \text{ and } \varrho = 1.19.$$

Thus, the stator yoke of rather complicated configuration in Fig. 1-7 has been replaced by a single body with parameters $h = 112$ cm, $b_0 \gamma l = 581$ cm² and $\varrho = 1.19$.

The method here expounded would be absolutely exact if the method proposed in section 3-1 were observed. On account of the above-mentioned deviations from this rule, an error, though a very small one, is committed in determining the flux, owing to the transition from $\varrho = 1$ to $\varrho = 1.19$ in the first body. Yet owing to the transition from $\varrho = 1.44$ to $\varrho = 1.19$ in the second body, an error of about the same magnitude but of the opposite sign is committed, whence the value of the resultant flux is determined with fairly good accuracy.

Other tasks concerning compound-connected ferromagnetic bodies can be solved in a similar way.

CHAPTER FOUR

THE NOMOGRAPHIC DETERMINATION OF THE MAGNETIC RELATIONS IN THE REGION OF THE TOOTH AND THE MAGNETICALLY PARALLEL SLOT

4-1. Longitudinal Fluxes in the Open Slot

In determining the reluctance of ferromagnetic bodies of different shape we have so far neglected the fluxes passing parallel to the ferromagnetic body through the adjacent air gap. We shall now develop a method for finding these fluxes, i.e. for determining the reluctance of the body with due regard to the parallel-connected air gaps.

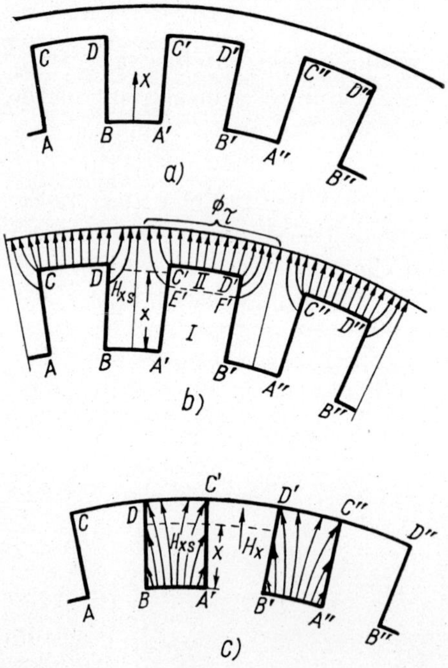

Fig. 4-1

In the study of this problem, the open slot with parallel walls (Fig. 4-1a), a frequent feature of the rotors in d.c. machines, will be chosen as the fundamental case.

In such slots there arise fluxes directed in general along the height of the slot and termed therefore longitudinal fluxes.

These fluxes are due to two factors: to the fall of potential along the air gap between the stator and the rotor and to the potential difference along the teeth.

The first factor creates a flux (Fig. 4-1b) obtained by assuming that the potential drop V along the teeth and the field intensity in the ferromagnetic material of the teeth are equal to zero. In this case the slot is magnetically parallel-connected to that part of the air gap which is located between the pole and the crown of the teeth, i.e. the slot flux is created by the potential difference V_0—V acting along the slot of the pertaining tooth.

The second factor creates a flux (Fig. 4-1c) obtained by assuming that the air gap and the potential difference V_0—V are decreased to zero. In this case, under the influence of the potential difference V along the tooth the flux will pass partly through the slot magnetically parallel-connected to the tooth.

In reality both these fluxes are acting simultaneously and create a definite resultant flux density.

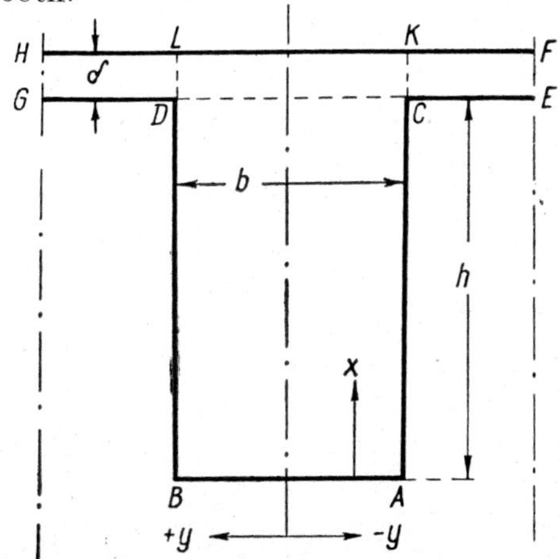

Fig. 4-2

Let us investigate analytically the distribution of these fluxes in the open slot and their influence upon the magnetic condition of the tooth. Take an open armature slot (Fig. 4-2) and the parts of the air gap limiting it within one slot pitch having the contour ACEFHGDBA. Assume that both teeth limiting the slot are equally saturated, whence there is a symmetrical distribution of the flux density.

It may be assumed with fair accuracy that the potential P_{FH} along the line FH representing the surface of the pole shoe will have a constant value, the potential $P_{EC} = P_{GD}$ along the lines EC and GD will also have a constant, yet somewhat different value. It may also be assumed that, owing to saturation, in the tooth, an even less but constant potential will act along the line AB, which can be regarded as zero.

Let the teeth be wedge-shaped. Thus the field intensity H_x along AC and BD will increase the more, the closer the relevant point will be to the bottom of the slot. In order to have boundary conditions coming close enough to the actual ones, let H_x be assumed to increase parabolically

$$H_x = -C_1 - C_2 \frac{h-x}{h} - C_3 \frac{(h-x)^2}{h^2} \tag{4-1}$$

where $h = \overline{AC} = \overline{BD}$ = depth of slot
x = distance from line AB
C_1, C_2, C_3 = constants, without any restrictions.

In this case

$$V = \int_h^0 H_x\, dx = h\left(C_1 + \frac{C_2}{2} + \frac{C_3}{3}\right) \tag{4-2}$$

Let the potential along EF and GH be assumed to increase proportionally from $P_{EC} = P_{DG}$ to P_{FH}.

The distribution of the longitudinal slot fluxes can be determined by means of two operations. The potential along CA and DB is first assumed to be distributed according to Eq. (4-1), while the potential along the whole contour $CEFHGD$ to have the value $P_{EC} = P_{DG}$. In the second step the potential along the contour $ECABDG$ is assumed to equal zero, while along the lines EF and GH to increase linearly to P_{FH}—P_{EC}.

By determining in both cases the slot flux, then adding up the results, we shall obtain the slot flux pertaining to the actual boundary conditions, because the distribution of the flux and the induction in the air is a linear function of the distribution of the potential. The first case corresponds to the longitudinal slot flux due to the saturation of the teeth, and the second to the slot flux due to the potential drop in the air gap when the teeth are not saturated.

Let us start by examining the first case.

If the potential along the line AB is zero and along the contour $CEFHGD$ it equals P_{EC}, then the magnetic force lines will obviously be perpendicular to the lines CE, KF, HL and GD. Owing to the screening effect of these lines of the rectangle $CEFK$ and $DGHL$, a relatively small quantity of force lines penetrate the slot, along which the potential drop can be neglected, i.e. it can be assumed that the potential along the portions CK and DL is the same and equals P_{EC}.

These boundary conditions are satisfied by the equation

$$P_1 = -\sum \frac{4b^2}{n^3\pi^3} f_n(y) \frac{C_2 + 2C_3}{h}\left[\operatorname{sh}\frac{n\pi(h+\delta)}{b} - \right.$$

$$\left. -\operatorname{sh}\frac{n\pi(h+\delta-x)}{b} - \operatorname{sh}\frac{n\pi x}{b}\operatorname{ch}\frac{n\pi\delta}{b}\right] +$$

$$+\sum\frac{4b^2}{n^3\pi^3}f_n(y)\frac{2C_3}{h}\left[\frac{x}{h}\operatorname{sh}\frac{n\pi(h+\delta)}{b}-\operatorname{sh}\frac{n\pi x}{b}\operatorname{ch}\frac{n\pi\delta}{b}-\right.$$

$$\left.-\frac{b}{n\pi h}\operatorname{sh}\frac{n\pi x}{b}\operatorname{sh}\frac{n\pi\delta}{b}\right]-$$

$$-\sum\frac{4b}{n^2\pi^2}C_1 f_n(y)\operatorname{sh}\frac{n\pi x}{b}\operatorname{sh}\frac{n\pi\delta}{b}+(C_1+C_2+C_3)x-$$

$$-\frac{C_2+2C_3}{2h}x^2+\frac{C_3}{3h^2}x^3 \tag{4-3}$$

which determines the potential due to the saturation of the teeth in points corresponding to $h > x > 0$, i.e. within the slot $ABDC$.

And also

$$f_n(y)=\frac{\sin\frac{n\pi}{2}\cos\frac{n\pi y}{b}}{\operatorname{sh}\frac{n\pi}{b}(h+\delta)} \tag{4-4}$$

For points $h < x < h+\delta$, i.e. for those lying within the contour $LDCK$ we may write

$$P_{\rm II}=-\sum\frac{4b^2}{n^3\pi^3}f_n(y)\frac{C_2+2C_3}{h}\operatorname{sh}\frac{n\pi(h+\delta-x)}{b}\left(\operatorname{ch}\frac{n\pi h}{b}-1\right)+$$

$$+(C_2+2C_3)\frac{h}{2}+$$

$$+\sum\frac{4b^2}{n^3\pi^3}f_n(y)\frac{2C_3}{h}\operatorname{sh}\frac{n\pi(h+\delta-x)}{b}\left(\operatorname{ch}\frac{n\pi h}{b}-\frac{b}{n\pi h}\operatorname{sh}\frac{n\pi h}{b}\right)-$$

$$-\frac{2}{3}C_3 h-\sum\frac{4b}{n^2\pi^2}C_1 f_n(y)\operatorname{sh}\frac{n\pi(h+\delta-x)}{b}\operatorname{sh}\frac{n\pi h}{b}+C_1 h \tag{4-5}$$

The correctness of these equations can easily be shown by taking into account that $P_{\rm I}$ and $P_{\rm II}$ for the points of the contour $ACKLDBA$ must coincide with the given potential values. In addition, $P_{\rm I}$ and $P_{\rm II}$ must satisfy the equation

$$\frac{\partial^2 P}{\partial x^2}+\frac{\partial^2 P}{\partial^2 y}=0$$

and for the straight line CD the following relations prevail:

$$P_{\mathrm{I}} = P_{\mathrm{II}}$$

$$\left(\frac{\partial P_{\mathrm{I}}}{\partial y}\right)_{x=h} = \left(\frac{\partial O_{\mathrm{II}}}{\partial y}\right)_{x=h}$$

$$\left(\frac{\partial P_{\mathrm{I}}}{\partial x}\right)_{x=h} = \left(\frac{\partial P_{\mathrm{II}}}{\partial x}\right)_{x=h}$$

By differentiating P_{I} (Eq. 4-3) according to x, integrating this expression according to y from $+b/2$ to $-b/2$ and dividing the result by 2, we obtain the mean field intensity of the longitudinal slot flux due to the saturation of the teeth:

$$H_{xs} = \sum \frac{8b}{n^3\pi^3} \frac{C_2 + 2C_3}{h} \frac{1}{\mathrm{sh}\,\dfrac{n\pi x\,(h+\delta)}{b}} \left[\mathrm{ch}\,\frac{n\pi\,(h+\delta-x)}{b} - \right.$$

$$\left. - \mathrm{ch}\,\frac{n\pi x}{b}\,\mathrm{ch}\,\frac{n\pi\delta}{b}\right] +$$

$$+ \sum \frac{8b}{n^3\pi^3} \frac{2C_3}{h} \left[- \frac{b}{hn\pi} + \frac{\mathrm{ch}\,\dfrac{n\pi x}{b}\,\mathrm{ch}\,\dfrac{n\pi\delta}{b} + \dfrac{b}{hn\pi}\,\mathrm{ch}\,\dfrac{n\pi x}{b}\,\mathrm{sh}\,\dfrac{n\pi\delta}{b}}{\mathrm{sh}\,\dfrac{n\pi\,(h+\delta)}{b}} \right. +$$

$$+ \sum \frac{8}{n^2\pi^2} C_1 \frac{\mathrm{ch}\,\dfrac{n\pi x}{b}\,\mathrm{sh}\,\dfrac{n\pi\delta}{b}}{\mathrm{sh}\,\dfrac{n\pi\,(h+\delta)}{b}} -$$

$$- (C_1 + C_2 + C_3) + \frac{C_2 + 2C_3}{h}\,x - \frac{C_3\,x^2}{h^2} \qquad (4\text{-}6)$$

Let us examine the physical significance of the different parts of Eq. (4-6). According to our assumption (see Eq. 1-4), the members

$$- (C_1 + C_2 + C_3) + \frac{C_2 + 2C_3}{h}\,x - \frac{C_3\,x^2}{h^2}$$

express the field intensity H_x in the teeth. This will prevail in every case, independently of the pattern according to which H_x is distributed. Those parts of the infinite sets in which sh $n\pi\delta/b$ prevails, illustrate the decrease of the longitudinal slot flux due to saturation, determined by the air gap. These parts disappear if $\delta = 0$. Let us now examine which members of the sets may be neglected if $x = 0$. The fundamental of the third set ($n = 1$)

$$C_1 \frac{8 \operatorname{sh} \dfrac{\pi\delta}{b}}{\pi^2 \operatorname{sh} \dfrac{\pi(h+\delta)}{b}}$$

is for the other values h/b insignificant as compared to the member C_1 even if δ is great. The other harmonics can be neglected even without that much consideration. In the case of $x = 0$, similar considerations allow us to neglect the expression $\operatorname{ch} n\pi\delta/b$ even for large values of δ as compared to the expression

$$\operatorname{ch} \frac{n\pi(h+\delta)}{b}$$

and likewise the expression $\operatorname{sh} n\pi\delta/b$ as compared to the expression

$$\operatorname{sh} \frac{n\pi(h+\delta)}{b}$$

A comparison of

$$\sum \frac{8b}{n^3\pi^3} \left(\operatorname{cth} \frac{n\pi(h+\delta)}{b} \right) \frac{C_2}{h}$$

with the member C_2 shows that in the usual case of $h/b > 2$, the fundamental even for $\delta = 0$ is smaller than C_2, in a ratio of about 13 : 100. The third harmonic is not greater than 0.5 per cent of C_2.

A comparison of

$$\sum \frac{8b}{n^3\pi^3} \left(\operatorname{cth} \frac{n\pi(h+\delta)}{b} - \frac{b}{hn\pi} \right) \frac{2C_3}{h}$$

with the member C_3 shows that if $h/b > 2$ the fundamental equals 23 per cent of C_3 and the third harmonic is smaller than 1 per cent of C_3. Consequently, each member of the infinite sets can be neglected for $x = 0$, i.e. for the point where the possible error in the flux due to great saturation would have the greatest effect on the field intensity in the tooth. Thus it may be assumed that

$$(H_{xs})_{x=0} \approx (H_x)_{x=0}$$

Let us now examine where the members of the infinite sets can be neglected for $x > 0$. With the increase of x the set containing C_2 decreases, then equals zero and finally changes its sign. If $x = h$ and $\delta = \infty$, its fundamental will be about $-8bC_2/\pi^3 h$, but if $\delta = 0$, it will be $-8bC_2/\pi^3 h$, i.e. will have the same value as in case of $x = 0$ but with the opposite sign. Thus, by neglecting this set altogether, the increase of x will not only be accompanied by the decrease of the absolute magnitude of the error committed, but also the error committed in the upper and lower parts of the slot will partly be compensated.

The same applies to the set of Eq. (4-6) containing $2C_3$. Its value and, therefore, also the error due to its being neglected, will decrease with the increase of x.

As to the set containing C_1, it will assume, for $x = h$, the form

$$\sum \frac{8C_1}{\pi^2 n^2} \frac{1}{1 + \operatorname{th} \dfrac{n\pi h}{b} \operatorname{cth} \dfrac{n\pi\delta}{b}}$$

Since $\operatorname{th} n\pi h/b \approx 1$, we obtain

$$\sum \frac{8C_1}{\pi^2 n^2} \frac{1}{2} \left(1 - e^{-2n\pi\delta/b}\right) \tag{4-7}$$

Considering that

$$e^{-2n\pi\delta/b}$$

is for $n = 1$ equal to $1/e$ even in case of $\delta = b/2\pi$, no greater error will be committed in case of small values of δ than by substituting the expression

$$1 - e^{-2n\pi\delta/b}$$

by $2n\pi\delta/b$, because both differential quotients are equal for $\delta = 0$. This slight error may partly be eliminated by substituting $\pi\delta/b$ for $n\pi\delta/b$.

Since

$$\sum \frac{8}{n^2 \pi^2} = 1$$

we obtain, instead of the set containing the value C_1, the simple expression $+ C_1\pi\delta/b$ which is valid for $\delta < b/2\pi$ but is equal to zero for $\delta \geq b/2\pi$. Since $(H_x)_{x=h} = C_1$, the formula (4-6) for $x = h$ can be written as

$$(H_{xs})_{x=h} = (H_x)_{x=h}\left(1 - \frac{\pi\delta}{b}\right) \tag{4-8}$$

which is valid for $\delta < b/2\pi$. For $\delta \geqq b/2\pi$ it may be assumed that

$$(H_{xs})_{x=h} = (H_x)_{x=h}\,\frac{1}{2} \tag{4-9}$$

The above considerations allow of the following conclusion. Whereas for $x = 0$ the field intensity of the longitudinal slot flux due to saturation is approximately equal to the field intensity of the tooth at the same height, the increase of x affects this equality under the influence of the air gap, and a certain difference arises between the field intensities which, with the increase of x to h, can attain half the field strength of the tooth.

If we neglect this difference and assume that $H_{xs} = H_x$ at any height x, then the slot flux will, for the high values of x, be greater than in reality, while the corresponding tooth flux will be smaller. In any case, in wedge-shaped teeth the field strength and the longitudinal slot flux rapidly decrease with the increase of x, while the magnetic permeability of the steel suddenly increases. Therefore, the error in computing fluxes will affect but very slightly the potential difference V in the tooth. Yet if the tooth has parallel walls or a small coefficient a, this error may increase substantially.

Let us assume, for example, that $a = 1$. In this case the field intensity H along the tooth will be constant. Thus — $C_1 = H$, $C_2 = 0$, $C_3 = 0$, i.e.

$$H_{xs} = H\left(1 - \sum \frac{8}{n^2\pi^2}\,\frac{\operatorname{ch}\dfrac{n\pi x}{b}\operatorname{sh}\dfrac{n\pi\delta}{b}}{\operatorname{sh}\dfrac{n\pi(h+\delta)}{b}}\right) \tag{4-10}$$

For values of x close to h

$$\operatorname{ch}\frac{n\pi x}{b} \approx \frac{e^{n\pi x/b}}{2}$$

and

$$\operatorname{sh}\frac{n\pi h}{b} \approx \operatorname{ch}\frac{n\pi h}{b} \approx \frac{e^{n\pi x/b}}{2}$$

whence

$$H_{xs} = H\left[1 - \sum \frac{8}{n^2\,\pi^2}\, e^{-n\pi(h-x)/b}\, \frac{1-2^{-2n\pi\delta/b}}{2}\right] \tag{4-11}$$

When substituting the expression

$$\frac{1-e^{-2\,n\pi\delta/b}}{2}$$

by $\pi\delta/b$, and the expression

$$e^{-n\pi(h-x)/b}$$

by

$$\left[1 - \frac{\pi}{b}(h-x)\right]$$

we obtain

$$H_{xs} = H\left\{1 - \left[1 - \frac{\pi}{b}(h-x)\right]\frac{\pi\delta}{b}\right\} \tag{4-12a}$$

valid for

$$\frac{h-x}{b} < \frac{1}{\pi}$$

For

$$\frac{h-x}{b} \leq \frac{1}{\pi}$$

we shall have

$$H_{xs} = H \tag{4-12b}$$

In order to find out whether or not the above-mentioned error can be neglected, it should first be examined how the longitudinal slot flux due to the potential difference V_0—V along the air gap is distributed.

To this end we must find the potential distribution within the slot, which determines the potential difference P_{FH}—P_{EG} acting between the lines *FH* and *EG*.

Should the slot *ACDB* be absent, the field strength would be distributed evenly throughout the air gap.

Owing to the presence of the slots, this distribution is disturbed and the force lines are condensed in the corners *C* and *D*. This phenomenon, however, cannot develop fully because of the saturation of the steel near the corner points C and D.

Relying on the analytical examination, which is omitted here, it may be concluded that the field intensity along the stretches LD and KC may be regarded as constant without any serious error.

It can readily be seen that in such boundary conditions, the task of finding the potential within the rectangle $ACDB$ is reminiscent of the problem determined by Eq. (4-5).

Eq. (4-5) yields the potential in the rectangle $CKLD$ of height δ, which is determined by the given distribution of the longitudinal field intensity along AC and BD if the adjacent rectangle is h high. In this case the potential within the rectangle $ABDC$ of height h should be determined, the potential being defined by the given distribution of the longitudinal field strength along the stretches CK and DL of the adjacent rectangle of height δ.

In addition to this, Eq. (4-5) relies on the assumption that the longitudinal field strength along AC and BD is distributed according to the formula (4-1), while in the given case we must also assume the constancy of the field strength

$$\frac{V_0 - V}{\delta}$$

along the lines CK and DL.

Finally, the direction of the field intensity acting along CK and DL is, as compared to the rectangle $ABCD$, opposite to the direction of the field strength acting along AC and BD, as compared to the rectangle $CKLD$.

Considering these changes the potential P'_I in the slot, due to the potential difference acting along the air gap, can be expressed by Eq. (4-5) if the values h, δ, $(h + \delta - x)$ and C_1 are substituted by the values δ, h, $(h + \delta - x)$, x and

$$-\frac{V_0 - V}{\delta}$$

respectively, and the constants C_2 and C_3 are zero:

$$P'_\mathrm{I} = \sum \frac{4b}{n^2 \pi^2} \frac{V_0 - V}{\delta} \cdot \frac{\sin \frac{n\pi}{2} \cos \frac{n\pi y}{b} \operatorname{sh} \frac{n\pi x}{b} \operatorname{sh} \frac{n\pi\delta}{b}}{\operatorname{sh} \frac{n\pi(h+\delta)}{b}} \mp (V_0 - V) \tag{4-13}$$

Since

$$\frac{\operatorname{sh}\dfrac{n\pi\delta}{b}}{\operatorname{sh}\dfrac{n\pi(h+\delta)}{b}} = \frac{1}{\operatorname{sh}\dfrac{n\pi h}{b}\operatorname{cth}\dfrac{n\pi\delta}{b} + \operatorname{ch}\dfrac{n\pi h}{b}}$$

and by differentiating P_I according to x and integrating the expression obtained according to y from $+b/2$ to $-b/2$ and dividing the result by b, the mean longitudinal field strength is obtained as

$$H'_{xs} = \sum \frac{8}{n^2\pi^2}\frac{V_0 - V}{\delta}\frac{\operatorname{ch}\dfrac{n\pi x}{b}}{\operatorname{sh}\dfrac{n\pi h}{b}\operatorname{cth}\dfrac{n\pi\delta}{b} + \operatorname{ch}\dfrac{n\pi h}{b}} \tag{4-14}$$

This formula, as also Eq. (4-12a), can be replaced by the expression

$$H'_{xs} = \frac{V_0 - V}{\delta}\left[1 - \frac{\pi}{b}(h - x)\right]\frac{\pi\delta}{b} \tag{4-15}$$

On multiplying it by 0.4 πbl and introducing $x = h$, the longitudinal slot flux Φ'_{xs} at a height h is obtained as

$$(\Phi'_{xs})_{x=h} = 0.4\,\pi bl\frac{V_0 - V}{\delta}\frac{\pi\delta}{b} \tag{4-16}$$

On the other hand, however,

$$\Phi_\tau = \frac{V_0 - V}{\delta k_c}(b_0 + b)\,l \cdot 0.4\pi \tag{4-17}$$

where k_c = the coefficient of the air gap (Carter's factor) and
b = width of the slot,
while the tooth flux at the crown is

$$\Phi_t = 0.4\pi\frac{V_0 - V}{\delta}b_0 l = \Phi_\tau - (\Phi'_{xs})_{x=h} \tag{4-18}$$

wherefrom

$$(\Phi'_{xs})_{x=h} = 0.4\pi\frac{V_0 - V}{\delta}\,l\left[\frac{b_0 + b}{k_c} - b\right] = \Phi_\tau\left[1 - \frac{b_0 k_c}{b_0 + b}\right] \tag{4-19}$$

Transforming these expressions we obtain a simplified formula

$$H'_{xs} = 0 \text{ for } \frac{h - x}{b} \geq \frac{1}{\pi} \tag{4-20a}$$

respectively

$$H'_{xs} = \frac{\Phi_\tau}{0.4\pi\, bl}\left(1 - \frac{b_0\, k_c}{b_0 + b}\right)\left[1 - \frac{\pi}{b}(h - x)\right] \tag{4-20b}$$

for

$$\frac{h - x}{b} < \frac{1}{\pi}$$

Let us now return to the problem of evaluating the formula (4-12a).

It has been stated that in case of wedge-shaped teeth, the field intensity H_{xs} of the longitudinal slot flux may be regarded in the whole slot as equal to the field intensity H_x of the tooth. For teeth with parallel walls it may be assumed that the same condition applies to the total height of the tooth, except for a relatively small part of the slot lying between the limit $h > x > h - b/\pi$.

In the case of the normal relation between b_0, δ, b and k_c, the longitudinal slot flux due to the potential difference $V_0 - V$ is a comparatively great part of flux Φ_τ. Thus the fact that it passes along the tooth in the range of $h > x > h - b/\pi$, decreases the flux density and the field strength acting here, and considerably diminishes the absolute error $H_{xs} - H_x$ committed by assuming that $H_{xs} = H_x$. The error committed in the computation of V by assuming that the flux $0.4\pi\ (H_x - H_{xs})\, bl$ passes through the slot and not through the tooth will be even smaller owing to the increase in the permeability of the tooth in this region.

On the strength of the above considerations we are now entitled to say that also for teeth of a low a value or with $a = 1$, the above error can be neglected and it may be presumed that $H_{xs} = H_x$ in every case. To sum up, the following fairly accurate formulae can be advanced for the over-all field intensity of the longitudinal flux:

$$(H_{xs} + H'_{xs})_{x > h - b/\pi} = H_x + \frac{\Phi_\tau}{0.4\,\pi bl}\left(1 - \frac{b_0\, k_c}{b_0 + b}\right)\left[1 - \frac{\pi}{b}(h - x)\right] \tag{4-21a}$$

whence

$$(H_{xs} + H'_{xs})_{x < h - b/\pi} = H_x \tag{4-21b}$$

which may serve as a basis for developing a simple nomographic computation method for the influence of the said flux.

4-2. The Necessity of the Nomographic Consideration of the Longitudinal Flux in a Parallel-Walled Open Slot, Due to the Potential Differences Acting in the Air Gap

The formulae (4-21a) and (4-21b) characterizing the distribution of the over-all longitudinal slot flux have been deduced in section 4-1. Accordingly, both kinds of longitudinal slot fluxes depend on entirely different factors.

Consequently, in our system of nomographic methods different approaches should be made to the computation of their influence.

The examples in section 1-2 show that the longitudinal slot flux due to the saturation of the tooth considerably unloads the tooth and substantially diminishes the value V, which makes it necessary to take it into account. The situation is completely different in the case of the slot flux due to the potential difference $V_0—V$.

If $a = 1$, both the flux density of the tooth and the value H_x along the entire tooth are practically constant and H_{xs} unloads the tooth throughout its height. On the other hand, H'_{xs} unloads the tooth along part of its height only, to wit, within the range from $x = h$ to $x = h - b/\pi$. If $a < 1$, then H_{xs} relieves the tooth at its bottom only, while H'_{xs} has but a slight influence upon V because, in wedge-shaped teeth, the said unloading takes place in the maximum cross-section of the tooth i.e. at a point of minimum flux density. Since in case of low flux density the derivative dH/dB sharply decreases, the slight decrement of flux density in the upper part of the tooth, due to the longitudinal slot flux, causes the field intensity to decrease but slightly and has but a slight influence upon V, which is determined first of all by the field strength near the minimum cross-section.

Thus the question arises whether it is at all necessary to take into account the influence of H'_{xs} upon the magnetic conditions of the tooth.

This problem will be tackled in the following manner.

The first step is to develop a nomographic method for the computation of the influence of H'_{xs} upon the values Φ_τ and V. This will then be used to examine, by an example, the quantitative aspect of this influence to find out whether it is at all necessary to consider it.

Our nomographic method has so far relied on the assumption that the flux passing through a ferromagnetic body (tooth) is equal at each value x of the height. Flux Φ_τ (if H_{xs} is neglected), however, passes the tooth only below $h - b/\pi$. Beyond this height there is a linear decrement, because part of it leaves through the side walls of the tooth and becomes a component of the longitudinal slot flux.

Let us assume that the tooth (Fig. 4-1b) is divided into two parts, one of which has a height $h_{\mathrm{I}} = h - b/\pi$, and the other b/π. Without incurring the danger of serious error, we obviously can assume that the whole flux passes through part I, whence the relationship of V and Φ in this part can be determined by the methods expounded in chapter 2 in the same manner as for the wedge-shaped body having a height of $h_{\mathrm{I}} = h - b/\pi$, a minimum width $b_{2\mathrm{I}} = b_2$ and a maximum width

$$b_{0\mathrm{I}} = b_2 + (b_0 - b_2)\frac{h_{\mathrm{I}}}{h}$$

According to Eq. (4-21a), the field strength increases linearly from zero for $x = h - b/\pi$ to its maximum for $x = h$. Therefore, the part of the tooth flux leaving the tooth in the region $h - b/\pi < x < h$ and entering the slot will have a constant density along the height of part II, whence its magnetic relations in this part can be determined in the same manner as for the body of Fig. 2-10.

The said body replacing part II of the tooth has a height $h_{\mathrm{II}} = b/\pi$, a maximum width $b_{0\mathrm{II}}$, a minimum width $b_{2\mathrm{II}} = b_{0\mathrm{I}}$, while the flux passing through its minimum cross-section will be $\Phi_t = \Phi_\tau$, the flux passing through the maximum cross-section

$$\Phi_0 = \Phi_\tau \frac{b_0\,k_c}{b_0 + b} \tag{4-22}$$

(cf. Eq. 4-19), and the flux leaving its side walls in two branches will be

$$\Phi_\tau\left[1 - \frac{b_0\,k_c}{b_0 + b}\right]$$

The factor k for the body replacing part II is

$$k = \frac{b - b_0(k_c - 1)}{2\,(b_0 + b)} \tag{4-23}$$

while the factor ϱ_{II} can be determined with the formula (2-21).

Since, according to Eq. (4-22), the minimum flux density

$$B_0 = \frac{\Phi_0}{b_0 \gamma l} = \Phi_\tau \frac{k_c}{(b_0 + b)\gamma l}$$

the magnetic conditions do not change if, on the one hand, the flux passing through the crown of the tooth will be Φ_τ instead of Φ_0 and, on the other, if the maximum width of part II changes according to the ratio

$$\frac{b_0 + b}{b_0 k_c} : 1$$

The factor of the air gap should, however, be computed with respect to the actual width by using, for instance, the formula

$$k_c = \frac{10\delta + b + b_0}{10\delta + b_0} \tag{4-24}$$

Thus part II of the tooth is replaced by a body having the parameters

$$h_{II} = \frac{b}{\pi}, \quad b_{0II} = \frac{b_0 + b}{k_c}, \quad b_{2II} = b_{0I}$$

and the factors ϱ_{II} to be computed according to Eqs. (4-23) and (4-21).

Since, according to our assumption, the flux passing through part II is the same as the one passing through part I, both parts can be replaced by a single tooth of h height on the strength of the method developed in chapter 3.

Let these considerations be illustrated in a practical example.

Example 60. The tooth, the slot and the air gap of Fig. 4-1b have the following parameters: $b_2 = 1$ cm, $b_0 = 1$ cm, $h = 2$ cm, $b = 1$ cm, $\gamma l = 20$ cm, $\delta = 0.5$ cm. Replace this configuration by an equivalent tooth having no longitudinal slot flux.

Compute for part I the height $h_I = 1.682$ cm, the minimum width $b_{2I} = 1$ cm, the maximum width $b_{0I} = 1$ cm, and the factor $\varrho_I = 1$ according to the formula (2-6).

For part II we have the height $h_{II} = 0.318$ cm, the minimum width $b_{2II} = b_{0I} = 1$, the factor $k_c = 1.166$ and from Eq. (4-23) the factor $k = 0.208$.

We determine the factor ϱ_{II} with Eq. (2-21) whereas

$$b_{0II} = \frac{b_0 + b}{k_c} = 1.71$$

Determine the parameters $b_{0\text{res}}$ and ϱ_{res} by using the method explained in section 3-2. In this case we have

$$h_{\text{res}} = h_{\text{I}} + h_{\text{II}} = h$$

Replace part I and part II by a resultant tooth, presuming that $\Phi_\tau = 480{,}000$ M, find for the abscissa $B_{0\text{I}} = 24{,}000$ G the ordinate 2,260 A/cm on curve $\varrho_{\text{I}} = 1$, i.e. $P_{\text{I}} = 3{,}800$ A. On curve $\varrho_{\text{II}} = 1.71$ the ordinate 510 A/cm pertains to the abscissa 14,000 G, i.e. $P_{\text{II}} = 160$ A. The ordinate

$$\frac{V_{\text{I}} + V_{\text{II}}}{h_{\text{I}} + h_{\text{II}}} = 1{,}980 \text{ A/cm}$$

yields for $\varrho_{\text{res}} = 1.44$ the flux density $B_{0\text{res}} = 19{,}000\ \text{G} = 480{,}000/b_{0\text{res}} \cdot 20$.

Accordingly, the actual tooth can be replaced by one having the parameters $h = 2$ cm, $b_{0\text{res}} = 1.265$ cm and $\varrho_{\text{res}} = 1.44$.

Let us check now the influence of the longitudinal slot flux upon the magnetic conditicns in the tooth.

In the new tooth flux $\Phi_\tau = 480{,}000$ M creates a density $B_0 = 19{,}000$ G. On curve $\varrho = 1.44$ the ordinate pertaining to this abscissa is $V/h = 1{,}980$ A/cm, i.e. $V = 3{,}960$ A.

Should we have a tooth without longitudinal slot flux, the abscissa pertaining to the magnitude $V = 3{,}960$ A and $V/h = 1{,}980$ A/cm on curve $\varrho = 1$ would be $B_0 = 23{,}650$ G, i.e. $\Phi = 473{,}000$ M would be obtained instead of the actual flux 480,000 M.

This shows that by neglecting the influence of the longitudinal slot flux upon the magnetic conditions in the tooth, the error committed in determining the flux amounts to no more than 1.5 per cent.

In this example we have examined instances not frequently encountered with open slots and parallel-walls teeth under heavy magnetic demand.

Obviously a decrement of a involves a decrease of V_{II} as compared to V_{I}, whence the said error will be even smaller. Consequently, the unloading effect of this kind of slot flux upon the magnetic conditions in the tooth can justly be neglected altogether.*

* The fact that we shall neglect the unloading effect of this flux does not mean that it has no significance for our computations. Its influence on the distribution of the magnetic flux in the air gap will be taken into account in chapter 6 by using Carter's factor.

4-3. *The Nomographic Determination of the Longitudinal Flux in the Open Slot with Parallel Walls, Due to the Saturation of the Adjacent Teeth*

Let us first investigate the case when both slots and teeth have parallel walls, i.e. $\alpha = 1$ and $\varrho = 1$ (Fig. 4-3a). Under such conditions both the flux density and the field strength will be identical at all heights, whence both the tooth and slot fluxes should be identical throughout the height. The formula

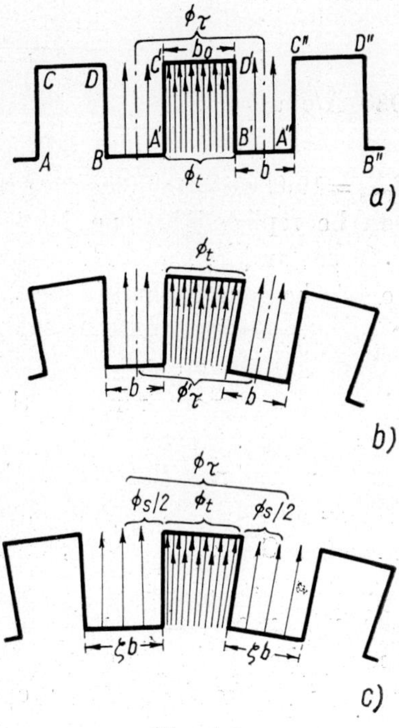

Fig. 4-3

$$0.4\pi \frac{V}{h} b' l = \Phi_s$$

can be used for calculating the longitudinal slot flux, while for the computation of the tooth flux we have the formula

$$\Phi_\tau - 0.4\pi \frac{V}{h} b' l = \Phi_t$$

In these formulae, b' is the effective width of the slot including the space between the steel sheets (if any), which can be determined with the formula (1-4) for wedge-shaped bodies.

The relation of the slot flux and of the tooth flux can readily be determined with the nomographic method in the following manner.

Let us plot a set of straight lines extending from point O (Fig. 4-4) to the left of the ordinate axis. Dividing the tooth flux by the value of the maximum tooth cross-section $b_0 \gamma l$, we obtain the value B_0 which is connected through our set of curves with the value V/h. Let us select from the said set of straight lines (Fig. 4-4) the line OA for which the tangent of the inclination angle enclosed with the axis of the ordinate equals $0.4\ \pi b'/b_0\gamma$. The next step is to find, on the curve $\varrho = 1$ characterizing the given tooth form and on the straight line OA, the points C and M having identical ordinates and a distance of $\Phi_\tau/b_0\gamma l$ between them.

The ordinate of these points $\overline{CK}$ yields the value V/h, the length $\overline{ML}$ corresponds to the value of

$$0.4\pi \frac{b' l}{b_0 \gamma l} \cdot \frac{V}{h} = \frac{\Phi_s}{b_0 \gamma l}$$

while $\overline{LC}$ to B_0.

With the given parameters the pertaining tooth flux $\overline{LC} \cdot b_0\gamma l$, the longitudinal slot flux $\overline{ML} \cdot b_0\gamma l$ and the mean field strength in the tooth $\overline{CK} = V/h$ can be determined for any flux Φ_τ or vice

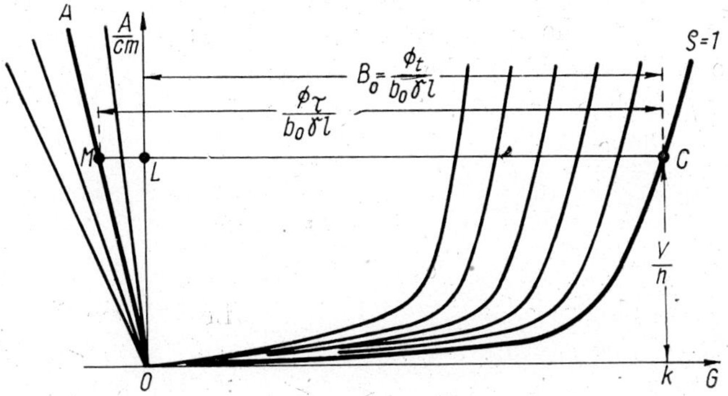

Fig. 4-4

versa; the flux Φ_τ passing through the tooth pitch and its branches for V/h. In other words, Fig. 4-4 enables us to determine in a simple manner the reluctance of the entire region of a tooth and the parallel slot.

This nomographic method can, however, only be applied to the case of $a = 1$. Take now, for instance, a wedge-shaped tooth with $a < 1$. In this case we have a longitudinal slot flux as shown in Fig. 4-1c. The distribution of the slot flux and the tooth flux in the case of constant Φ_τ changes in relation to the distribution according to Fig. 4-3a. Around the crown of the tooth, both the slot flux and the tooth flux will decrease, while around the slot they will increase.

Since the determination of the magnetic relations with the help of the set of curves in the nomogram relies on the assumption that the flux passing through the tooth is constant, while in plotting the straight lines OA of Fig. 4-4 the constancy of the slot flux along the height x was also presumed, the above method cannot be applied directly to the case of $a < 1$.

If the flux Φ_τ were not distributed according to Fig. 4-1c but as in Fig. 4-3b, i. e. if it were divided into slot flux and tooth flux, this method could be applied with the sole difference that point C should be located not on curve $\varrho = 1$, but on a curve pertaining to the value ϱ for the given tooth.

On substituting the distribution of flux Φ_τ of Fig. 4-3b for the distribution in Fig. 4-1c, a certain error will anyway be committed because, in the case of constant values of V/h, the flux Φ'_τ obtained in Fig. 4-3b is somewhat smaller than the actual flux Φ_τ. This will be evident from the following considerations:

The field strength of the slot flux in Fig. 4-3b is constant and equals V/h, while in Fig. 4-1c it changes along the height and equals H_x. Since

$$\frac{1}{h}\int_0^h H_x\,dx = \frac{V}{h}$$

a certain height x_k exists at which the field strength H_x in Fig. 4-1c equals V/h of Fig. 4-3b. In the range $0 < x < x_k$ the value $H_x > V/h$, and in the range $x_k < x < h$ the value $H_x < V/h$.

Let us start by examining the range for which $0 < x < x_k$ is valid. In Fig. 4-1c the slot flux is $0.4\,\pi H_x b'l$ at a height x, while in Fig. 4-3b at the same height it equals $0.4\,\pi b'l\,V/h$, i. e. it is smaller by

$$0.4\pi\left(H_x - \frac{V}{h}\right)b'\,l$$

because within this range $H_x > V/h$. Accordingly, the tooth flux in Fig. 4—1c is by the same value smaller than in Fig. 4-3b. In a similar manner it can be ascertained that within the range $x_k < x < h$ the tooth flux is, according to Fig. 4-1c, greater by

$$0.4\pi\left(\frac{V}{h} - H_x\right)b'\,l$$

than in Fig. 4-3b.

Let us presume that in some way or other the above-mentioned flux difference

$$0.4\pi \left(H_x - \frac{V}{h} \right) b' \, l$$

has been transposed, in the range $0 < x < x_k$, from the slot into the tooth, which would correspond to the transition from Fig. 4-1c to Fig. 4-3b. In this case the tooth flux density would increase by

$$\frac{0.4\pi \left(H_x - \frac{V}{h} \right) b' \, l}{b_x \gamma l}$$

and the pertaining field strength by

$$\frac{0.4\pi \left(H_x - \frac{V}{h} \right) b' \, l}{b_x \gamma l \, \mu_x}$$

The potential difference between points $x = 0$ and $x = x_k$ would increase by a certain value that could be denoted $\Delta V_{0<x<x_k}$. It is thus evident that

$$\Delta V_{0<x<x_k} = \int\limits_0^{x_k} \frac{0.4\pi \left(H_x - \frac{V}{h} \right) b' \, l}{b_x \gamma l \, \mu_x} dx \tag{4-25}$$

If within the range $x_k < x < h$ the flux difference of

$$0.4\pi \left(\frac{V}{h} - H_x \right) b' \, l$$

could be transposed from the tooth into the slot (which would mean, in this range too, a transition from Fig. 4-1c to Fig. 4-3b), the potential difference between points $x = x_k$ and $x = h$ would decrease by a certain value $\Delta V_{x_k<x<h}$ whose magnitude is

$$\Delta V_{x_k<x<h} = \int\limits_{x_k}^{h} \frac{0.4\pi \left(\frac{V}{h} - H_x \right) b' \, l}{b_x \gamma l \, \mu_x} dx \tag{4-26}$$

Should b_x and μ_x remain constant with an increasing x, the value $\Delta V_{0<x<x_k} + \Delta V_{x_k<x<h}$ (around which the potential difference pertaining to the entire tooth would increase) would be

$$\frac{0.4\,\pi\,b'\,l}{b_x\,\gamma\,l\,\mu_x}\int_0^h\left(\frac{V}{h}-H_x\right)dx$$

i. e. zero according to the formula (1-2a). In other words, the value V would not change in this case.

Since, however, the parameters b_x and μ_x in the range $0 < x < x_k$ are smaller than in the range $x_k < x < h$, obviously $\Delta V_{0<x<x_k}$ will be greater than $\Delta V_{x_k<x<h}$. This is why V as a whole increases. Since it has been assumed that Φ_τ undergoes no change, we find that in the transition from Fig. 4-1c to Fig. 4-3b, the resultant reluctance of the region of a tooth and a slot increases, which again means that flux Φ_τ, in the case of equal V values, is smaller in Fig. 4-3b.

This error can, however, be taken into account and corrected by a certain modification of the nomographic method.

The correction can be achieved by substituting for the slot width b' another, somewhat higher value, $\zeta b'$ (Fig. 4-3c), i.e. by substituting for the slot flux $0.4\ \pi b'l\ V/h$ the flux

$$\Phi_s = 0.4\,\pi\zeta\,b'\,l\,\frac{V}{h} \tag{4-27}$$

This solution would be correct if the factor ζ were at least approximately constant for the different magnetic demands.

4-4. The Theoretical Foundation of the Possibility of Replacing the Actual Slot Flux by an Equivalent Flux Constant Along the Height of the Slot

Let us clarify the error involved in replacing the flux distribution in the tooth pitch as shown in Fig. 4-1c by its distribution according to Fig. 4-3b and check the possibility of correcting it by the aid of the factor ζ having an approximately constant value for the different magnetic demands.

The actual flux density in any point of the tooth is

$$B_x = \frac{\Phi_\tau - 0.4\pi\,H_x\,b'\,l}{b_x\,\gamma l} \tag{4-28}$$

By introducing $0.4\ \pi\zeta b'l\ \dfrac{V}{h}$ for $0.4\ \pi H_x b'l$, the error committed amounts to

$$\Delta B_x = \frac{0.4\pi b'}{b_x \gamma}\left(\frac{V}{h}\zeta - H_x\right) \tag{4-29}$$

when computing the tooth flux density. Again, when calculating the field strength at the same point, the error committed is ΔH_x.

Since these errors are not great, it can be assumed with fair accuracy that

$$\frac{\Delta H_x}{\Delta B_x} = \frac{dH_x}{dB_x}\,. \tag{4-30}$$

where dH_x/dB_x is the derivative, corresponding to B_x, of the magnetizing curve. We can, therefore, write

$$\Delta H_x = \Delta B_x \frac{dH_x}{dB_x} = \Delta B_x \frac{dH_x}{dx}\;\frac{dx}{db_x}\;\frac{db_x}{dB_x} \tag{4-31}$$

On the strength of the equation

$$b_x = b_0\left[1 - (1-a)\frac{h-x}{h}\right] \tag{4-32}$$

we obtain

$$\frac{dx}{db_x} = \frac{h}{b_0(1-a)} \tag{4-33}$$

and

$$\frac{dB_x}{db_x} = d\,\frac{\left(\dfrac{\Phi_t}{b_x \gamma l}\right)}{db_x} \tag{4-34}$$

Since Φ_t cannot essentially change along the slot and since what we are concerned with here is not the field strength but the flux density, Φ_t can be taken as constant, whence

$$\frac{db_x}{dB_x} = -\frac{b_x^2 \gamma l}{\Phi_t} = -\frac{\gamma l b_0^2\left[1-(1-a)\dfrac{h-x}{h}\right]^2}{\Phi_t} \tag{4-35}$$

The relationship between the values H_x, V and dH_x/dx can be expressed analytically on the basis of the following considerations.

If the flux is increased to its possible maximum value encountered in practical computations (i.e. if we take the highest possible value

B_0), in general H_x will be distributed according to

$$H_{x\max} = f_{\max}\left(\frac{x}{h}\right) \tag{4-36}$$

In this case the following equations can be derived

$$\frac{1}{h}\int_0^h H_x\,dx = \frac{V}{h}$$

$$\frac{1}{h}\int_0^h H_{x\max}\,dx = \int_0^1 f_{\max}\left(\frac{x}{h}\right) d\,\frac{x}{h} = \frac{V_{\max}}{h} \tag{4-37}$$

In the given tooth form, i. e. with the given value a, the ratio $V/V_{\max}$ depends only on the magnitude of the flux (i. e. on the value B_0), whence we may write

$$\frac{V}{V_{\max}} = f(B_0) \tag{4-38}$$

Let us assume that

$$\frac{H_x}{H_{x\max}} = \frac{V}{V_{\max}}$$

i. e. that

$$H_x = f(B_0)\,f_{\max}\left(\frac{x}{h}\right) \tag{4-39}$$

and examine the error now involved. In the case of maximum magnetic demand, when $V = V_{\max}$, the function $f(B_0) = 1$, the field strength $H_x = H_{\max}$, i. e. Eq. (4-39) will yield an accurate result.

In the case of a decrease in the flux Eq. (4-39) cannot be used without committing some slight error. Since, however, with the decrease of the flux the decrease of the field strength H_x will be essentially more rapid, the absolute value of this error will be very small.

It can readily be understood that the mean value of all values H_x computed with Eq. (4-39) for different magnitudes of x will correspond to the actual value because

$$\int^1 f(B_0)\,f_{\max}\left(\frac{x}{h}\right) d\left(\frac{x}{h}\right) = V\int_0^1 \frac{H_{x\max}}{V_{\max}}\,d\left(\frac{x}{h}\right) = \frac{V}{h} = \int_0^1 H_x\,d\left(\frac{x}{h}\right) \tag{4-40}$$

In other words, if for some magnitude x/h Eq. (4-39) yields too low values of the fields strength H_x, it will yield too high ones for other magnitudes of x/h.

All this entitles us to regard Eq. (4-39) as a sufficiently accurate one. By substituting H_x into Eq. (4-29) from Eq. (4-39) and b_x from Eq. (4-32), we obtain the magnitude of the error ΔB_x.

By determining the differential quotient

$$\frac{dH_x}{dx} = f(B_0) f'_{max}\left(\frac{x}{h}\right) \tag{4-41}$$

and introducing the corresponding values from Eqs. (4-29), (4-41), (4-33) and (4-35) into Eq. (4-31), the error ΔH_x can be determined, and by integrating it within the range $x = 0$ and $x = h$, the error ΔV involved in the computation of the potential fall along the tooth can be obtained:

$$\Delta V = \int_0^h \Delta H_x\, dx = \frac{0.4\,\pi\, b'\, h^2\, l}{(1-a)\,\Phi_t}[f(B_0)]^2 \int_0^1 f'_{max}\left(\frac{x}{h}\right)\left[1-(1-a)\frac{h-x}{h}\right]\times$$
$$\times\left[f_{max}\left(\frac{x}{h}\right) - V_{max}\frac{\zeta}{h}\right] d\left(\frac{x}{h}\right) \tag{4-42}$$

Let us assume that for certain given values of Φ_t, $f(B_0)$ and a the factor ζ has been so computed that the integral

$$\int_0^1 f'_{max}\left(\frac{x}{h}\right)\left[1-(1-a)\frac{h-x}{h}\right]\left[f_{max}\left(\frac{x}{h}\right) - V_{max}\frac{\zeta}{h}\right] d\left(\frac{x}{h}\right)$$

in Eq. (4-42) should be zero, i.e. with a view to eliminating the error. Then, as shown by the formula, the said integral will not be dependent on the degree of the magnetic demand, i.e. on Φ_t and $f(B_0)$, whence the error ΔV will equal to zero for every possible magnetic demand.

4-5. Theoretical Considerations Underlying the Nomographic Determination of the Magnetic Relations in the Region of Tooth and Slot in Wedge-Shaped Teeth and Slots with Parallel Walls

In the previous section we have seen that the factor ζ preserves with sufficient accuracy its value under different magnetic demands, whence the effect of the longitudinal slot flux due to the saturation of the tooth can be determined with the help of the set of curves taken from the nomogram. Let us find now a method for determining this factor.

The actual distribution of the longitudinal slot flux for a definite configuration and a definite flux pertaining to the tooth pitch can be obtained on the basis of the given magnetizing curve. Relying on the same characteristic we can compute the value of the equivalent longitudinal flux $0.4\ \pi\zeta b'lV/h$ necessary to obtain the same value V/h for an unchanged flux Φ_τ. Such computations can be performed for different configurations and the factor ζ can be obtained as the graphical function of the configuration of the body.

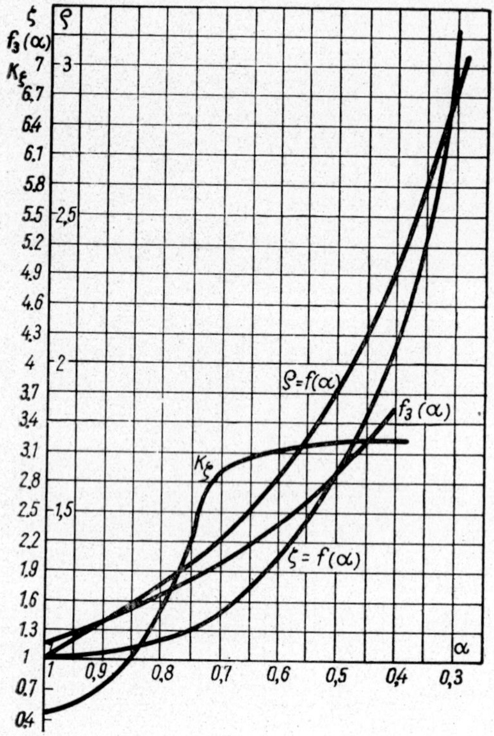

Fig. 4-5

It should be remembered that the integral, contained in Eq. (4-42) and equalling zero in the case of the proper choice of ζ, does not depend upon the parameters b', b_0, l and h. Beside x/h, only the values a and ζ are behind the sign of the integral, consequently, for every value a there exists a given value ζ with which the error ΔV disappears. Thus the factor ζ only depends on a and can be represented by a single curve. The function $\zeta = f(a)$ can be determined in the following manner.

Let us draw a tooth with a given a value and the adjacent slot. The relation of the width of the tooth to that of the slot should be normal. By assuming a maximum flux density $B_{0\max}$ we obtain at this point the pertaining field strength $H_{x\max}$, the actual value of the longitudinal slot flux $0.4\,\pi\,H_{x\max} b' l$ and the flux

$$\Phi_\tau = a\, b_0\, l\, \gamma\, B_{0\max} + 0.4\,\pi\, H_{x\max}\, b'\, l$$

Then compute the distribution of flux Φ_τ between the tooth and the slot in the other tooth cross-section and on this basis determine the value of V. By the aid of the set of curves it is possible to determine

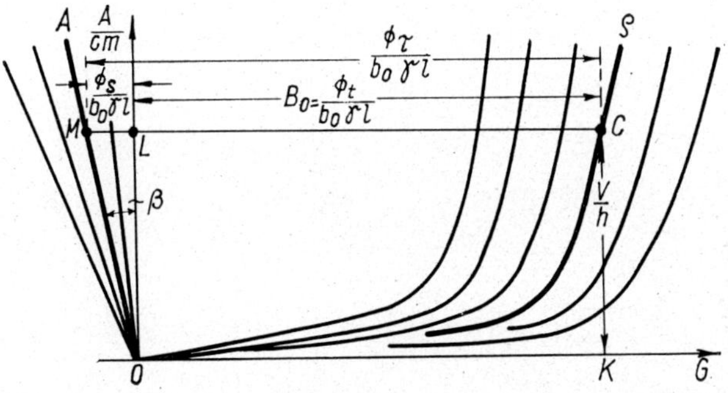

Fig. 4-6

nomographically the equivalent constant tooth flux Φ_t that would cause the same potential drop V in the tooth. Then ζ can readily be computed from the equation

$$\Phi_\tau = \Phi_t + 0.4\,\pi\, b'\, l \zeta\, \frac{V}{h}$$

where ζ is the only unknown value.

By repeating similar computations for every a value we obtain the required curve $\zeta = f(a)$ shown in Fig. 4-5.

Thus by using the factor ζ, the same nomographic method for the computation of the influence of the parallel slot can be applied for teeth with any arbitrary a as for teeth with $a = 1$ (cf. section 4-3).

4-6. Approach to the Practical Determination of the Magnetic Relations in the Region of Tooth and Slot in the Case of Wedge-Shaped Teeth and Slots with Parallel Walls

On the basis of theoretical considerations (section 4-5) the magnetic relations in the region of a tooth and a parallel slot, in the case of

TABLE 4-1

No. of Ex.	Relation of max. width of tooth to min. width	Given value of V A	α	ζ	ϱ	B_0 pertaining to ordinate V/h of curve ϱ G	Φ_t M	Φ_s M	Flux Φ_τ M according to nomogr. method	Flux Φ_τ M according to usual exact method	Remarks
1	2	3	4	5	6	7	8	9	10	11	12
61	1.6	729	0.625	1.9	1.55	14,150	22,600	580	23,180	23,350	See Ex. 8
62	1.6	1,860	0.625	1.9	1.55	15,500	24,800	1,480	26,280	26,440	See Ex. 11
63	2.2	381	0.455	3.4	2.07	10,300	22,700	540	23,240	23,350	See Ex. 9
64	2.2	968	0.455	3.4	2.07	11,300	24,900	1,480	26,380	26,440	See Ex. 12 ϱ computed for $\alpha = 0.4$
65	3.4	198	0.294	7.6	2.34	9,000	22,500	640	23,140	23,350	See Ex. 10 ζ computed for $\alpha = 0.294$
66	3.4	498	0.294	7.6	2.34	9,850	24,600	1,570	26,170	26,440	See Ex. 13 B_0 determined for $h = 1.875$ cm and $b_0 = 2.5$ cm; Φ_s determined for $h = 3$ cm

wedge-shaped teeth and slots with parallel walls, can be determined in the following order of succession.

A) The determination of magnetic paramenters for a given flux Φ_τ

1. Compute a and, with Eq. (2-6), determine the factor ϱ.

2. Determine the factor $\zeta = f(a)$ with the help of Fig. 4-5.

3. Among the set of straight lines diverging radially from point O in Fig. 4-6, find the line OA for which the tangent of the angle made with the ordinate axis is

$$\tan\beta = 0.4\pi\zeta \frac{b'l}{b_0 \gamma} \tag{4-43}$$

4. Find, on the curve corresponding to ϱ, the point C whose horizontal distance from the straight line AO is $\overline{MC} = \Phi_\tau / b_0 \gamma l$.

5. The ordinate $\overline{KC}$ multiplied by the tooth height h yields the potential difference V.

6. The ordinate $\overline{KC}$ multiplied by $0.4\ \pi\zeta b'l$ yields the equivalent slot flux Φ_s.

7. The abscissa of point K (section LC) multiplied by $b_0 \gamma l$ yields the equivalent tooth flux Φ_t.

B) The determination of magnetic parameters for a given value of the potential difference V

1. Compute the factors a and ϱ and determine the position of the straight line OA as in points 1, 2 and 3 of part A.

2. Determine, on the curve pertaining to ϱ, the point C whose ordinate is V/h.

3. The abscissa $\overline{LC}$ multiplied by $b_0 \gamma l$ yields the equivalent tooth flux Φ_t.

4. The ordinate $\overline{KC}$ multiplied by $0.4\ \pi b' \zeta l$ yields the equivalent slot flux Φ_s.

5. The sum $\Phi_s + \Phi_t$ is the flux of the tooth pitch Φ_τ.

The application of this method will be illustrated by some examples, which will also serve to check the degree of its accuracy. For this purpose let us determine nomographically, for given geometrical forms (Exs. 61 to 66 in Table 4-1), the magnetic relations and collate them with the values obtained by using the exact, but very cumbersome, approach of the usual method.

We shall proceed from slot and tooth configurations as in Exs. 8 to 13 and regard the values V computed in Table 1-3 (column 5) as given. The task consists in determining nomographically the corresponding fluxes Φ_τ to be compared with the fluxes Φ_τ computed for Exs. 8 to 13.

Let us replace in Exs. 65 and 66 the actual tooth by a tooth having the parameters $a = 0.4$ and $h = 1.875$ cm, compute ϱ for $a = 0.4$ and ζ for the actual value $a = 0.294$.

As shown by columns 10 and 11 in Table 4-1, the deviation of the values Φ_τ obtained by the two different methods does not exceed 1 per cent, even within the wide range of tooth configurations and magnetic demand. Consequently, the simple nomographic method yields results just as accurate as the extremely involved and cumbersome usual method.

4-7. Theoretical Considerations Underlying the Nomographic Determination of the Magnetic Relations in the Region of Tooth and Slot in the Case of Parallel-Walled Teeth and Wedge-Shaped Slots

In some electrical machines the rotors have parallel-walled teeth and wedge-shaped slots (Fig. 4-7). In examining such configurations we shall proceed from Fig. 4-3a in which both teeth and slot have parallel walls. Let the teeth in Fig. 4-7 be assumed to have the same dimensions as in Fig. 4-3a and in both cases an identical flux Φ_τ to pass through the tooth pitch, whence there will be an approximately identical distribution of flux density and field strength in both teeth. In this case the slot flux in Fig. 4-7 will be, at a height x,

$$\left[b_b + (b_l - b_b)\frac{x}{h}\right] 0.4\,\pi H_x l$$

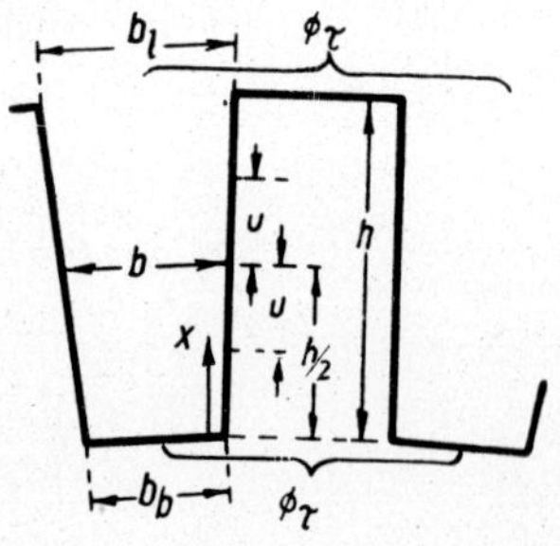

Fig. 4-7

where b_b = the width of the slot at the bottom,

b_l = the width at $x = h$.

If we presume that the width of the slot in Fig. 4-7 at $x = h/2$ equals width b of the slot in Fig. 4-3a, then at $x = h/2 - u$ the slot flux in Fig. 4-7 will be less by

$$0.4\,\pi l H_x \frac{u}{h}(b_l - b_b)$$

and at $x = h/2 + u$ greater by the same value than the slot flux in Fig. 4-3a. Accordingly, at a height $x = h/2 - u$ the slot flux in Fig. 4-7 will be greater by the same value, and at $x = h/2 + u$ less than the slot flux in Fig. 4-3a. The change in the flux density in the tooth at a distance of $\pm u$ from the height $h/2$ will be

$$\Delta B_x = \pm \frac{0.4\,\pi\, H_x\,(b_l - b_b)\,\frac{u}{h}}{b_0\,\gamma} \tag{4-44}$$

and the corresponding change in the field strength

$$\Delta H_x \approx \Delta B_x \frac{d\,H_x}{d\,B_x} = \pm \frac{0.4\,\pi\, H_x\,(b_l - b_b)\,\frac{u}{h}}{b_0\,\gamma} \frac{d\,H_x}{d\,B_x} \tag{4-45}$$

For teeth with parallel walls it may be assumed that the values dH_x/dB_x at different heights are practically constant. It may therefore be presumed that with any change in the slot flux the field strength in the tooth at $h/2 + u$ will increase by the same value as its decrement at $h/2 - u$, i.e. that with identical fluxes Φ_τ along the teeth of both figures identical potential differences V will be acting. This means that the teeth in Fig. 4-7 and in Fig. 4-3a are magnetically equivalent, and therefore the nomographic method can be applied also to the form in Fig. 4-7 if the slot width is taken as

$$b = \frac{b_l + b_b}{2} \tag{4-46}$$

and the factors ζ and ϱ as equalling unity.

4-8. *Approach to the Practical Determination of the Magnetic Relations in the Region of Tooth and Slot in the Case of Parallel-Walled Teeth and Wedge-Shaped Slots*

Relying on the considerations expounded in section 4-7, the magnetic relations in the regions of a tooth with parallel walls and the parallel wedge-shaped slot can be determined in the following order of succession.

1. Compute b according to Eq. (4-46).
2. Compute b' according to Eq. (1-4) and assume $\tau = 1$, $\varrho = 1$.

In the following the process is identical with the one in section 4-6.

Example 67. The following values are known: $b_b = 0.95$ cm, $b_t = 1.91$ cm, $b_0 = b_2 = 1$ cm, $h = 3$ cm, $\gamma = 0.95$, $l = 10.5$ cm, $V = 1{,}500$ A.

Determine flux Φ_τ. Compute with Eqs. (4-46) and (1-4) the width $b' = 1.48$ cm. On the curve $\varrho = 1$ for ordinate $V/h = 500$ A/cm determine the point C whose abscissa $\overline{LC} = 20{,}700$ G.

By using the method of section 4-6, the corresponding fluxes are obtained as

$$\Phi_t = 207{,}000 \text{ M}, \quad \Phi_s \approx 9{,}300 \text{ M}, \quad \Phi_\tau = 216{,}300 \text{ M}.$$

4-9. Theoretical Considerations Underlying the Determination of he Magnetic Relations in the Region of Tooth and Slot with Cylindrical Walls

In electrical machines with circular or half-closed slots the configurations shown in Fig. 4-8 may occur.

Such a configuration contains two series-connected fields $DD'O'O$ and $OO'C'C$ having identical magnetic reluctances and each consisting of a tooth with cylindrical walls $A'C'$ and CB and two parallel-connected half slots OBC and $O'A'C'$. Since in Fig. 4-8 the magnetic flux Φ_τ is distributed in an involved pattern between the ferromagnetic body $BA'C'C$ and the two half slots OBC and $O'A'C'$, this case escapes the application of the method explained in section 4-6, because the factor ζ is computed there with assumption of a wedge-shaped tooth and a parallel-walled slot. With a view to considering the new conditions, such as a tooth with cylindrical walls and a slot bounded by a circular arc, let us examine their influence upon the distribution of the magnetic parameters.

Divide tooth $BA'C'C$ into two symmetrical parts by the line EF and replace both half slots OBC and $A'O'C'$ by the slot $EE'F'F$ (Fig. 4-8b) having a constant width b equal to the actual maximum width $2\,\overline{OB}$ of the slot. Place the slot $EE'F'F$ between the two halves $EFCB$ and $E'F'C'A'$ of the tooth and assume the above flux Φ_τ to pass through the region $BA'C'C$ (Fig. 4-8b).

This substitution leaves the field strength in sections BE and $E'A'$ as well as at the bottom EE' of the slot unchanged. Nor does it change actually in the other tooth cross sections $EFCB$ and $E'F'C'A'$ located close to the line BA' because an increase of x causes their width to change according to the same rule as in Fig. 4-8a. The field strength in the slot also changes but slightly, because the width of the slot in Fig. 4-8a changes but insignificantly with small changes in the value of x.

Thus, in that part of the configuration where the greatest field intensities arise, having a decisive influence upon the creation of potential differences V, the region $BA'C'C$ (Fig. 4-8b) is almost equivalent to the region $OO'C'C$ (Fig. 4-8a). If x increases considerably, the width of the slot in Fig. 4-8a decreases rather rapidly. Nevertheless, the cross-section of the tooth changes here too in the same way as in Fig. 4-8b, whence it may be assumed, as a first approximation, that there is an identical distribution of field strength along the height for both con-

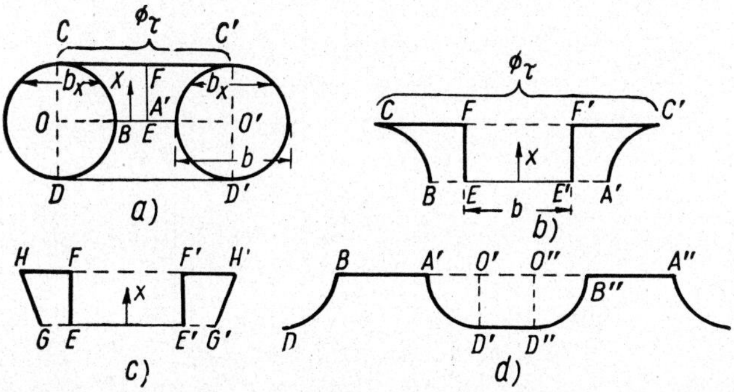

Fig. 4-8

figurations. Thus, with high values of x, the magnetic difference between the two configurations will be the difference of the form of their slots which determines the increment of the slot flux by $(b - b_x)\, lH_x$ for Fig. 4-8b, as compared to the slot flux in Fig. 4-8a.

The decrement of the tooth flux will obviously be very small and, owing to the low values of flux density in this region, will not involve significant changes in the magnitude of the field intensity of the teeth. Considering again that the part of the potential difference V of the tooth in this region is very small, we may conclude that the error in computing V, involved in the above substitution, exerts a very small effect on the magnitude of the resultant reluctance in the tooth and the slot, whence $OO'C'C$ (Fig. 4-8a) can be replaced by $BA'C'C$ (Fig. 4-8b).

Let us examine now the problems connected with the computation of the factor ζ. Assume that the teeth $BEFC$ and $E'A'C'F'$ (Fig. 4-8b) are replaced by the wedge-shaped teeth $GEFH$ and $E'G'H'F'$ (Fig. 4-8c) with identical parameters h, b_2, γl and ϱ. Should the magnetic flux Φ_τ responsible for the potential differences V pass through the field $GG'H'H$, it could, according to the method of the section 4-6, be replaced by the flux Φ_s and the tooth flux Φ_t, constant at all heights.

Let us examine the error involved in replacing the actual distribution of Φ_τ within the region $BA'C'C$ (Fig. 4-8b) by the constant fluxes Φ_s and Φ_t. Obviously, owing to the identity of the slots in both configurations, the flux Φ_s creates along the slot in Fig. 4-8c the same potential difference V as along the slot in Fig. 4-8b. Owing to some difference in the form of the teeth in Fig. 4-8c, the flux Φ_t will create a somewhat different distribution H_x along the height than in the teeth in Fig. 4-8b.

Since, however, with identical parameters b_2, γl, h and ϱ, i.e. identical reluctance, the flux Φ_t necessarily creates an identical potential drop V in both teeth, the above-mentioned change in the distribution of the field strength H_x will exert practically no effect on the magnitude of V.

Relying on the above considerations, the substitution of $GG'H'H$ for $BA'C'C$ (Fig. 4-8b) also seems to be permissible. The factor ζ can therefore be computed from a obtained from ϱ according to Eq. (2-6) or to the curve $\varrho = f(a)$ (Fig. 4-5) plotted in compliance with Eq. (2-6).

4-10. Approach to the Practical Determination of the Magnetic Relations in the Region of Tooth and Slot with Cylindrical Walls

Relying on the considerations expounded in section 4-9, the magnetic relations in the field $OO'C'C$ (Fig. 4-8a) between two slots with cylindrical walls can be determined in the following order of succession.

1. Determine for the body $BA'C'C$ the values ϱ, b_0 and h or h' with the method of section 2-10.

2. For the value of ϱ thus obtained determine, according to Fig. 4-5, the factor a and from the latter, the corresponding values of ζ.

3. Take for the slot width the maximum width of the actual slot.

The remaining steps are identical with those listed in section 4-6.

Example 68. A geometrical configuration is given corresponding to the area $DD'C'C$ in Fig. 4-8a with the following parameters: $\overline{BA'} = 0.8$ cm, $\overline{OB} = r = h = 0.5$ cm, $\gamma l = 1$ cm.

Determine Φ_τ passing through the said field under the effect of the potential difference $V = 2{,}000$ A.

For the body $BA'C'C$ we have, in Ex. 31, the factor $\varrho = 1.79$ and $b_0 = 1.34$ cm. Determine for this ϱ, according to Fig. 4-5, the value of $\zeta = 2.55$. The product ζb yields $2.55 \cdot 2 \cdot 0.5 = 2.55$ cm and the value V/h is 2,000 A/cm.

From the values ϱ and V/h we obtain nomographically:

$$B_0 = 16{,}300 \text{ G}$$
$$\Phi_t = 16{,}300 \cdot 1.34 = 21{,}900 \text{ M}$$
$$\Phi_s = 0.4\,\pi \cdot 2{,}000 \cdot 2.55 = 6{,}400 \text{ M}$$
$$\Phi_\tau = 28{,}300 \text{ M}$$

A similar method can be applied in computing the slot of the configuration in Fig. 4-8d which occurs in reaction motors or high-frequency generators. In this case the teeth in $DBA'D'$ are similar to those in $DBA'D'$ of Fig. 4-8a, and the slots consist of three parallel-connected parts of which part $D'D''O''O'$ is one with parallel walls, while parts $A'O'D'$ and $D''O''B''$ correspond to parts $A'D'O$ and DBO of Fig. 4-8a. It may readily be seen that here too the factor ϱ is determined according to the dimensions of the teeth, the factor ζ in Fig. 4-5 according to the value $\varrho = f(a)$ obtained, and for the width of the equivalent slot $\overline{A'B''}$ is selected.

CHAPTER FIVE

SERIES CONNECTION OF THE REGION OF TOOTH AND MAGNETICALLY PARALLEL SLOT

5-1. The Formulation of the Problem and the Approach to its Solution

In the magnetic circuits of electrical machines and devices there often occur configurations which are essentially the series connection of two or more parallel regions of tooth and slot.

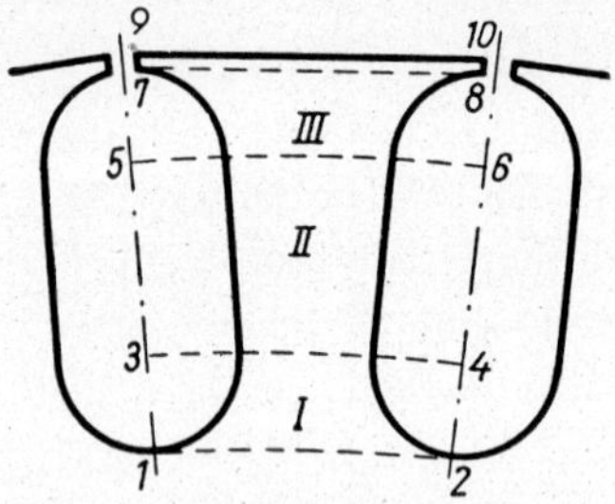

Fig. 5-1

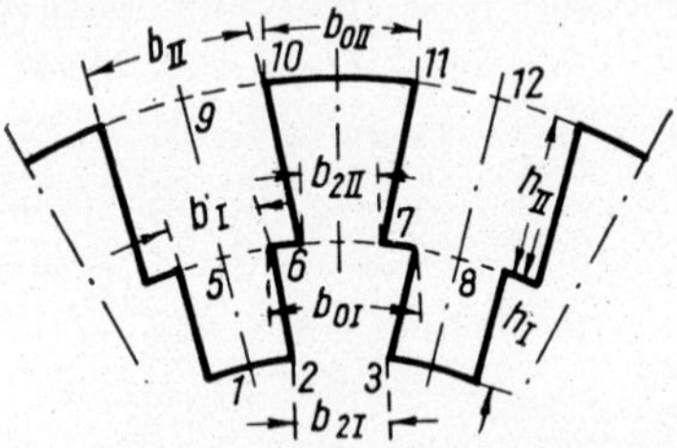

Fig. 5-2

They can be found in rotors with half-open slots (Fig. 5-1), in rotors with gradual slots (Fig. 5-2) and in rotors of asynchronous machines with a double squirrel-cage (Fig. 5-3).

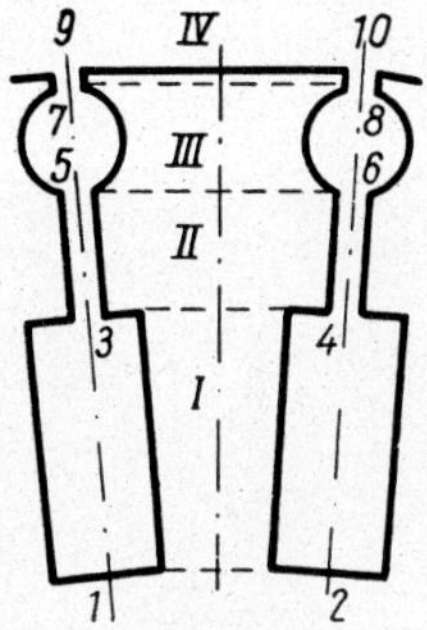

Fig. 5-3

In the first case, the tooth pitch consists of three series-connected regions of tooth and parallel-connected slot, of which field II is a wedge-shaped tooth and a slot with parallel walls, fields I and III being similar to field $OO'C'C$ in Fig. 4-8a.

In the second case the tooth pitch consists of series-connected regions of tooth and parallel-connected slot, each consisting, in turn, of a wedge-shaped tooth and a slot with parallel walls.

In the third case we find a series connection of three such regions. The first (1-2-3-4) and the second (3-4-5-6) regions correspond to the regions of wedge-shaped tooth and parallel-walled slots, while the third (5-6-8-7) to the region $DD'C'C$ of Fig. 4-8a. (The region 7-8-10-9 may be neglected.)

In chapter 3 it has been demonstrated that several series-connected ferromagnetic bodies may be connected into a single resulting body. It has, however, been presumed as a basic assumption that the magnetic flux passing through the series-connected bodies is a constant one.

In the cases shown in Figs. 5-1 to 5-3 the conditions are entirely different because parts of the flux that pass through the ferromagnetic body may, in different series-connected regions, have different values.

This is illustrated by the example of the fields 1-2-3-4 and 3-4-6-5 in Fig. 5-3.

An examination of this configuration shows that the flux density in the tooth of region II, and the pertaining field strength, are materially smaller than in region I. The induction in the slots of these regions is distributed accordingly (in region I it will be considerably higher than in region II).

Consequently, the slot flux of region II will be much smaller than the one in region I, and vice versa, the flux through the tooth in region II will be greater than the flux crossing the tooth in region I.

In order to find a solution for the problem of similar series-connected regions, let us examine Fig. 5-4a, which is part of the configuration in Fig. 5-3. A flux Φ_τ, distributed in a rather complicated form between the tooth and the slot, crosses each region of tooth and parallel slot in Fig. 5-4a.

We shall prove that the said complicated distribution of flux Φ_τ and the given configuration may be substituted by a single region of tooth and parallel slot (Fig. 5-4f), which is crossed by the same flux Φ_τ in the form of two parallel branches of the slot flux Φ_{sres} and the tooth flux Φ_{tres}, both being constant at all heights and causing the same potential drop V as in Fig. 5-4a.

In order to check this proof, let us examine the inverse case of replacing the configuration and the flux distribution in Fig. 5-4f by the configuration and the flux distribution in Fig. 5-4a.

As is known from chapter 4, the configuration and flux distribution in Fig. 5-4f are magnetically equivalent to the configuration and the flux distribution in Fig. 5-4e where the tooth is of the same size as in Fig. 5-4f, the slot being ζ times less wide, and the flux is

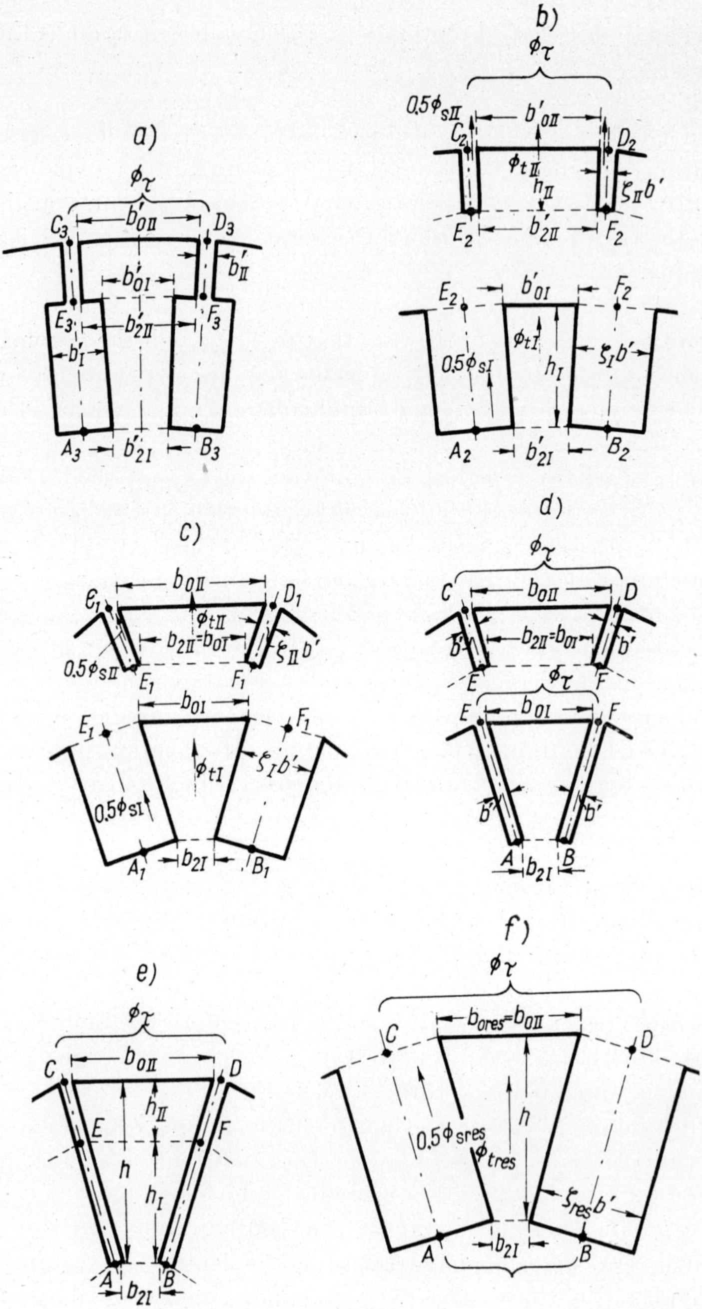

Fig. 5-4

distributed between the tooth and the slot in a natural, complicated manner.

The condition of equivalence is the correspondence of the factor ζ computable from Fig. 4-5 (in this case ζ_{res}) to the factor a of the given tooth (in this case $a = 0.25$).

Let the field $ABCD$ (Fig. 5-4e) be divided by the line EF in two independent fields $ABFE$ and $EFDC$ (Fig. 5-4d) magnetically series-connected to one another so that the magnetic flux Φ_τ should produce a potential difference V_I in the field $ABFE$ and a potential difference V_{II} in the field $EFDC$. Since the distribution of Φ_τ has not changed throughout the field $ABDC$, the sum of potential differences $V_I + V_{II}$ has remained the same as in Figs. 5-4e and 5-4f.

The fields $ABFE$ and $EFDC$ (Fig. 5-4d) may, in turn, be replaced by equivalent fields $A_1B_1F_1E_1$ and $E_1F_1D_1C_1$ (Fig. 5-4c), in which the flux Φ_τ divides into slot fluxes Φ_{sI} and Φ_{sII}, and tooth fluxes Φ_{tI} and Φ_{tII}, having a constant value all along the height.

Thus, in fields $A_1B_1F_1E_1$ and $E_1F_1D_1C_1$ we shall have teeth identical with the corresponding teeth of fields $ABEF$ and $EFCD$, and slots whose width will be by ζ_I and ζ_{II} greater than the width of the slots in fields $ABFE$ and $EFDC$, respectively.

Since in our example the tooth in Fig. 5-4a has been divided by the line EF so that the factor a_I should equal 0.33 and $a_{II} = 0.75$, we obtain from the curve in Fig. 4-5 $\zeta_I = 5.8$ and $\zeta_{II} = 1.3$. We could, obviously, select any other position for the line EF and obtain thereby any other value for a_I and a_{II} and, accordingly, any other values for the widths of the slots in Fig. 5-4c and a different distribution of the fluxes Φ_s and Φ_t.

It follows from the theory of the factor ζ (chapter 4) that flux Φ_τ creates along the field $A_1B_1F_1E_1$, as before, a potential difference V_I, and along the field $E_1F_1D_1C_1$ a potential difference V_{II}, whereas, in the case of the series-connection of the two fields, the sum of the potential differences will be $V = V_I + V_{II}$.

Since in the given example $V_I/h_I > V_{II}/h_{II}$, the following inequalities prevail:

$$\Phi_{sI} > \Phi_{sII} \text{ and } \Phi_{tI} > \Phi_{tII}$$

The equivalent fields $A_1B_1F_1E_1$ and $E_1F_1D_1C_1$ thus obtained (Fig. 5-4c) may be subject to further transformations, replacing them by other equivalent fields.

As has been shown on page 67, any ferromagnetic body with given values of b_0 and ϱ may be substituted by another body with correspondingly greater or smaller values of b_0 and ϱ. Let us replace, accordingly, the tooth of the field $A_1B_1F_1E_1$ (Fig. 5-4c), having a maximum width $b_{0\mathrm{I}}$ and a minimum width $b_{2\mathrm{I}}$, by an equivalent tooth (Fig. 5-4b) characterized by the parameters $b'_{0\mathrm{I}}$ and $b'_{2\mathrm{I}}$. In the same manner let the tooth of the field $E_1F_1D_1C_1$ (Fig. 5-4c), having a maximum width $b_{0\mathrm{II}}$ and a minimum width $b_{2\mathrm{II}}$, be replaced by an equivalent tooth (Fig. 5-4b) with the parameters $b'_{0\mathrm{II}}$ and $b'_{2\mathrm{II}}$. In the case of such substitution the values V_I and V_II created by the previous fluxes $\Phi_{t\mathrm{I}}$ and $\Phi_{t\mathrm{II}}$ remain unchanged; consequently, by retaining in Fig. 5-4b the same slot widths as in Fig. 5-4c, the same flux Φ_τ will pass through the series-connected fields $A_2B_2F_2E_2$ and $E_2F_2D_2C_2$ of Fig. 5-4b as in Fig. 5-4c, and the resultant potential difference V will remain unchanged for both fields.

By resorting to the method explained in chapter 4, we can, in the same way as the substitution of Fig. 5-4e for Fig. 5-4f, replace the configurations $A_2B_2F_2E_2$ and $E_2F_2D_2C_2$ in Fig. 5-4b, as well as the corresponding flux distributions by the configurations $A_3B_3F_3E_3$ and $E_3F_3D_3C_3$ in Fig. 5-4a, respectively, by the natural, complicated distribution of Φ_τ between the teeth and the slots. These fields will differ from the fields $A_2B_2F_2E_2$ and $E_2F_2D_2C_2$ of Fig. 5-4b only in the changed width of the slots, each of which decreases in compliance with the changed factor ζ. As a result of the transformation of Fig. 5-4c into Fig. 5-4b the factor a of the teeth changes, and the factors ζ are determined by the new factors a according to Fig. 4-5. Thus we have

$$b'_\mathrm{I} = \frac{\zeta_\mathrm{I}\, b'}{\zeta'_\mathrm{I}} \quad \text{and} \quad b'_\mathrm{II} = \frac{\zeta_\mathrm{II}\, b'}{\zeta'_\mathrm{II}}$$

where ζ'_I for the given case equals 1.3 and $\zeta'_\mathrm{II} \approx 1$.

Thus we have demonstrated that the configuration and the flux distribution in Fig. 5-4f are equivalent to those in Fig. 5-4a.

Consequently, the configuration of Fig. 5-4a consisting of two series-connected regions of tooth and parallel slot can be replaced by one region consisting of one resultant tooth and one parallel slot. The actual complicated distribution of flux Φ_τ between the teeth and the slots is replaced by a magnetically equivalent distribution of flux Φ_τ consisting of two constant components $\Phi_{s\mathrm{res}}$ and $\Phi_{t\mathrm{res}}$ throughout.

A similar substitution, i.e. the transition from the configuration of Fig. 5-4a to that of Fig. 5-4f, requires the following operations:

1. Replace the ferromagnetic bodies with the parameters h_{I}, $b'_{0\text{I}}$, ϱ_{I}, γl, respectively, h_{II}, $b'_{0\text{II}}$, ϱ'_{II}, γl by a single body having the parameters $h = h_{\text{I}} + h_{\text{II}}$, $b_{0\text{res}}$, ϱ_{res}, γl.

2. Determine from the values $\zeta_{\text{I}} b'$ and $\zeta_{\text{II}} b'$ the value $\zeta_{\text{res}} b'$ of the resultant slot.

The solution of the first task is known from chapter 3. For the solution of the second problem it must be demonstrated that the substitution of the actual slot flux by a constant flux passing through a slot of width $\zeta_{\text{res}} b'$ is possible and correct for any magnetic demand. Such a proof is given in section 5-2.

The factor ζ_{res} is determined in the following manner. The first thing to do is to determine, for any flux Φ_τ, the values V'_{I} and V'_{II} created in each of the series-connected regions of tooth and parallel slot, then to find nomographically flux $\Phi_{tr\ s}$ due to the potential difference prevailing along a body characterized by the parameters $h_{\text{I}} = h_{\text{II}}$, $b_{0\text{res}}$, ϱ_{res} and γl, and to compute the difference

$$\Phi_\tau - \Phi_{t\text{res}} = \Phi_{s\text{res}} = \zeta_{\text{res}}\, b'\, l \frac{0.4\,\pi(V_{\text{I}} + V_{\text{II}})}{h_{\text{I}} + h_{\text{II}}}$$

in which the sole unknown value is the value ζ_{res}.

Relying on similar considerations, it can be demonstrated that this method is valid for any configuration, and for any number of series-connected regions.

5-2. The Theoretical Foundation of the Possibility of Using the Factor ζ_{res}

Let us assume that the width of the tooth in the region of tooth and parallel slot changes from $x = 0$ to $x = \Sigma h$ according to any $b_x = f_1(x/\Sigma h)$, and that the width of the parallel slot according to any $b'_{sx} = f_2(x/\Sigma h)$. In this case the actual flux density at a height x will be

$$B_x = \frac{\Phi_\tau - 0.4\,\pi\, H_x\, l f_2\left(\dfrac{x}{\Sigma h}\right)}{\gamma\, l f_1\left(\dfrac{x}{\Sigma h}\right)} \tag{5-1}$$

By replacing the actual flux of the slot at x by

$$0.4\,\pi \frac{\Sigma V}{\Sigma h} l\,\zeta_{\text{res}}\,b'$$

which will be the same at any height, we obtain the tooth flux throughout the height as

$$\Phi_\tau - 0.4\,\pi \frac{\Sigma V}{\Sigma h} l\,\zeta_{\text{res}}\,b'$$

As a result of this substitution, the flux density at any height will differ from the actual value by

$$\Delta B_x = \frac{0.4\pi\left[H_x f_2\left(\frac{x}{\Sigma h}\right) - \frac{\Sigma V}{\Sigma h}\zeta_{\text{res}}\,b'\right]}{\gamma f_1\left(\frac{x}{\Sigma h}\right)} \tag{5-2}$$

and the error involved with respect to the magnitude of H_x in the tooth will be approximately

$$\Delta H_x = \Delta B_x \frac{dH_x}{dB_x} = \Delta B_x \frac{dHx}{d\left(\frac{x}{\Sigma h}\right)} \frac{d\left(\frac{x}{\Sigma h}\right)}{df_1\left(\frac{x}{\Sigma h}\right)} \frac{df_1\left(\frac{x}{\Sigma h}\right)}{dB_x} \tag{5-3}$$

We shall introduce the following expressions:

$$\frac{df_1\left(\frac{x}{\Sigma h}\right)}{d\left(\frac{x}{\Sigma h}\right)} = f'_1\left(\frac{x}{\Sigma h}\right)^* \tag{5-4}$$

$$\frac{dB_x}{df_1\left(\frac{x}{\Sigma h}\right)} = \frac{d\,\frac{\Phi_s}{\gamma\, l f_1\left(\frac{x}{\Sigma h}\right)}}{df_1\left(\frac{x}{\Sigma h}\right)} = \frac{\Phi_s}{\gamma\, l f_3\left(\frac{x}{\Sigma h}\right)} \tag{5-5}$$

Let us presume that when the practically possible maximum flux passes through the investigated region, the field strength along height

* Here and in the following f' as'll exceptionally denote the derivative of function f.

x will be distributed according to the expression

$$H_{x\max} = f_{\max}\left(\frac{x}{\Sigma h}\right)$$

and the mean field strength will equal

$$\int_0^1 H_{x\max}\, d\left(\frac{x}{\Sigma h}\right) = \frac{\Sigma V_{\max}}{\Sigma h}$$

If the flux is less, the field strength will have a value of H_x and the mean field strength will equal

$$\int_0^1 H_x\, d\left(\frac{x}{\Sigma h}\right) = \frac{\Sigma V}{\Sigma h}$$

Let us assume that

$$\frac{H_x}{H_{x\max}} = \frac{V}{\Sigma V_{\max}}$$

i.e.

$$H_x = \frac{\Sigma V}{\Sigma V_{\max}} f_{\max}\left(\frac{x}{\Sigma h}\right) \tag{5-6}$$

which is correct for $H_x = H_{x\max}$.

If the flux decreases, Eq. (5-6) gives a certain error. Nevertheless, since the field strength H_x decreases much more rapidly than the flux, the absolute value of the error involved in the application of Eq. (5-6) will be insignificant.

In addition to this, the mean value of all magnitudes H_x calculated with Eq. (5-6) for different heights x will be equal to the actual value of the mean field strength, because

$$\int_0^1 \frac{\Sigma V}{\Sigma V_{\max}} f_{\max}\left(\frac{x}{\Sigma h}\right) d\left(\frac{x}{\Sigma h}\right) = \frac{\Sigma V}{\Sigma V_{\max}}\,\frac{\Sigma V_{\max}}{\Sigma h} = \int_0^1 H_x\, d\left(\frac{x}{\Sigma h}\right) \tag{5-7}$$

That is why, if Eq. (5-) yields for the determination of $x/\Sigma h$ somewhat higher values, it gives somewhat lower ones for other $x/\Sigma h$ values.

Relying on these considerations, on the analogy of section 4-4 with respect to Eq. (4-3), Eq. (5-6) may be regarded as sufficiently exact.

It follows from Eq. (5-6) that

$$\frac{dH_x}{d\left(\frac{x}{\Sigma h}\right)} = \frac{\Sigma U}{\Sigma U_{\max}} f'_{\max}\left(\frac{x}{\Sigma h}\right) \tag{5-8}$$

By substituting H_x from Eq. (5-6) into Eq. (5-2) we obtain the value ΔB_x. Transforming Eqs. (5-2), (5-8), (5-4), (5-5) and (5-3), compute the error ΔH_x whose integration within the range from $x/\Sigma h = 0$ to $x/\Sigma h = 1$ yields the error

$$\Delta V = \Sigma h \int_0^1 \Delta H_x \, d\left(\frac{x}{\Sigma h}\right) = \frac{0.4\,\pi\, l\,(\Sigma V)^2\,\Sigma h}{\Sigma V_{\max}\,\Phi_t} \times$$

$$\times \int_0^1 \frac{\left[\dfrac{f_{\max}\left(\frac{x}{\Sigma h}\right) f_2\left(\frac{x}{\Sigma h}\right)}{\Sigma V_{\max}} - \dfrac{\zeta_{res}\, b'}{\Sigma h}\right] f'_{\max}\left(\frac{x}{\Sigma h}\right) f_3\left(\frac{x}{\Sigma h}\right)}{f_1\left(\frac{x}{\Sigma h}\right) f'_1\left(\frac{x}{\Sigma h}\right)}\, d\left(\frac{x}{\Sigma h}\right) \tag{5-9}$$

involved in the computation of the potential difference.

If the value $\zeta_{res} b'$ is computed so that for a given flux Φ_τ the error is $\Delta V = 0$, then the expression integrated in Eq. (5-9) must also

TABL

No. of Ex.	Form	Data of the series-connected regions: I				II				III				ϱ_I	ϱ_{II}	ϱ_{III}
		h_I cm	b_{0I} cm	$(\gamma l)_I$ cm	b_I cm	h_{II} cm	b_{0II} cm	$(\gamma l)_{II}$ cm	b_{II} cm	h_{III} cm	b_{0III} cm	$(\gamma l)_{III}$ cm	b_{III} cm			
1	2	3	4	5	6	7	8	9	10	11	12	13	14	15	16	17
69 (see Exs. 43 and 31)		0.5	1.34	10	1	1	0.8	10	1	0.5	1.34	10	1	1.79	1	1.7
70 (see Ex. 50)		1.2	1.5	1	1	1.8	1.8	1	1.8	—	—	—	—	1.465	2.12	—

be zero. Nevertheless, in this case the integrated expression, depending only on the geometrical configuration of the tooth and the slot, will be zero also for all other possible magnetic demands. This fact permits the conclusion that the substitution of the actual slot flux by a constant flux passing through a slot of a definite width $\zeta_{res} b'$ is possible and correct for any magnetic demand.

5-3. Approach to the Practical Substitution of Several Series-Connected Regions of Tooth and Parallel Slot by a Single Resultant Region

Relying on the theoretical considerations expounded in sections 5-1 and 5-2, we can proceed with the substitution of several series-connected regions of tooth and parallel slot by a single resultant region, in the following manner.

1. Replace all the teeth by one resultant according to the method expounded in sections 3-3 or 3-5, and determine the values ϱ_{res} and $b_{0r\,s}\gamma l$ obtained.

2. Assume any arbitrary flux to pass through all series-connected regions of tooth and parallel slot, and determine according to the method of section 4-6 the corresponding values V for all regions.

3. By summing up the values V and at dividing their sum by the sum of all heights, we obtain the ratio $\Sigma V/\Sigma h$.

-1

ζ_I	ζ_{II}	ζ_{III}	Values obtained nomographically		Assumed flux Φ_τ M	V/h A/cm obtained nomographically for regions			$\frac{\Sigma V}{\Sigma h}$ A/cm	Abscissa $\overline{LC} = \frac{\Phi_{tres}}{b_{0res}\gamma l}$ G	Slot flux $\Phi_{sres} = \Phi_\tau - \Phi_{tres}$ M	Required value $\zeta_{res}\, b'l$ cm²
according to Fig. 4-5			ϱ_{res}	b_{0res} cm		I	II	III				
18	19	20	21	22	23	24	25	26	27	28	29	30
2.55	1	2.55	1.44	1.045	237,600	1,180	3,000	1,180	2,090	19,100	37,600	1.44
1.65	3.45	—	1.44	1.39	29,000	1,260	870	—	1,020	17,300	4,900	3.85

4. Determine, on the curve ϱ_{0res}, the point C whose ordinate is equal to $\Sigma V/\Sigma h$. The abscissa $\overline{LC}$ of this point, multiplied by $b_{0res}\gamma l$ yields the flux Φ_{tres}.

5. Compute the flux $\Phi_{sres} = \Phi_\tau - \Phi_t$

6. Compute

$$\zeta_{res} = \frac{\Phi_{sres}}{0.4\,\pi \dfrac{\Sigma V}{\Sigma h} b'l} \quad \text{and} \quad \tan\beta_{res} = \frac{\Phi_{sres}}{b_{0\,res}\,\gamma l\, \dfrac{\Sigma V}{\Sigma h}}$$

Examples of the application of this method are given in Table 5-1. In Ex. 69 of the Table a tooth and a slot are examined similar to those of the field 1-2-8-7 of Fig. 5-1. This tooth has been replaced by a resultant body in Ex. 43. Ex. 70 refers to the tooth and slot of Fig. 5-2. The substitution of the tooth by a resultant body was performed in Ex. 50.

Thus by connecting the principle of substituting series-connected ferromagnetic bodies by one resultant body with the principle of replacing the actual tooth and slot fluxes by equivalent fluxes constant throughout the height, the nomographic method can be applied to determine the magnetic relations in intricate configurations, consisting of several ferromagnetic bodies and of air gaps connected between one another in series and in parallel.

CHAPTER SIX

NOMOGRAPHIC DETERMINATION OF MAGNETIC RELATIONS IN THE REGION OF TOOTH, SLOT AND AIR GAP IN ELECTRICAL MACHINES

6-1. The Theoretical Background of the Nomographic Computation of the Air Gap

We have hitherto determined the reluctance V/Φ in the region of tooth and parallel slot. In practice, however, those computing electrical machines are mostly concerned with the value of the resultant reluctance of the tooth, slot and the pertaining air gap (field 4-5-6-7, Fig. 1-10). Our set of curves is again a useful help ensuring a very simple solution of the problem.

Let it be assumed that the potential difference V_0 between the points 1 and 3 of Fig. 1-10 is to be determined as a first task, according to the given value Φ_τ. Proceeding from the dimensions of the tooth and the slot, our method expounded in section 4-6 yields the point C with the parameters $\overline{CM} = \Phi_\tau/b_0\gamma l = B_\tau$ and $\overline{CK} = V/h$.

The potential difference set up by flux Φ_τ in the air gap of length δ can be computed with the formula

$$\frac{\Phi_\tau \delta k_c}{\tau_s l 0.4 \pi}$$

where k_c = the factor of the air gap (Carter coefficient),

$\Phi_\tau/\tau_s l$ = flux density in the air gap, and

τ_s = size of the slot (or tooth) pitch.

The total potential drop between the surface of the pole and the slot bottom can be determined with the following expression

$$V_0 = V + \frac{\Phi_\tau \delta k_c}{\tau_s l 0.4 \pi}$$

whence

$$B_\tau = \overline{MC} = \frac{\Phi_\tau}{b_0 \gamma l} = \frac{V_0 - V}{h} \frac{0.4 \pi h \tau_s}{\delta k_c b_0 \gamma} \qquad (6\text{-}1)$$

Let the point F on the axis of the abscissa be determined so that

$$\overline{OF} = \frac{V_0}{h} \quad \frac{0.4\,\pi\, h\, \tau_s}{\delta k_c\, b_0\, \gamma} \tag{6-2}$$

From these two formulae it follows that

$$\overline{MC} : \overline{OF} = \frac{V_0 - V}{h} : \frac{V_0}{h} \tag{6-3}$$

that is, if points F and C are connected by a straight line, the latter intersects the continuation of the straight line OM at a point D whose ordinate is

$$\overline{DE} = \frac{V_0}{h} \tag{6-4}$$

Relying on these considerations it is easy to determine the values of Φ_τ, Φ_s and Φ_t as well as of V for a given value V_0.

This requires the determination of only point D having an ordinate V_0/h and of point F having an abscissa computable with the formula (6-2), as well as their connection by means of the straight line DF intersecting the curve for the corresponding ϱ at a point C.

The sections $\overline{ML}$, $\overline{LC}$, $\overline{MC}$ thus obtained, when multiplied by $b_0\gamma l$, yield the values Φ_s, Φ_t and Φ_τ while the section $\overline{CK}$, when multiplied by h, yields V. The flux density in the air gap is computed with the formula

$$B_\delta = \frac{B_\tau \gamma\, b_0}{\tau_s} = \frac{\Phi_\tau}{l\,\tau_s}$$

A similar method is used for determining the magnitude of $\overline{OF}$ for a given Φ_τ or the potential difference V. For this purpose it is most expedient to express the section $\overline{OF}$ as

$$\overline{OF} = \overline{LC} + \overline{KF} = \overline{LC} + \overline{KC}\,\frac{\overline{EO} + \overline{OF}}{\overline{ED}} =$$

$$= \overline{LC} + \overline{KC}\,\frac{0.4\,\pi\left(\zeta b' + \dfrac{h\,\tau_s}{\delta\, k_c}\right)}{b_0\,\gamma} \tag{6-5}$$

which permits the computation of its value on the basis of the lines $\overline{LC}$ and $\overline{KC}$ which, in turn, can be determined with the method expounded in section 4-6.

By connecting points C and F the position of point D can be found, i.e. the value V_0/h can be determined.

6-2. *Approach to the Practical Determination of the Magnetic Relations in the Region of Tooth, Slot and Air Gap*

A) Determination of the potential difference V_0 for a given Φ_τ

1. Determine the factor ϱ and $\tan \beta$, and compute the factor k_c with some known equation, for instance (4-24).

2. Determine by the method of section 4-6 the lines $\overline{ML}$, $\overline{LC}$ and $\overline{CK}$ (Fig. 6-1).

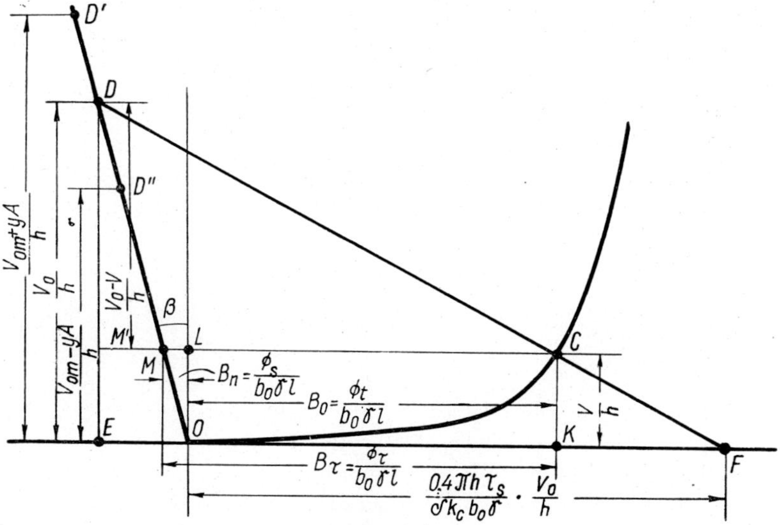

Fig. 6-1

3. Compute the line $\overline{OF}$ with Eq. (6-5).

4. Connect points F and C with a straight line, and compute the point of intersection D of this line and the straight line OM.

5. Multiplying the ordinate $\overline{ED}$ by h we obtain V_0.

B) Determination of fluxes Φ_t, Φ_s and Φ_τ as well as of the value V for a given value of V_0

1. Determine the factor ϱ and $\tan \beta$ as well as the factor k_c, as in part *A)*.

2. Determine, on the straight line corresponding to $\tan \beta$, point D having the ordinate $\overline{ED}$ V_0/h.

3. Compute the abscissa of point F with the formula (6-2).

4. Connect points D and F by a straight line, and determine point C where it intersects the curve corresponding to ϱ.

5. Multiplying lines $\overline{ML}$, $\overline{LC}$ and $\overline{MC}$ by $b_0 \gamma l$, the fluxes Φ_s, Φ_t and Φ_τ are obtained.

6. Multiplying the line $\overline{CK}$ by h, we obtain the value V.

C) Determination of the value of the air gap δ, at which the potential difference V_0 sets up flux Φ_τ

1. Determine ϱ and $\tan \beta$ as in part *A)*.

2. On the straight line corresponding to $\tan \beta$, determine point D having the ordinate $\overline{ED} = V_0/h$.

3. Determine, according to section 4-6, point C proceeding from the flux Φ_τ.

4. Connect points D and C by a straight line, and determine point F where this intersects the axis of the abscissa.

5. Use Eq. (6-2) for computing (δk_c), then determine the value δ at which the factor k_c equals the ratio

$$\frac{(\delta k_c)}{\delta}$$

In applying the nomographic method, it may happen that point F or point D is found to lie outside the nomogram.

In such cases, the method to be followed is this.

Beside the curves A constructed for the field corresponding to a maximum field strength of 3,000 A/cm and a maximum flux density of 30,000 G, the nomogram (Supplement I) also features curves B constructed, in a reduced scale, for field strengths above 3,000 A/cm and flux densities exceeding 30,000 G. When using the curves B the scale values, plotted against the axes of ordinates and abscissae, should be multiplied by 5 (in Supplement II the range of curves B begins with the values 4,500 A/cm and 45,000 G, respectively).

The field occupied by the curves A in the reduced scale of the curves B corresponds to the rectangle *abcd*.

If, in using the nomograms, the points D and F are found to lie outside the field of the nomogram, then the curves B should be resorted to, reducing the abscissae and ordinates of point D by 5. In this case there are two possible alternatives.

1. The straight line DF may intersect the field of curves B beyond the boundaries of the rectangle *abcd*. In this case, the abscissa and the

ordinate of the required point C, obtained by the intersection with the corresponding curve, should be multiplied by 5.

2. The straight line DF may intersect the field of curves within the rectangle (where the curves B are not indicated). In this case the points where the straight line DF and the sides da, ab, bc, cd of this rectangle intersect should be transferred into the field of curves A, increasing five times the corresponding lines (from points d, a or c to the points where the sides of the rectangle intersect with the straight line DF). Thus the straight line DF can be plotted within the field of curves A.

Here are a few examples to illustrate the application of this method.

Example 71. Determine the flux density $B_{\delta m}$ in the air gap under the mid-pole of a traction engine of the DPE-340 type. The potential difference is $V_0 = 14{,}300$ A.

The configuration of the region of tooth, slot and air gap is characterized by the following parameters:* $h = 5.79$ cm, $b_2 = 1.365$ cm, $\gamma = 0.95$, $l = 30.5$ cm, $b_0 = 2.005$ cm, $\tau_s = 3.5$ cm, $b = 1.455$ cm, $\delta = 0{,}63$ cm. Use Eq. (1-4) for computing $b' = 1.54$ cm and the factor $a = 0.68$. From Fig. 4-5 determine $\zeta = 1.6$ and with Eq. (2-6) compute the factor $\varrho = 1.43$ and with Eq. (4-43) $\tan\beta = 1.62$.

Determine the values $k_c = 1.18$, $V_0/h = \overline{DE} = 2{,}470$ A/cm and $0.4\,\pi h\tau_s/\delta k_c \gamma b_0 = 18$.

Now the line $\overline{OF} = 44{,}500$ G can be computed for the point lying beneath the middle of the pole. Point F is found to lie outside the field covered by the nomogram in Supplement I.

By decreasing lines $\overline{OF}$ and $\overline{DE}$ five times, we obtain point F on the abscissa axis of the nomogram, a point corresponding to $\overline{OF} = 8{,}900$ G and on the straight line for $\tan\beta = 1.62$, point F corresponding to the ordinate

$$\overline{DE} = \frac{2{,}470}{5}\ \text{A/cm}.$$

The straight line DF intersects the field of the curves B within the rectangle $abcd$, and its point of intersection with the side ad had the ordinate 460 A/cm, and with the side bc, the ordinate 150 A/cm.

* Советские магистральные электровозы (Soviet main-line electrical locomotives), Трансжелдориздат, 1940, p. 347, Fig. 399.

In the field of curves A this corresponds to the following points: one having the ordinate 0 and the abscissa $460 \cdot 5$ A/cm, the other having the abscissa 30,000 G and the ordinate $150 \cdot 5$ A/cm. By connecting these points with a straight line, we find its point of intersection with the curve for $\varrho = 1.43$ (point C) having the abscissa $B_0 = 18{,}000$ G and the ordinate $V/h = 1{,}330$ A/cm.

The ordinate 1,330 A/cm corresponds on the straight line for $\tan \beta = 1.62$ to point M with the abscissa $B_s = 2{,}100$ G.

Thus we have: $B_\tau = B_0 + B_s = 20{,}100$ G.

The flux density in the air gap is then $B_\delta = B_\tau \gamma b_0/\tau_s = 10{,}900$ G.

6.3 Theoretical Considerations Underlying the Computation of the Air Gap for Stators and Rotors with Teeth and Slots

In the practice of electrical engineering one often comes across cases when not only the revolving parts but also the stators are designed with teeth and slots (Fig. 1-11). Such designs are preferably used for asynchronous machines, commutator motors with compensation windings, for synchronous machines with damping windings and so on. In all these cases, the magnetic flux passes through the region of tooth and parallel slot in the rotor, through the air gap and the region of tooth and parallel slot in the stator.

For determining the magnetic relations in a similar construction, the two series-connected regions of tooth and parallel slot in both stator and rotor may be connected, and the air gap may be computed with the method expounded in the previous section of this chapter.

If the same magnetic flux passes through the region of tooth and parallel slot in the stator as through that in the rotor, i.e. if the tooth pitch of the stator and the rotor has angles of identical degree, then, according to the method of chapter 5, they can be replaced by a single resultant region having the parameters $h_{\text{I}} + h_{\text{II}}$, $\varrho_{\text{r s}}$, $b_{0\text{res}}$ and $\zeta_{\text{res}} b'$.

The effective air gap is then taken as

$$\delta_{\text{eff}} = \delta \, k_{c1} \, k_{c2} \tag{6-6}$$

where k_{c1} is the Carter coefficient in the stator and k_{c2} is that of the rotor. These factors are computed according to the actual configuration of both regions of tooth and parallel slot and to the actual value of the air gap.

If the tooth pitch of the stator has a greater or smaller number of angular degrees than the tooth pitch of the rotor, then this case can be reduced to the previous one on the basis of the following considerations.

The tooth pitches of the stator may, for instance, be decreased, i.e. their number increased, so that a smaller flux should pass through each pitch. By a simultaneous and proportional decrease of the width of the slot and the tooth, with h constant, the flux density will not change at any point of the tooth and slot, whence the potential drop in the region of tooth and slot of the stator will not change either, Thus the ratio of Φ_τ to $V_{\text{I}} + V_{\text{II}}$, i.e. the reluctance of both regions. will also remain unaltered.

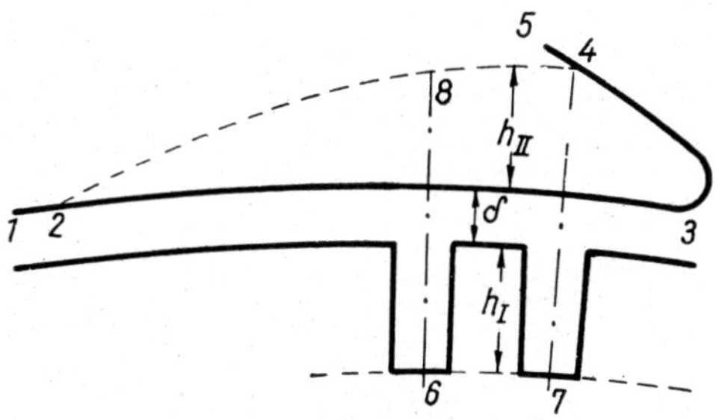

Fig. 6-2

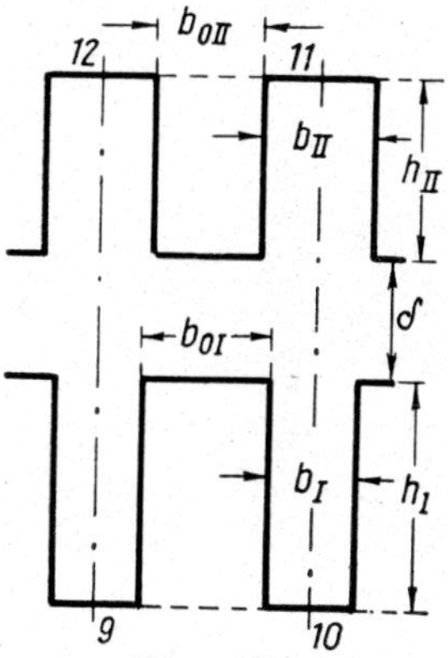

Fig. 6-3

Consequently, if the tooth pitch of the stator has a number of angular degrees different from that of the rotor, they can always be made identical by changing correspondingly the width of the tooth and the slot in one of them (in identical proportion), with the height h unchanged.

In this connection it should be noted that in computing the Carter coefficient the slot pitch to be assumed should be the actual one, and not the changed one, because the reluctance of the air gap depends on the former.

The configuration of the pole shoe shown in Fig. 6-2, in which the sheets having the shape 1-2-3-4-5 alternate with those having a shape 1-2-4-5, can be reduced to a similar case. As a result we obtain a layer 2-3-4-2, half of which consists of steel, the other half being parallel-connected air spaces. Since it is magnetically irrelevant whether these air spaces are perpendicular to the axis of the machine (as shown in Fig. 6-2), or parallel to it, the distribution of the spaces filled with steel and with air within a field 6-7-4-8 (Fig. 6-2) can be replaced by an equivalent distribution within the field 9-10-11-12 (Fig. 6-3).

6-4. Approach to the Practical Determination of the Magnetic Relations in the Region of Tooth, Slot and Air Gap in Toothed Stator and Rotor

A) Two regions of tooth and parallel slot divided by an air gap

On the strength of the considerations expounded in section 6-3 the space consisting of an air gap and two series-connected regions of tooth and parallel slot can be replaced by a space consisting of the same air gap and a single series-connected region of tooth and parallel slot in the following manner:

1. If the tooth pitch of the stator has a greater (or smaller) angle than the tooth pitch of the rotor, then the parameters b_0, b_1, b_2 and b' pertaining to the stator should be decreased (or increased) until both angles become identical.

2. Replace, according to section 5-3, the region of tooth and parallel slot of the rotor and the region of tooth and parallel slot of the stator, as reduced in point 1, by a single resultant region with the parameters B_{0res}, γl, ϱ_{res}, $b'\zeta_{res}$, $h_{res} = h_{I} + h_{II}$.

3. Compute for the actual configuration Carter coefficient k_{c1} and k_{c2} whose product yields the resultant factor k_c.

The application of this method is illustrated by the following examples.

Example 72. Let both the stator and the rotor of a machine have regions of tooth and slot consisting of wedge-shaped teeth and slots with parallel walls and divided by an air gap of $\delta = 0.7$ cm. Determine the magnetically equivalent region consisting of the same air gap and a single region of tooth and slot.

The tooth pitch of the stator is characterized by the following parameters: $h_{I} = 5.9$ cm, $b_{0I} = 1.58$ cm, $b_{2I} = 1.18$ cm, $l = 35.5$ cm, $\gamma = 0.95$, $b_{I} = 1.12$ cm, and that of the rotor by $h_{II} = 4$ cm, $b_{0II} = 0.9$ cm, $b_{2II} = 0.635$ cm, $b'_{II} = 1.4$ cm, $l = 35.5$ cm, $\gamma' = 0.95$.

Compute the factors $a_{I} = 0.745$, $a_{II} = 0.71$, $\zeta_{I} = 1.3$, $\zeta_{II} = 1.45$, $\tan \beta_{I} = 1.21$, $\tan \beta_{II} = 2.98$, $\varrho_{I} = 1.32$, $\varrho_{II} = 1.39$.

Determine nomographically the ordinate $\overline{CK}_{I} = 95$ A/cm for $\varrho_{I} = 1.32$ and $\Phi_\tau/b_{0I}\gamma l = 14{,}300$ G in case of an arbitrary flux

$\Phi_\tau = 760{,}000$ M, and the ordinate $\overline{CK}_{II} = 2{,}020$ A/cm for $\varrho_{II} = 1.39$ and $\Phi_\tau / b_{0II}\gamma l = 25{,}000$ G.

Choose any flux $\Phi_t = 54 \cdot 10^4$ M and determine for $\varrho_I = 1.32$ and $\overline{LC}_I = 10{,}000$ G the ordinate $\overline{CK}_I = 10$ A/cm, and for $\varrho_{II} = 1.39$ and $\overline{LC}_{II} = 18{,}000$ G the ordinate $\overline{CK}_{II} = 1{,}110$ A/cm. For $\varrho_{res} = 1.44$, $\overline{CK} = 455$ A/cm and $h = (5.9 + 4)$ cm determine the section $\overline{LC} = 15{,}900$ G, whence compute $b_{0res}\gamma' l = 33.9$ cm². For $\varrho = 1.44$ and $\overline{CK} = 870$ A/cm we obtain $\overline{LC} = 17{,}000$ G. For the chosen flux $\Phi_\tau = 76 \cdot 10^4$ M and the computed value $B_{0res}\gamma l$ find the section $\overline{MC} = 22{,}400$ G and the pertaining section $\overline{LM} = 22{,}400—17{,}000 = 5{,}400$ G. The result will be $b'\zeta_{res} = 4.8$ cm.

Thus the resultant region of tooth and parallel slot is characterized by the parameters $h = 9.9.$ cm, $b_0\gamma_1 = 33.9$ cm², $\varrho = 1.44$, $b'\zeta = 4.8$, and the air gap 0.7 cm, the Carter coefficient $k_c = 1.13 \cdot 1.18 = 1.33$.

Example 73. Replace the active region of a machine with wedge-shaped teeth in the rotor and the stator divided by the air gap $\delta = 0.7$ cm, by a magnetically equivalent region consisting of the same air gap and a single region of tooth and parallel slot.

The teeth and the slots of the stator have the following characteristics: $h_I = 5.9$ cm, $b_{0I} = 1.9$ cm, $b_{2I} = 1.42$ cm, $b'_I = 1.34$ cm, while those of the rotor by $h_{II} = 4$ cm, $b_{0II} = 0.9$ cm, $b_{2II} = 0.635$ cm, $b'_{II} = 1.4$ cm.

The length of the iron body along the axis is 35.5 cm if $\gamma = 0.95$. Since the tooth pitch on the stator is greater by the ratio 6 : 5 to that on the rotor, multiply b_{0I}, b_{2I} and b'_I by 5/6 which yields the following parameters for the tooth pitch in the stator, reduced to that of the rotor: $h_I = 5.9$ cm, $b_{0I} = 1.58$ cm, $b_{2I} = 1.18$ cm, $b'_I = 1.12$ cm.

The computation is continued as in Ex. 72 with the use of the parameters obtained. Thus the Carter coefficient for the stator is computed with the actual values of the tooth pitch $k_c = 1.15$.

B) The region of tooth and parallel slot, and the region separated from it by the air gap, consisting of alternating iron sheets of different profiles

For determining the magnetic relations in the configuration of Fig. 6-2 the following steps should be performed:

1. The field 6-7-4-8 in Fig. 6-2 is replaced by the field 9-10-11-12 in Fig. 6-3.

Thus the height of the "stator tooth" will equal the height h_{II} of the field 2-3-4-2 at a given point, its width being equal to that of the parallel-connected slot, i.e. half the width of the tooth pitch of the rotor calculated for the stator.

2. The configuration in Fig. 6-3 is then replaced by a resultant region of gap, tooth and slot in the same manner as in the case of two regions of tooth and parallel slot divided by the air gap. Thus the Carter coefficient in the stator is computed proceeding from the actual tooth pitch having a width equal to that of two iron sheets. If the gaps are large, the Carter coefficient gap in the stator can be assumed to be unity.

Here is an example to show this computation method.

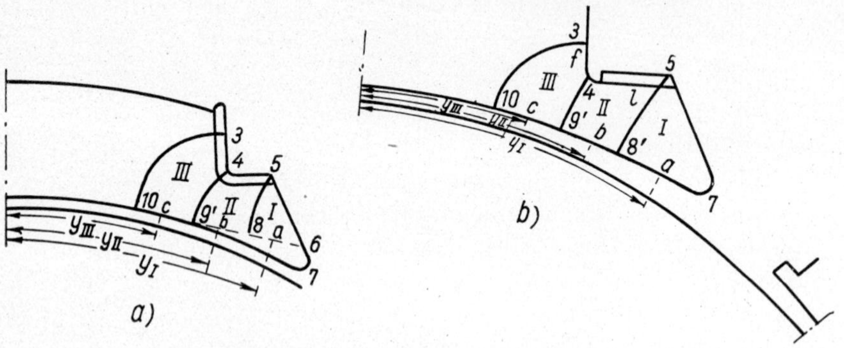

Fig. 6-4

Example 74. In a traction motor DPE—340 the laminated pole shoe (the field 10-6-7 in Fig. 6-4a) composed of sheets of different profile is 1 cm high, $h_{II} = 1$ cm, at a distance $y = +14.6$ cm from the middle of the pole (on the periphery of the armature). The region of tooth, slot and gap, as well as the pertaining series-connected region of the above layer of the pole shoe, should be replaced by a resultant region of tooth, slot and gap.

Since the tooth pitch of the rotor computed for the stator is approximately 3.5 cm, the above-mentioned layer of the pole shoe is replaced by the region of tooth and parallel slot with the following parameters:

$$b_{0II} = b_{2II} = 1.75 \text{ cm}, \quad \varrho_{II} = 1.$$

The saturation factor of the iron is $\gamma_{II} = 0.97$, whence $b'_{II} = 1.8$ cm.

The tooth pitch of the rotor has the following parameters: $h_{\mathrm{I}} = 5.79$ cm, $b_{0\mathrm{I}} = 2.005$ cm, $b_{2\mathrm{I}} = 1.365$, $\gamma_{\mathrm{I}} = 0.95$, $b'_{\mathrm{I}} = 1.53$, $\varrho_1 = 1.43$, $l = 30.5$ cm.

Choose any arbitrary flux $\Phi_\tau = 10^5$ M.

By assuming first that the entire flux passes through the tooth ($\Phi_t = \Phi_\tau$), for the region of tooth and parallel slot in the rotor we have $B_{0\mathrm{I}} = 17{,}200$ G, whence for $\varrho = 1.43$ determine nomographically $V'_{\mathrm{I}}/h' = 900$ A/cm and $V' = 5{,}200$ A.

In the region of tooth and parallel slot of the stator we shall have $B_{0\mathrm{II}} = 19{,}300$ G, whence for $\varrho_{\mathrm{II}} = 1$ we obtain nomographically $V'_{\mathrm{II}}/h_{\mathrm{II}} = 240$ A/cm and $V'_{\mathrm{II}} = 240$ A.

On curve $\varrho_{r\ s} = 1.44$, for the resultant value

$$\frac{V'_{\mathrm{I}} + V'_{\mathrm{II}}}{h_{\mathrm{I}} + h_{\mathrm{II}}} = 800 \text{ A/cm}$$

find point C whose ordinate is 800 A/cm. The abscissa of this point corresponds to $B_{0\mathrm{res}} = 16{,}900$ G, whence $\gamma b_{0\mathrm{res}} = 1.94$ cm.

Let it then be assumed that flux $\Phi_\tau\ \gamma = 10^5$ M also passes through the slots. Thus we have, for the region of tooth and parallel slot of the rotor, $\tan\beta_{\mathrm{I}} = 1.58$, $\varrho_{\mathrm{I}} = 1.43$ and $B_{\tau\mathrm{I}} = \Phi_\tau / b_{0\mathrm{I}}\gamma_{\mathrm{I}} l = 17{,}200$ G, whence we determine nomographically $V_{\mathrm{I}}/h_{\mathrm{I}} = 550$ A/cm and $V_{\mathrm{I}} = 3{,}190$ A. For the region of tooth and parallel slot in the stator $\varrho_{\mathrm{II}} = 1, \zeta = 1, \tan\beta = = 0.4\pi \cdot 1.8/1.75 \cdot 0.97 = 1.32$ and $B_{\tau\mathrm{II}} = \Phi_\tau / b_{0\mathrm{II}}\gamma_{\mathrm{II}} l = 19{,}300$ G, whence we have nomographically $V_{\mathrm{II}}/h_{\mathrm{II}} = 220$ A/cm and $V_{\mathrm{II}} = 220$ A.

For the resultant value

$$\frac{V_{\mathrm{I}} + V_{\mathrm{II}}}{h_{\mathrm{I}} + h_{\mathrm{II}}} = 505 \text{ A/cm}$$

we find, on curve $\varrho = 1.44$ the section $\overline{LC}$ corresponding to $B_{0\mathrm{res}} = \Phi_{t\mathrm{res}}/l\gamma b_{0\mathrm{res}} = 16{,}100$ G.

Hence the value $\Phi_{s\mathrm{res}} = \Phi_\tau - \Phi_{t\mathrm{res}} = 47{,}000$ M and $\tan\beta_{\mathrm{res}} = 800/505 = 1.58$ can be determined.

Thus for point $y = \pm 14.6$ cm we obtain the resultant region of tooth and slot with the parameters $\tan\beta_{\mathrm{res}} = 1.58$, $\varrho_{\mathrm{res}} = 1.44$, $h_{\mathrm{res}} = 6.79$ cm, and $\gamma b_{0\mathrm{res}} = 1.94$ cm.

In the same manner we have for point $y = \pm 10.5$ cm, where $h_{\mathrm{II}} = 0.3$ cm, $\tan\beta_{\mathrm{res}} = 1.58$, $\varrho_{\mathrm{res}} = 1.44$, $\gamma b_{0\mathrm{res}} = 1.92$, $h_{\mathrm{res}} = 6.09$ cm.

For point $y = \pm 12$ cm, where $h_{II} = 0.5$ cm, $\tan \beta_{res} = 1.58$ $\varrho_{res} = 1.44$, $\gamma b_{0res} = 1.93$, $h_{res} = 6.29$ cm.

For point $y = \pm 13.5$ cm, where $h_{II} = 0.75$ cm, $\tan \beta_{res} = 1.58$, $\varrho_{res} = 1.44$, $\gamma b_{0res} = 1.935$, $h_{res} = 6.54$ cm.

For point $y = \pm 16.5$ cm, where $h_{II} = 1.37$ cm, $\tan \beta_{res} = 1.58$, $\varrho_{res} = 1.44$, $\gamma b_{0res} = 1.95$, $h_{res} = 7.16$ cm.

6-5. Theoretical Principles Underlying the Nomographic Assessment of the Effect of the Configuration of the Air Gap and the Armature Reaction upon the Magnetic Conditions in the Active Region of d. c. Machines

Having developed the method for determining the magnetic relations in a region corresponding to a tooth pitch, consisting of part of the air gap and possibly of series-connected regions of tooth and slot, we can now examine the effect exerted by the form of the air gap and the armature reaction upon the magnetic relations in the active layer* of d.c. machines.

Let us examine first the solution of this problem by the usual method.

In order to find, for a given exciting flux Φ_e, the pertaining potential drop in the active layer under the middle of the pole at no load, first the "ideal" width of the pole arc b_i is assessed, for instance, according to the formula

$$b_i = b_p + 2\,\delta \tag{6-7}$$

where b_p = the width of the pole shoe. Dividing the exciting flux Φ_e by $b_i l_a$ (where l_a is the length of the armature), we obtain the flux density

$$B_{\delta m} = \frac{\Phi_e}{b_i\, l_a} \tag{6-8}$$

in the air gap under the middle of the pole. Its multiplication by $\tau_s l_a$ yields the flux Φ_τ passing through the corresponding tooth pitch, and by one of the methods listed in chapter 1, we can determine the V of the tooth. Having computed the potential difference

$$0.8\,\frac{\Phi_e}{b_i\, l_a}\,\delta\, k_c$$

* The "active layer" will be understood to comprise the air gap as well as the regions of tooth and slot of the stator and the rotor.

between the crown of the tooth and the pole and added it to the potential difference V, we obtain the potential difference V_{0m} in the middle of the pole.

By repetition of this computation for different values of Φ_e, different points on curve $\Phi_e = f(V_{0m})$ are obtained.

The above construction of curve $\Phi_e = f(V_{0m})$ is not valid unless the air gap is constant and the machine operates at no load.

If, however, the air gap increases toward the ends of the pole, flux Φ_e considerably decreases in the case of a given value $B_{\delta m}$, i.e. also b_i decreases according to Eq. (6-8). Thus the notion of the "ideal

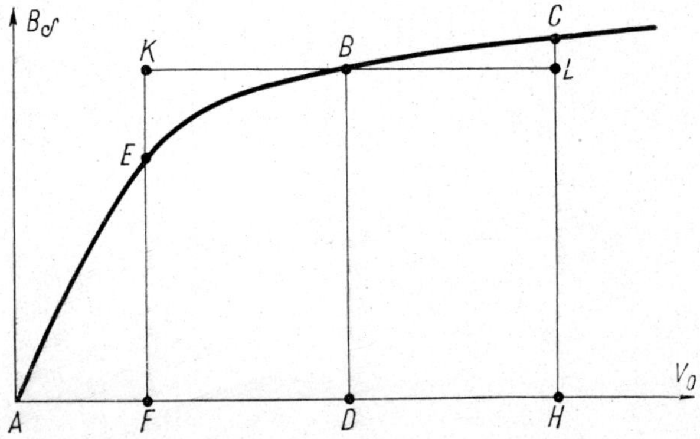

Fig. 6-5

width of the pole arc" becomes meaningless and its value cannot be assessed even approximately.

Even greater difficulties are involved in determining the relation between Φ_e and V_{0m} under load.

In this case flux Φ_e for a given value of $B_{\delta m}$, owing to armature reaction, will be even less than at no load, whence the maintenance of the earlier flux Φ_e requires an even greater potential difference V_{0n} in the region of air gap, tooth and slot. This effect is taken into consideration by the usual method to a certain extent in the following manner.

Curve $AEBC$ (Fig. 6-5) is constructed, whose ordinates are the values B_δ pertaining to the different abscissae V_0 acting upon the region of air gap, tooth and slot. By assuming that the ordinate $\overline{BD}$ corresponds to the flux density in the air gap $B_{\delta m}$ due to the potential difference $V_{0m} = \overline{AD}$ and that the section $\overline{FD} = \overline{DH}$ equals

$Ab_i/2$ (where A is the armature ampere-turn density), we may say that the area *FEBCHDF* represents, on a corresponding scale, flux Φ_e under load, and the area *FKLHF*, the flux Φ_e at no load.

This method is pregnant with considerable shortcomings.

In the first place, it relies on the assumption that the air gap is uniform because the curve *AEBC* shows the relation between B_δ and V_0 at a given value δ. If the air gap is not uniform, the shape of the actual flux may, obviously, differ from the form of curve *AEBC*.

In the second place, in spite of the said simplification, the construction of this curve is rather cumbersome, because it is very difficult to determine the relation between B_δ (i.e. Φ_τ) and V_0 with due regard to the effect of the slot, as has been explained in chapter 1. If this effect is neglected, the method will not yield exact results.

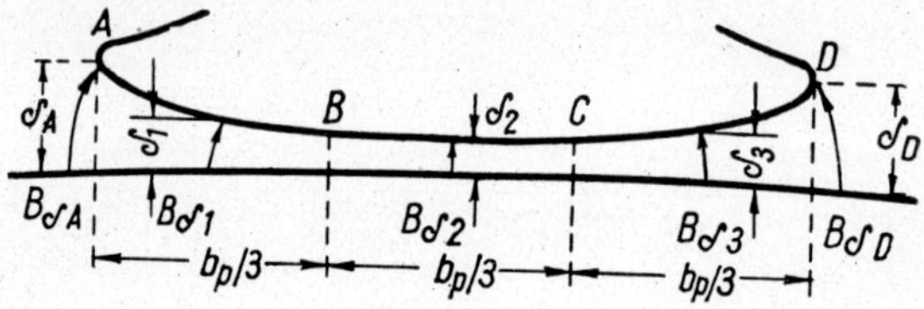

Fig. 6-6

Unlike this cumbersome method, the nomographic determination of the relation between Φ_e and V_{0m} takes into account the lack of uniformity of the air gap, the saturation of the teeth and armature reaction. This method proceeds from the following considerations.

Should the air gap be uniform, the flux Φ_e could be calculated at no load with the formula

$$\Phi_e = \Phi_{e1} + \Phi_{e2} \tag{6-9}$$

where

$$\Phi_{e1} = B_{\delta m} b_p l \tag{6-10}$$

is the flux passing through the pole of the armature,

$$\Phi_{e2} = B_{\delta m} 2\delta l \tag{6-11}$$

is the part of the flux bypassing the air gap, and $B_{\delta m}$ the flux density under the middle of the pole. In the case of a non-uniform air gap (Fig. 6-6) and under load the flux density at the left end of the pole shoe will have another value $B_{\delta A}$ than the flux density $B_{\delta D}$ at its right end.

Therefore flux Φ_{e2} will be determined by the expression

$$\Phi_{e2} = (B_{\delta A}\, \delta_A + B_{\delta D}\, \delta_D)\, l \qquad (6\text{-}12)$$

where δ_A = air gap at the left end

δ_D = air gap at the right end of the pole.

If the air gap is divided along the periphery of the armature into three equal parts AB, BC and CD, then the mean flux densities $B_{\delta 1}$, $B_{\delta 2}$, $B_{\delta 3}$ will act in each of them under load, while the mean flux density along the entire pole shoe will be, instead of $B_{\delta m}$, equal to

$$\frac{B_{\delta 1} + B_{\delta 2} + B_{\delta 3}}{3}$$

With an accuracy sufficient for the computation of Φ_{e2} it may be assumed that the flux density is distributed along the armature periphery according to a quadratic parabola, whence we have

$$B_{\delta A} = \frac{15\, B_{\delta 1} - 10\, B_{\delta 2} + 3\, B_{\delta 3}}{8} \qquad (6\text{-}13)$$

and

$$B_{\delta D} = \frac{3\, B_{\delta 1} - 10\, B_{\delta 2} + 15\, B_{\delta 3}}{8} \qquad (6\text{-}14)$$

Instead of Eq. (6-10) this yields

$$\Phi_{e1} = \frac{B_{\delta 1} + B_{\delta 2} + B_{\delta 3}}{3}\, b_p\, l \qquad (6\text{-}15)$$

and, instead of Eq. (6-9), we have

$$\frac{\Phi_e}{l} = B_{\delta 1}\frac{45\,\delta_A + 9\,\delta_D + 8\,b_p}{24} + B_{\delta 2}\frac{-30\,\delta_A - 30\,\delta_D + 8\,b_P}{24} +$$

$$+ B_{\delta 3}\frac{9\,\delta_A + 45\,\delta_D + 8\,b_P}{24} \qquad (6\text{-}16)$$

Thus we could obtain, for different values of V_{0m}, the function $\Phi_e = f(V_{0m})$ allowing for the armature reaction, the non-uniformity, the non-symmetry of the air gap, for the saturation in the teeth and the unloading effect of the slots, provided the values $B_{\delta 1}$, $B_{\delta 2}$, and $B_{\delta 3}$ pertaining to some given V_{0m} could be determined with due regard to all the above-listed factors.

This task can be solved by applying the results obtained in section 6-1.

6-6. Approach to Assessing the Effect of the Form of the Air Gap and the Armature Reaction upon the Magnetic Relations in the Active Layer of d.c. Machines

Relying on the theoretical results obtained in section 6-5, the function $\Phi_e = f(V_{0m})$ (Fig. 6-7), can be determined in the following order of succession.

1. Compute for the *AB* part of the gap the mean value δ_1 (Fig. 6-6) and the pertaining factor k_{c1}.

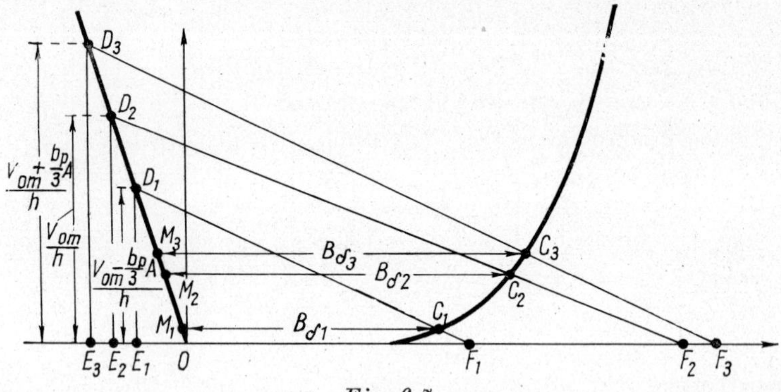

Fig. 6-7

2. With the method of section 6-2 determine the section $\overline{M_1C_1} = B_{\delta 1}\,\tau_t/b_0\gamma$ for the value $V_{0m} \pm Ab_p/3$ and for the computed values δ_1 and k_{c1}.

Here the signs — and + apply to the decrease or increase, respectively, of V_0 owing to the armature reaction toward the left end of the pole shoe.

3. Compute for the *BC* part of the gap the mean value δ_2 (Fig. 6-6) and the pertaining factor k_{c2}.

4. With the method of section 6-2 determine the section $\overline{M_2C_2} = B_{\delta 2}\tau_t/b_0\gamma$ for V_{0m} and the values δ_2 and k_{c2}.

5. Compute for the *CD* part of the gap the mean value δ_3 (Fig. 6-6) and the pertaining factor k_{c3}.

6. With the method of section 6-2 compute the section $\overline{M_3C_3} = B_{03}\tau_t/b_0\gamma$ for $V_{0m} \pm b_pA/3$ and for the value δ_3 and k_{c3}.

7. Determine the air gap δ_A and δ_D at the ends of the pole shoe.

8. Compute flux Φ_e with Eq. (6-16).

Repeating the computation for different values V_{0m} we obtain the function $\Phi_e = f(V_{0m})$.

Example 75. Determine the flux Φ_e of a DMP—151 type d.c. motor (Fig. 6-4b) for a linear demand of $A = 441$ A/cm (I = 300 A).

The motor is characterized by the following parameters:

$V_{0m} = 7{,}400$ A, $b_p = 22$ cm, $\delta_1 = \delta_3 = 0.6$ cm, $\delta_2 = 0.5$ cm, $\delta_A = \delta_D = 1.02$ cm,

$b_0 = 1.98$ cm, $b_2 = 1.32$ cm, $b = 1.42$ cm, $\gamma = 0.95$, $l = 41.2$ cm, $\tau_s = 3.4$ cm, $h = 3.95$.

Compute the factor $a = 2/3$; according to Eq. (2-7) factor $\varrho = 1.467$; from Fig. 4-5 we have $\zeta = 1.6$, Eq. (1-4) yields $b' = 1.5$ cm and Eq. (4-43) yields $\tan\beta = 1.6$.

The Carter coefficients pertaining to δ_1, δ_2, δ_3 are equal to $k_{c2} = 1.205$, $k_{c1} = k_{c3} = 1.18$.

Determine $\overline{E_2D_2} = 1{,}870$ A/cm and $\overline{OF_3} = 27{,}700$ G and, for the part corresponding to the middle of the pole shoe and find nomographically the section $\overline{M_2C_2} = 17{,}500$ G. $B_{\delta 2} = 9{,}700$ G belongs to this section.

The same process should be repeated for the section to the left of the middle of the pole: $\overline{E_1D_1} = 2{,}670$ A/cm, $\overline{OF_1} = 33{,}700$ G, $\overline{M_1C_1} = 19{,}250$ G, $B_{\delta 1} = 10{,}700$ G and for the section to the right of the middle of the pole: $\overline{E_3D_3} = 1{,}080$ A/cm, $\overline{OF_3} = 13{,}600$ G, $\overline{M_3C_3} = 12{,}800$ G, $B_{\delta 3} = 7{,}100$ G. Compute $\Phi_e = 8.9 \cdot 10^6$ M with Eq. (6-16).

6-7. Approach to the Practical Determination of Curve $F_e = f(\Phi_e)$ at No Load and under Load in d.c. Machines

The magnetomotive force of the exciting winding F_e can be determined, as is known, by the formula

$$F_e = V_{0m} + V_p + V_a + V_{st} = f(I_e) \tag{6-17}$$

where

V_p = the potential drop in the body of the pole,

V_a = the potential drop in the armature yoke,

V_{st} = the potential drop in the stator yoke due to the magnetic flux Φ_e (obtained from the full current along the lines *abcd* and *abef* of Fig. 6-8a).

Let us investigate first the case of no load.

For determining the potential drop V_a in the rotor at no load, the nomogram for one body is used with $\varrho = 1$ and flux Φ_e crossing it. When determining the potential drop V_p in the pole body at no load it should be remembered that beside the exciting flux, also leakage fluxes pass through the pole body. At no load these are created by the windings on the main poles and pass through the interpolar space between the stator and the pole shoe, and between the latter and the auxiliary pole. The distribution of these fluxes is shown by the lines of force in Fig. 1-14 from which the magnitude of the conductivity of the leakage fluxes, i.e. the value of the leakage fluxes created by the unit m. m. f. (1A) can be computed with the formula

$$\lambda = 0.4\pi \frac{n_f}{n_e} l \qquad (6\text{-}18)$$

for the different parts of the ferromagnetic configuration surrounding the interpolar space. In this expression, n_f is the number of force tubes pertaining to the given section, and n_e is the number of the elements constituting the tube.

Let the conductivity of the flux passing between points 7 and 5 (Fig. 6-4) be λ_1 and the flux passing between points 5 and 4 be λ_2. The total value of the leakage fluxes is thus obtained as $(\lambda_1 + \lambda_2)F_e$ if there were no potential drop along the body of the pole and the stator yoke. Considering these potential differences, as well as Eq. (6-17). the leakage fluxes can be expressed by the formula

$$(F_e - V_p - V_{st})(\lambda_1 + \lambda_2) = (V_{0m} + V_a)(\lambda_1 + \lambda_2) \qquad (6\text{-}19)$$

We have here neglected the potential drop in the pole shoe, somewhat decreasing the leakage fluxes compared to the value obtained from Eq. (6-19). This error is compensated to a certain degree by neglecting the leakage fluxes passing through the frontal walls of the pole. Thus with an accuracy sufficient for this task we may obtain nomographically the value V_p by assuming a flux $\Phi_e + 2(\lambda_1 + \lambda_2)(V_{0n} + V_a)$ and computing the factor ϱ from the size of the pole body.

On the strength of similar considerations, we can determine nomographically for no load V_{st} relying on the assumption that a flux $(\Phi_e/2) + (V_{0m} + V_a)\ (\lambda_1 + \lambda_2)$ passes through the stator yoke.

If the cross-section of the yoke is constant, the nomographic problem reduces to $\varrho = 1$. If the cross-section of the yoke varies, the factor ϱ, the flux density and the potential drop can be determined for each constituent separately, or the resultant factor ϱ_{res} can be computed with the method of chapter 3.

Under load (Fig. 6-8b) the leakage fluxes increase in the interpolar space where the magnetomotive force in the winding of the

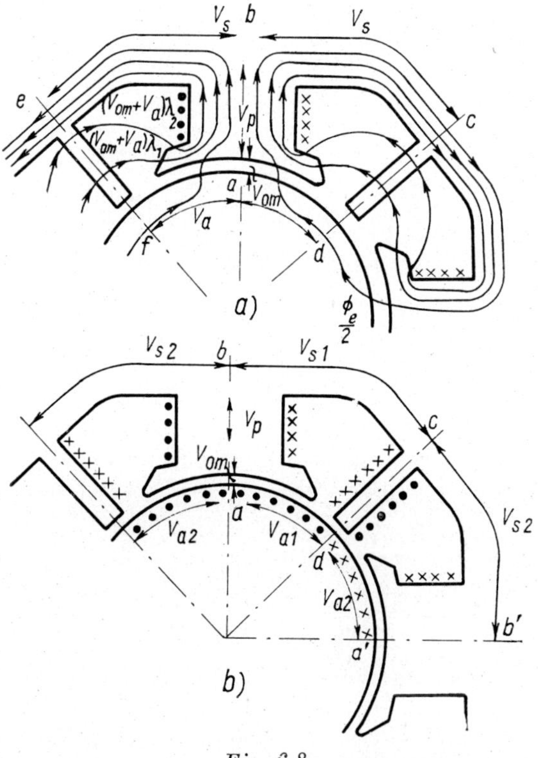

Fig. 6-8

auxiliary pole has the same direction as that of the exciting winding. In the space symmetrical to it, the leakage flux will be smaller. It may be assumed without appreciable error that the resultant leakage flux passing through the body of the pole remains unaltered, whence the relation between the potential drop V_p and flux Φ_e computed for no load remains unchanged also under load.

Yet the said redistribution of the leakage fluxes under load affects the potential drop in the stator. In the quadrant of the stator, through which increased fluxes pass, the potential difference V_{st1} will be greater than V_{st2} in the other quadrant. Thus not V_{st} but

$$\frac{V_{st1} + V_{st2}}{2}$$

should be substituted into the formula (6-17) determining the magnetomotive force F_e (according to the total current distribution, embracing the circuit *abcb'a'a* in Fig 6-8b). This value differs very little from V_{st}, wherefrom the difference will be neglected in the following.

Under the effect of armature reaction the potentials under load are redistributed also in the rotor yoke, whence the potential difference V_{a1} in one quadrant will be greater and V_{a2} in the other quadrant will be less than V_a. Since, however, the difference between

$$\frac{V_{a1} + V_{a2}}{2}$$

and V_a is extremely small, we may proceed not from the former but from the latter value obtained for no load.

Consequently, the fluxes passing through the pole, the rotor yoke and the stator yoke can be calculated, and the values V_a, V_p and V_{st} determined nomographically, for load in the same manner as for no load.

The above considerations show that from the standpoint of the nomographical method the determination of curve $F_e = f(\Phi_e)$ under load is in principle the same as its determination at no load, because the sole difference consists in the possible coincidence of points D_1 and D_3 with point D_2 (Fig. 6-7).

*6-8. Theoretical Considerations Underlying the Nomographic Determination of the Distribution over the Periphery of the Rotor, of the Magnetic Relations within the Active Layer of d. c. Machines at No Load and Under Load**

The construction of Fig. 6-7 renders it possible to assess approximately the flux density in three points of the air gap. Such an assessment is sufficiently accurate for the determination of curve $F_e = f(\Phi_e)$. Nevertheless, for other cases, as for instance, for finding the

* In this section the absence of saturation in the pole shoes will be investigated. The effect of their saturation will be dealt with in chapter 7.

distribution curve of the potentials along the periphery of the commutator, for the exact determination of iron losses and so on, it is indispensable to find the exact distribution of the radial component flux density B_δ in the gap and of V along the armature periphery.

Having developed in section 6-2 a method for determining the reluctance of a region consisting of one tooth, one slot and the pertaining part of the air gap, and in section 6-6 the method for determining the function $\Phi_e = f(V_{0m})$, from which the value of V_{0m} can be obtained for any arbitrary flux Φ_e, we may tackle the problem of determining the magnetic relations in the whole active layer.

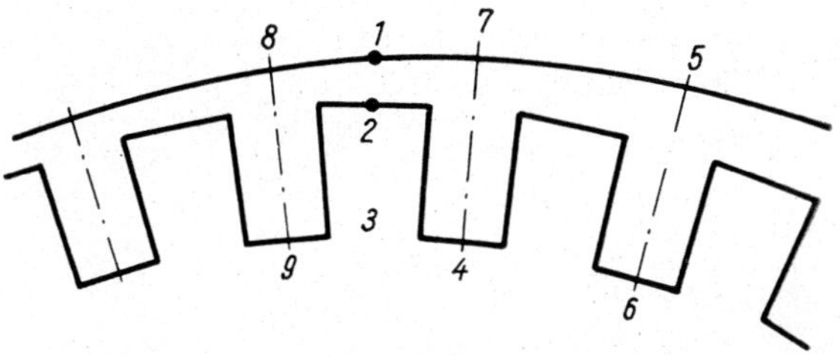

Fig. 6-9

This layer (Fig. 6-9) consists of parallel-connected fields 8-9-4-7 and 7-4-6-5 examined in section 6-1 and having, in the general case, air gaps of different lengths. At no load an identical potential difference V_0 acts upon all these fields.

At points where the form of the air gap changes continuously, i.e. within the edges of the poles, the size of the air gap in different peripheral points can be determined by direct measuring on the sketch.

In determining the air gap at the ends of the poles we proceed from the practically permissible assumption that if the corresponding teeth are saturated, only the fluxes passing through them change, while the general pattern of their distribution remains unchanged. In this case, under the ends of the poles, we find conditions in principle analogous to those under the middle of the pole where, with the teeth saturated, only the value $V_{0m} - V$ is subject to changes, whereas the reluctance of the gap, independently of the magnetic condition of the tooth, is always $0.8\delta\ k_c/\tau_s$. Owing to this, we can, without knowing the degree of saturation in the teeth, determine the reluctance of the air gap at the end of the pole, corresponding to one slot pitch, by the formula $0.8\delta_k k_{ck}/\tau_t$. The value δ_k is determined from the pattern of the lines of force valid for non-saturated teeth and the factor k_{ck} computed thereby.

As soon as the values of the corresponding parts of the air gap are found and the parameters of the tooth and the slot are known, we have all the necessary data for determining nomographically points F, D and C for any selected point on the periphery of the rotor.

In chapters 4 and 5 we have examined the problem of the distribution of the longitudinal slot flux and its effect on the potential difference along the tooth, relying on the assumption that the fluxes, flux densities and fields strengths are symmetrical in two adjacent teeth, whence the symmetrical flux distribution within the slot. In reality this assumption is valid only if the air gap is uniform, if the pole shoe is not saturated (when the potential drop along its height can be neglected) and if there is no load distorting the distribution of the exciting flux.

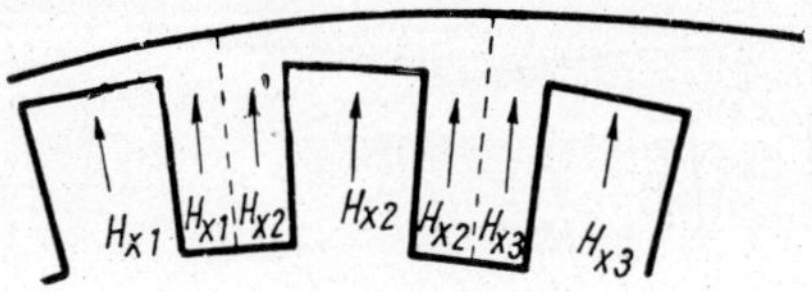

Fig. 6-10

Since we have set ourselves the task in this section to develop a method yielding correct results even in the case of a non-uniform air gap and any arbitrary magnetic demand, it is necessary to find out how the above conclusions will change without the starting assumption of the slot flux being symmetrical.

In the case of a non-uniform flux distribution along the periphery of the rotor, the field strength at a height x in one tooth will be H_{x1} (Fig. 6-10) and in the other, H_{x2}. This means that the longitudinal field strength in the slot will change uniformly from H_{x1} to H_{x2}, whence it may be presumed without great error that the mean field strength in the slot at x will be

$$\frac{H_{x1} + H_{x2}}{2}$$

In the same manner we find that in the following slot, between the second and the third tooth, the mean field strength at a height x will be

$$\frac{H_{x2} + H_{x3}}{2}$$

and so on. Obviously, the magnitude of the longitudinal slot fluxes thus obtained does not change materially if it is assumed that in the half of the first slot, adjacent to the first tooth, the field strength is H_{x1} and in the half adjacent to the second, it is H_{x2}. It may again be assumed that in the half of the second slot, adjacent to the second tooth, there is a field strength H_{x2} while in the half adjacent to the third we have H_{x3}. This means that in the two halves of a slot adjacent to any tooth, such field strengths are acting as correspond to that in the iron of the tooth, i.e. the conditions are analogous to those assumed in chapters 4 and 5. This fact entitles us to apply the above-mentioned nomographic method also to the case of the non-uniform distribution of the air gap.

In examining each slot pitch the only thing to do is to proceed from that magnitude of the air gap which determines the value of the magnetic relations in the tooth, i.e. from the magnitude of the gap in the middle of the crown of the tooth.

It can readily be seen that similar conditions prevail also for the longitudinal slot flux due to the presence of the air gap. Our results will be sufficiently accurate also in this case, if the value of the flux for the individual teeth is computed with the values δ and k_c pertaining to the middle of the tooth crown, according to the formula (4-19).

Beside the redistribution of the density of longitudinal fluxes within the slot (which, as has been shown, does not alter our method), in the case of different magnetic demands of adjacent teeth, transverse slot fluxes, mentioned in chapter 1, also occur.

Should the transverse flux entering the tooth through a side wall be greater or smaller than the transverse flux leaving it through the wall on the other side, then their difference partly passes through the tooth, as shown in Fig. (1-16b). In this case the basic condition underlying the nomographic method, to wit, the constancy of Φ_τ at any height x, is no longer strictly observed, whence a certain error in computing V. As will be shown in chapter 8, in all practical computation for determining the magnetic relations in the active layer of machines and devices, except for the determination of transverse slot fluxes, the effect of the latter upon the magnetic condition of the tooth can be neglected altogether.

Thus the nomographic method can be applied to determine the value of any flux Φ_τ passing through the slot pitches 9-4-7-8, 4-6-5-7-etc. (Fig. 6-9) even in case of a non-uniform air gap. It is only necessary to know the magnitude of V_{0y} acting along each slot pitch between the surface of the pole and the bottom of the slot.

Let us now ascertain the distribution of the magnetic relations in the region of tooth, slot and air gap along the periphery of the rotor under load when the distribution of V_0 over the periphery of the rotor changes on account of armature reaction.

This problem differs in principle from the above-examined problem of determining the distribution of the said relation at no load, inasmuch as the influence of the non-uniform distribution of V_0 can be taken into account in principle just as well as that of the non-uniformity of the air gap.

In using the nomographic method here developed, no-load operation and operation under load are in principle not two different regimes requiring the application of different methods, as is the case when employing the usual method. With the nomographic method, no-load operation is a special case of magnetic demand when V_{0y} acting at a given point over the periphery of the rotor equals V_{0m}, i.e. is identical for every tooth pitch, and point D does not change its position on the straight line OA. Consequently, with our nomographic method in the case of a load, only the different points D and F should be determined for each point under the pole, and we find the pertaining position of the straight line DF yielding point C determining, in turn, the potential drop in the tooth V and the flux density B_δ.

*6-9. Approach to the Practical Determination of the Distribution of Magnetic Relations over the Periphery of the Rotor within the Active Layer of a d.c. Machine at No Load and under Load**

Relying on the consideration expounded in section 6-8, the distribution of magnetic relations over the periphery of the rotor in the active layer of d.c. machines, at no load and under load, can be determined in the following manner:

A) Finding the distribution of the values $\Phi_t, \Phi_s, \Phi_\tau$, and V if V_{0m}, the form of the air gap and the linear demand A are given

At no load, that is, when $A = 0$, the ordinate $V_{0y}/h = V_{0x}/h$ can be obtained from the known function $\Phi_e = f(V_{0m})$ (see point

* See remark on p. 156.

D in Fig. 6-1). Under load, when the place examined is in the same part of the pole pitch in which the excitation coincides with the flux of the armature reaction, the ordinate

$$\frac{V_{0y}}{h} = \frac{V_{0m} + yA}{h}$$

(see point D'' in Fig. 6-1). When this place is in the part of the pole pitch where the flux of armature reaction is opposed to the exciting flux, the ordinate

$$\frac{V_{0y}}{h} = \frac{V_{0m} - yA}{h}$$

(see point D'' in Fig. 6-1).

1. Determine b', α, ϱ, ζ, $\tan\beta$ and find the distances y from the middle of the pole for the points, we are concerned with, on the periphery of the rotor.

2. On the straight line OM pertaining to $\tan\beta$, determine point D (or D' or D'') having the ordinate V_{0y}/h.

3. Compute, for the points we are concerned with over the periphery of the rotor, the values δ_y and k_{cy}, as well as the pertaining sections $\overline{OF}$ with the formula (6-2).

4. For point D (or, in the same manner, for point D' or D'') and for each point F_y use the method of section 6-2 for determining points C_y and the values Φ_t, Φ_s, Φ_τ and V. The division of Φ_τ by $\tau_t\, l$* yields the flux density B_δ at a given point over the periphery of the rotor.

B) Determining the form of the air gap required to obtain the curve $B_{\delta\gamma} = f(y)$ of definite form for given values of V_{0m} and of the linear value A

1. Same as in points 1 and 2 of paragraph *A)*.

2. Compute the sections $\overline{M_yC_y} = B_{\delta y}\tau_t/b_0\gamma$ for the investigated points of the air gap at a distance y from the middle of the pole and determine on the curve ϱ points C_y pertaining to the computed sections $\overline{M_yC_y}$.

3. Determine the points F_y of intersection of the abscissa axis and the straight lines connecting D (or D' or D'') with the different points C_y.

* Naturally, $\tau_t = \tau_s$, i.e. the tooth pitch and the slot pitch are identical.

4. Use Eq. (6-2) to compute, on the basis of the sections OF_y the values $\delta_y k_{cy}$ and those values δ_y for which

$$k_{cy} = \frac{\delta_y k_{cy}}{\delta_y} \tag{6-20}$$

C) Determining the form of the air gap required to obtain a curve $V_y = f(y)$ of the potential drop in the teeth of a definite form at given V_{om} and A

The process is the same as in paragraph B with the sole difference that points C_y are determined not through their abscissae but through their ordinates

$$\overline{C_y K_y} = \frac{V_y}{h}$$

This method clearly shows that the task of determining the magnetic relations of d.c. machines in the air gap can usually be reduced to determining, on the curve ϱ pertaining to the given dimensions of the teeth, different points C_y relating to the different tooth pitches 9-4, 4-6 etc. Since the determinations of these points (curve OC and the straight line OA being the same for each tooth pitch) requires very little time, the new method enables us to determine readily the magnetic relations throughout the active layer of the machine.

The method developed in section 6-9 is based on the assumption that V_0 equals $V_{0m} \pm yA$ throughout the air gap. In reality this assumption holds only when the potential drop along the pole shoe can be neglected.

If there is any doubt as to the possibility of neglecting it, a control computation should be performed according to chapter 7 (section 7-6). In the case of A we may proceed from the obtained values $B_{\delta y}$, in the case of B, from the given values $B_{\delta y}$ and in the case of C, from the values $B_{\delta y}$ computed for the sections $\overline{MC}$ pertaining to the given ordinates $\overline{CK}$.

The application of the method here developed is shown in the following examples.

Example 76. Compute for $V_{0m} = 7{,}400$ A the magnetic relations in the active layer of a d.c. traction motor of the DMP—151 type at no load.

The values $h, b_2, b_0, \gamma, l, b, \tau_t, b', a, \varrho, \zeta, \tan\beta$ for this motor have been calculated in Ex. 75.

The values of δ for different magnitudes y are determined from the sketch of the air gap in Fig. 4-6b and the factors k_{cy} are computed accordingly.

Using Eq. (6-4) compute $\overline{ED} = 1{,}870$ A/cm and for the values y find the magnitudes $\overline{OF} = 8.9\ \overline{ED}/\delta k_c$.

On the basis of points F thus obtained we find nomographically the sections $\overline{CK}$ and $\overline{CL}$ and compute, for the different points of the air gap, the potential drop $V = 3.98\ \overline{CK}$, flux $\Phi_t = 78\ \overline{CL}$, flux $\Phi_s = 125\ \overline{CK}$, flux $\Phi_\tau = \Phi_t + \Phi_s$ and the flux density $B_\delta = 0.0071\ \Phi_\tau$.

The process of computation and the values obtained for the parameters are given in Table 6-1.

Owing to the symmetrical flux, for the points of the air gap from $y = 0$ to $y = -12.18$ we obtain, correspondingly, the same parameters as in the range of $y = 0$ to $y = +12.18$.

Example 77. When designing a traction motor of the type DMP—151 it is required to determine the form of the gap ensuring at no load the distribution B_δ according to the column 13 in Table 6-1.

TABLE 6-1

y cm	δ cm	k_c	δk_c cm	$\overline{ED}$ A/cm	$\overline{OF}$ G	$\overline{CK}$ A/cm	V A	$\overline{CL}$ G	Φ_t 10^6 M	Φ_s 10^6 M	Φ_τ 10^6 MG	B_δ G
1	2	3	4	5	6	7	8	9	10	11	12	13
±12.18	2.7	1.05	2.83	1,870	5,900	0	0	5,900	0.46	0	0.46	3,300
±10.44	0.9	1.13	1.02	1,870	16,300	180	700	14,400	1.12	0.022	1.142	8,150
±8.70	0.71	1.16	0.82	1,870	20,300	390	1,660	15,450	1.20	0.05	1.25	8,900
±6.96	0.57	1.18	0.67	1,870	24,900	600	2,380	16,100	1.25	0.075	1.325	9,400
±5.22	0.51	1.2	0.61	1,870	27,300	680	2,660	16,300	1.27	0.085	1.355	9,700
±3.48	0.5	1.2	0.6	1,870	27,700	690	2,730	16,400	1.28	0.09	1.37	9,800
±1.74	0.5	1.2	0.6	1,870	27,700	690	2,730	16,400	1.28	0.09	1.37	9,800
0	0.5	1.2	0.6	1,870	27,700	690	2,730	16,400	1.28	0.09	1.37	9,800

Having computed $\overline{MC} = B_0\tau_t/b_0\gamma$ for different values B_δ determine nomographically $\overline{ED}$ and $\overline{OF}$, then compute with Eqs. (6-2) and (6-20) the values δk_c and δ. The process of the operation, and the parameters obtained, are given in Table 6-2.

TABLE 6-2

y cm	B_δ G	$\overline{MC}$ G	$\overline{ED}$ G	$\overline{OF}$ G	δk_c cm	δ cm
1	2	3	4	5	6	7
± 12.18	3,300	5,960	1,870	5,900	2.83	2.7
± 10.44	8,150	14,700	1,870	16,300	1.02	0.9
± 8.70	8,900	16,100	1,870	20,300	0.82	0.71
± 6.96	9,400	17,100	1,870	24,900	0.67	0.57
± 5.22	9,700	17,600	1,870	27,300	0.61	0.51
± 3.48	9,800	17,700	1,870	27,700	0.6	0.5
± 1.74	9,800	17,700	1,870	27,700	0.6	0.5
0	9,800	17,700	1,870	27,700	0.6	0.5

If, by the proper selection of the air gap, it is necessary to ensure a definite curve $V = f(y)$, then in using the nomographic method we should proceed, not from the values B_δ and $\overline{MC}$, but from V and $\overline{CK}$. The rest of the operation would remain the same.

Example 78. Compute for different points on the rotor periphery (from $y = +3.48$ to $y = -12.18$) the magnetic relations in the active layer of a DMP—151 type motor at a linear demand $A = 441$ A/cm and with $V_{0n} = 7{,}400$ A.

The parameters characterizing the geometric configuration of the active layer, the values δk_c as well as the formulae for the computation of the section $\overline{OF}$ and the values V, Φ_t, Φ_s and B_δ will remain the same as in Ex.76.

For computing the section $\overline{DE}$ use the formula

$$\overline{DE} = \frac{V_{0m} \pm 411\,y}{3.95}$$

The course of the operation and the parameters are given in Table 6-3.

TABLE 6-3

No.	y cm	yA A	$V_{0m} \pm yA$ A	δk_c cm	$\overline{DE}$ A/cm	$\overline{OF}$ G	$\overline{CK}$ A/cm	V A	Φ_s M	$\overline{LG}$ G	Φ_t 10^6 M	Φ_τ 10^6 M	$B\delta$ G
1	2	3	4	5	6	7	8	9	10	11	12	13	14
7	+3.48	+1,550	8,950	0.6	2,280	34,000	980	3,900	120,000	17,100	1.32	1.44	10,300
8	+1.74	+ 770	8,170	0.6	2,060	30,900	830	3,300	100,000	16,700	1.31	1.40	10,000
9	0	0	7,400	0.6	1,870	28,000	690	2,740	86,000	16,400	1.27	1.37	9,700
10	−1.74	− 770	6,630	0.6	1,680	25,000	540	2,150	67,000	16,000	1.25	1.317	9,400
11	−3.48	−1,550	5,850	0.6	1,480	22,200	390	1,540	49,000	15,500	1.20	1.249	8,900
12	−5.22	−2,300	5,100	0.61	1,280	19,000	250	990	31,000	14,900	1.15	1.181	8,400
13	−6.96	−3,040	4,360	0.67	1,100	14,800	90	360	11,000	13,300	1.03	1.041	7,400
14	−8.70	−3,810	3,590	0.82	900	9,900	10	40	1,250	9,700	0.76	0.76	5,400
15	−10.44	−4,650	2,750	1.02	700	6,100	3	10	400	5,400	0.42	0.42	3,000
16	−12.18	−5,400	2,000	2.83	500	1,600	0	0	0	1,600	0.12	0.12	850

Example 79. Find the distribution of flux density in the air gap of a DPE—340 type d.c. motor for a one hour current $I = 250$ A. The potential drop along the pole shoe and in the field 10-9′-8′-6-7-10 (Fig. 6-4a) are neglected for the time being.

We shall proceed from the form of the main pole (Fig. 6-4a).

According to the computation formula* find the value $V_{0m} = 14{,}300$ A acting under the middle of the pole with regard to the effect of armature reaction, as well as the air gap $\delta = 0.63$ cm.

For the point under the middle of the pole, the flux density was obtained in Ex. 71 as $B_\delta = 10{,}900$ G.

For the point at a distance $y = +3.5$ cm at A = 428 A/cm, we have

$$\overline{ED} = \frac{V_0}{h} = \frac{14{,}300 + 3.5 \cdot 428}{5.79} = 2{,}730 \text{ A/cm}$$

whence $\overline{OF} = 2{,}730 \cdot 18 = 49{,}000$ G.

For the above section we obtain from the nomogram $B_\delta = 11{,}300$ G.

For the flux densities pertaining to the other y values we have:

$y = +6.0$	cm	$B_\delta = 11{,}650$	G
$y = +8.8$	cm	$B_\delta = 12{,}000$	G
$y = +9.8$	cm	$B_\delta = 12{,}100$	G
$y = +12.0$	cm	$B_\delta = 12{,}250$	G
$y = +14.6$	cm	$B_\delta = 12{,}600$	G
$y = +16.5$	cm	$B_\delta = 12{,}800$	G

At a point lying to the left from the middle of the pole, at a distance $y = -3.5$ cm, we obtain in the same manner

$$\frac{V_0}{h} = \frac{14{,}300 - 3.5 \cdot 428}{5.79} = 2{,}210 \text{ A/cm}$$

and $B_\delta = 10{,}600$ G. In the same manner we have:

$y = -6.0$	cm	$B_\delta = 10{,}350$	G
$y = -8.8$	cm	$B_\delta = 10{,}000$	G
$y = -9.8$	cm	$B_\delta = 9{,}850$	G
$y = -12.0$	cm	$B_\delta = 9{,}550$	G
$y = -14.6$	cm	$B_\delta = 9{,}050$	G
$y = -16.5$	cm	$B_\delta = 8{,}800$	G

* *Советские магистральные электровозы* (Soviet elektric locomotives for main lines), Москва, Трансжелдориздат 1940, pp. 351, 352.

By assuming the iron surface equipotential, the distribution curve of the flux density in the air gap can be constructed (Fig. 6-11, curve I).

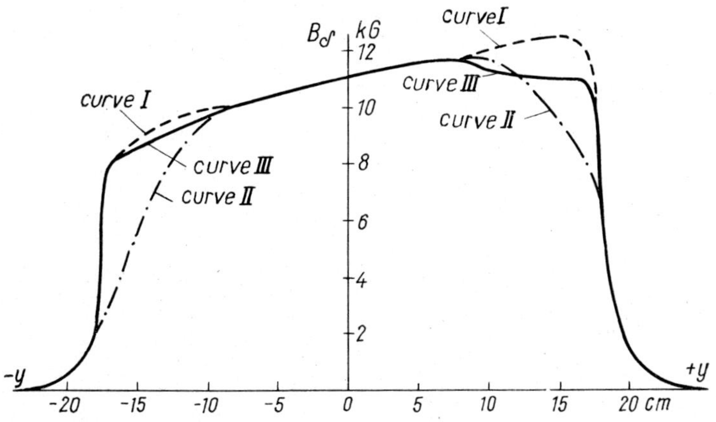

Fig. 6-11

Example 80. In the previous example we have found the distribution of flux density for a uniform air gap, $\delta = 0.63$ cm.

For the sake of comparison we shall show now how to proceed if δ changes along the periphery of the rotor. Let us assume the inner surface of the pole shoe to be 10-9′-8′-6 (Fig. 6-4a) and not 10-7. In this case the air gap will be $\delta = 0.83$ cm at points pertaining to $y = \pm 9.8$ cm, $\delta = 1.1$ cm at points pertaining to $y = \pm 12$ cm, $\delta = 1.7$ cm at points pertaining to $y = \pm 14.6$ cm and $\delta = 2.1$ cm at points pertaining to $y = \pm 16.5$ cm.

For point $y = +9.8$ cm we have

$$\frac{V_0}{h} = \frac{14{,}100 + 9.8 \cdot 428}{5.79} = 3{,}200 \text{ A/cm}$$

$k_c = 1.145$, $\overline{OF} = 50{,}500$ G and from the nomogram we obtain $B_\delta = 11{,}500$ G.

In the same manner we obtain

$y = +12.0$	cm	$B_\delta = 11{,}150$ G
$y = +14.6$	cm	$B_\delta = 10{,}350$ G
$y = +16.5$	cm	$B_\delta = 9{,}800$ G
$y = -9.8$	cm	$B_\delta = 9{,}350$ G
$y = -12.0$	cm	$B_\delta = 8{,}250$ G

$$y = -14.6 \text{ cm} \qquad B_\delta = 5{,}250 \text{ G}$$
$$y = -16.5 \text{ cm} \qquad B_\delta = 4{,}100 \text{ G}$$

On the basis of the values B_δ the distribution curve of flux density (Fig. 6-11, curve II) can be constructed for a non-uniform air gap increasing toward the ends of the poles.

The comparison with curve I clearly shows the effect of the increase of the air gap upon the distribution of flux density.

The preceding two examples make it evident that the load in the armature, or a non-uniform air gap (that is the factors which make all problems extremely complicated for the usual method of computation) do not affect the simplicity, the quickness and the accuracy of the solution when the nomographic method is applied.

In Fig. 6-12 the solid lines represent the distribution curve of the flux density B_δ in the air gap over the armature periphery of a DK—103 type motor with intensified field, without taking into account

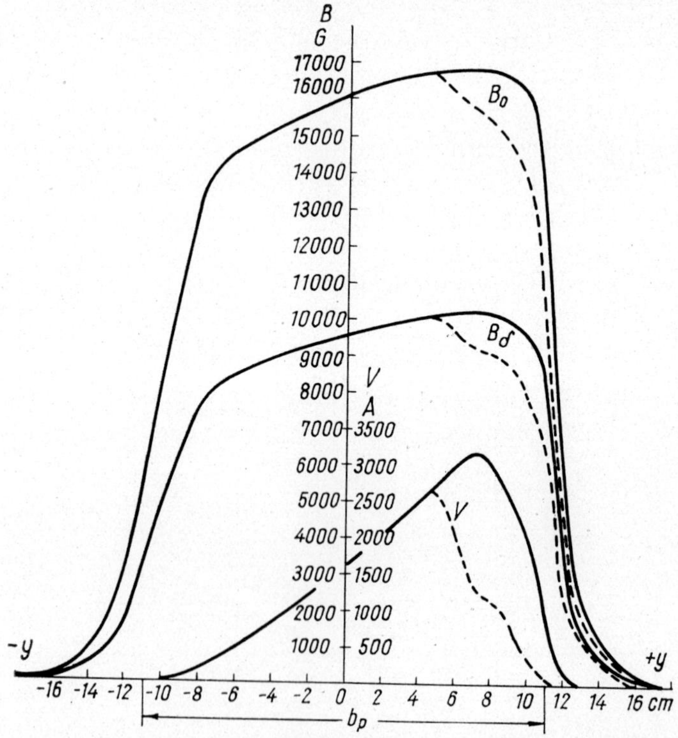

Fig. 6-12

the saturation of the pole shoe, as obtained by the nomographic method. The distribution curve of the values V under the same conditions is also plotted on the figure.*

The method of magnetic computations for cases when the pole shoe is composed of sheets of different configuration has been mentioned earlier. Let us show its application on an example.

Example 81. Determine the flux density in the air gap of a traction motor of the type DPE—340 at load, taking into account the actual configuration of the air gap (with sheets of different shape in the pole shoe). We shall, for the time being, neglect the potential drop along the pole shoe.

According to Ex. 74, the resultant region of tooth and parallel slot for the point $y = \pm 14.6$ cm, with due consideration of the sheets of different shape in the pole, is characterized by the following parameters: $\tan\beta = 1.58$, $\varrho_{res} = 1.44$, $\gamma b_{0 res} = 1.94$ and $h_{res} = 6.79$ cm.

Determine the flux density prevailing in the air gap and pertaining to the given point (V_{0n} and A are taken from Ex. 79).

Having calculated the value

$$\frac{V_0}{h} = \frac{14{,}300 + 14.6 \cdot 428}{6.79} = 3{,}020 \text{ A/cm}$$

and the section

$$\overline{OF} = 3{,}020 \frac{0.4\pi \cdot 6.79 \cdot 3.5}{0.63 \cdot 1.18 \cdot 1.94} = 62{,}500 \text{ G}$$

the nomogram yields $B_\delta = 12{,}300$ G.

For points $y = -14.6$ cm we have the same values of $\tan\beta_{res}$, ϱ_{res}, $\gamma b_{0 res}$, h_{res}, as for $y = +14.6$ cm; having computed the values $V_0/h = 1{,}165$ A/cm and $\overline{OF} = 24{,}600$ G, we obtain nomographically $B_\delta = 9{,}050$ G.

In a similar manner we have

$$y = +16.5 \text{ cm} \qquad B_\delta = 12{,}350 \text{ G}$$
$$y = -16.5 \text{ cm} \qquad B_\delta = 8{,}800 \text{ G}$$
$$y = +12.0 \text{ cm} \qquad B_\delta = 12{,}200 \text{ G}$$
$$y = -12.0 \text{ cm} \qquad B_\delta = 9{,}550 \text{ G}$$

* The curve is from the dissertation of V.A. Shilovski, *Исследование магнитной системы тяговых двигателей мотор-вагонного подвижного состава (секции C^p)* (Investigation of the magnetic system of the traction motors in motor coaches [section C^p]) who applied in his research the system of nomographic method developed by the author.

A comparison of these results with those of Ex. 79 makes it clear that there is great difference between them. Consequently, the magnitude of the flux density in the air gap in the said traction motor will be affected by the field 10-7-6 but slightly.

This can be explained by the fact that the teeth of the armature are much narrower than the iron "teeth" of the stator (in relation to the pertaining slots), whence the flux passing through the highly saturated rotor teeth causes almost no potential difference in the field 10-7-6.

Thus the field 10-7-6 in the DPE—340 type machine does not fulfil its function which, true enough, cannot be noticed because, as will be explained in chapter 7, the flux creates a great potential difference along the upper part of the pole shoe.

6-10. Method of Determining the Distribution of the Magnetic Values along the Periphery of the Active Layer in Other Electrical Machines

The sections 6-5, 6-6, 6-8, and 6-9 are devoted to the questions of nomographic computation only in respect to d.c. machines as usually manufactured. The results obtained in these sections can, however, be applied also to other electrical machines.

In the case of a single-phase series-connected commutator motor, for instance, the sole difference is that the fluxes and magnetomotive forces change as time functions. Let us, by way of example, determine the higher time harmonics of the load current and of the exciting flux. By determining, according to sections 6-5, 6-6 and 6-7, curve $F_e = f(\Phi_e)$ and assuming, as a first approximation, that Φ_e changes sinusoidally (sufficiently accurate in the case of high rpm), the function $F_e = f(\Phi_e)$, as well as the upper harmonic of the load current can be obtained. When examining the conditions at start, when both Φ_e and I may have considerable higher harmonics, we proceed from the following considerations:

It may be assumed in practice that the motor voltage at start maintains the equilibrium of the algebraic sum of two voltages, one being proportional to $d\Phi_e/dt$, the other to dI/dt whence also to dF_e/dt. By proceeding from the differential quotient to the quotients of small differences we find that the motor voltage changing sinusoidally with time equals the sum

$$C_1 \frac{\Delta F_e}{\Delta t} \left(\frac{\Delta I_e}{\Delta F_e} + C_2 \right)$$

in which C_1 and C_2 are constant. Since, for any arbitrary value of F_e, the pertaining value $\Delta\Phi_e/\Delta F_e$ can be read from curve $F_e = f(\Phi_e)$, the curve $F_e = f(t)$ and therefrom the curve $\Phi_e = f(t)$ can be determined. Thus the higher harmonics of both the exciting flux and the load current may be obtained.

Let us now examine, by way of example, the magnetic relations in the active layer of a d.c. machine in the rotor of which not only a transverse but also a longitudinal magnetomotive force prevails (e.g. Rosenberg's machine for the lighting of railway carriages).

Obviously, a certain part F_{lp} of the longitudinal mmf is linked with the entire pole arc and can therefore be added algebraically to the mmf F_e on the pole. Thus, depending on the direction of F_{lp}, the value F_e decreases or increases, respectively. At any arbitrary point under the pole arc at a distance of $\pm y$ from the middle of the pole there is, beside F_{lp} and the transverse mmf F_{qy}, a positive or negative remainder $F_{ly}—F_{lp}$ of the longitudinal mmf acting, which is created at the given point. By superposing the values F_{qy} and F_{ly} pertaining to the different distances, we obtain the actual distribution of the mmfs acting on the different points in the active layer. On the basis of this distribution, the mmfs pertaining to the flux densities $B_{\delta A}$, $B_{\delta 1}$, $B_{\delta 2}$, $B_{\delta 3}$, and $B_{\delta D}$ can be determined and with their help these flux densities obtained nomographically. Therefrom we have (section 6-6) the function $\Phi_e = f(V_{0n})$ and (section 6-7) the entire exciting mmf by substituting into Eq. (6-17) $F_e \pm F_{lp}$ instead of F_e.

As far as the problems listed in sections 6-8 and 6-9 are concerned, they can be solved in the same manner also in this case. The only thing to do is to take into account that points D, D', D'' etc. as well as the pertaining points F have a different position, being shifted even in relation to one another on account of the fact that the resultant mmfs pertaining to the different distances $\pm y$ are distributed in an entirely different manner.

In the case of, for instance, a three-phase synchronous machine, the proceedings will be the following:

The angle enclosed by the stator mmf (corresponding to the rotor mmf of commutator machines) and by the rotor mmf (representing the exciting mmf) can be read from the vector diagram.

Then the stator mmf is reduced to a component having the same axis as the rotor mmf (direct axis mmf) and to one perpendicular to it (quadrature axis mmf). The rest is, in principle, the same as in the previous case since the fact that both mmf components are distributed over the armature periphery, unlike in a commutator machine, has no theoretical significance for the application of the nomographic method.

In the case of an asynchronous machine the problems associated with the configuration of the air gap are eliminated since it is uniformly distributed throughout. On the other hand, the necessity may arise to determine the exact distribution and magnitude of the resultant flux for a given momentary space distribution (to be established from the vector diagram) of the mmfs in the rotor and the stator (required for a more accurate determination of the degree of saturation as well as the higher space harmonics of the flux). In this instance we should again proceed from the total mmf acting at a given point for each point in the active layer, and the relevant values B_δ can be determined nomographically by means of the pertaining points D and F.

CHAPTER SEVEN

NOMOGRAPHIC COMPUTATION OF THE INFLUENCE OF POLE SHOE SATURATION ON THE MAGNETIC FIELD IN THE REGION OF TOOTH, SLOT AND AIR GAP

7-1. Deduction of Formulae for Determining Leakage Fluxes Passing through the Saturated Pole Shoe

The determination of the magnetic field within the region of tooth, slot and air gap has been based upon the assumption that the value V_{0y} at any distance from the pole centre can be computed if the potential difference V_{0m} prevailing in the pole centre, as well as the magnitude and distribution of the rotor mmf, are known. The effect of pole shoe saturation upon the magnetic relations in this region has been neglected so far.

In reality, a certain part of V_{0y} is spent along the saturated pole shoe. Owing to this, the potential difference in the region of tooth, slot and air gap is smaller than V_{0y}. The basic difficulty in solving this problem is that the value of the fluxes crossing the air gap, and entering the shoe, cannot be determined unless the potential drop along the shoe V_{pv} is known and, not knowing these fluxes, there is no possibility of determining the potential drop V_{pv} caused by them in the shoe.

In addition to this, leakage fluxes, making the distribution of potentials rather involved, pass through the shoe simultaneously with the main flux.

To illustrate the method of determining leakage fluxes, let us resort to a practical example of a pole shoe (Fig. 7-1a) which has the same characteristics as the one in Fig. 1-13a or Fig. 1-13b and belong to a d.c. machine as shown in Fig. 7-2. Let the shoe be divided into parts I and II, and let part III be separated from the body of the pole. The next section is devoted to finding the exact boundaries between the above parts.

Let us determine the values of the leakage fluxes $\Phi_{\sigma I}$ and $\Phi_{\sigma II}$ set up by the windings of the main and commutating poles in the

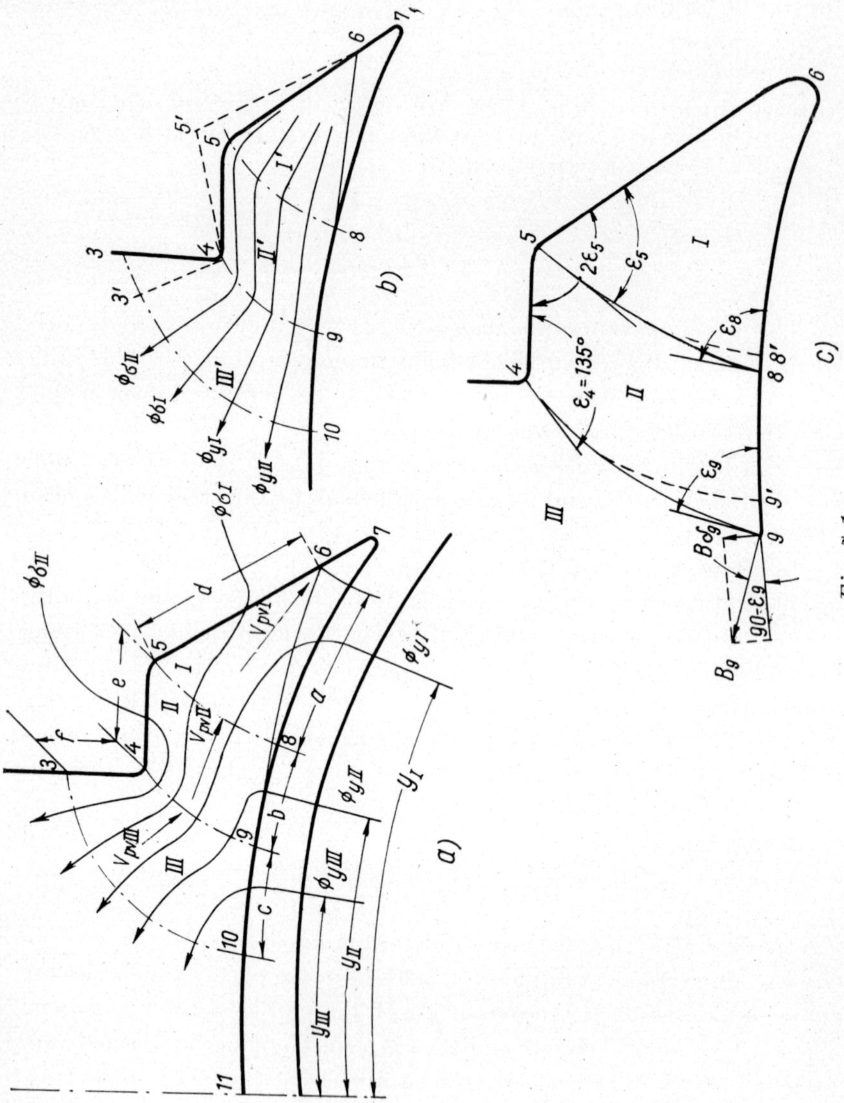

a)
b)
c)
$\varepsilon_4 = 135°$
$2\varepsilon_5$
ε_5
ε_8
ε_9
$90-\varepsilon_9$
B_9

Fig. 7-1

interpolar space. If the potential drop in the iron is neglected, their values $\Phi'_{\sigma I}$ and $\Phi'_{\sigma II}$ can readily be determined by constructing potential nets. These should be set up for three cases.

For the first net (Fig. 1-14) it is assumed that the magnetomotive force is uniformly distributed over the surface of the stator. This net corresponds to the mmf F_e created by the field coil.

The second net (Fig. 7-2a) is based on the assumption that the mmf is uniformly distributed over the surface of the armature and the commutating pole. This graph corresponds to the mmf of armature reaction F_a and to that part of the mmf of the commutating pole which compensates it.

The third net (Fig. 7-2b) relies on the assumption that the mmf is uniformly distributed over the surface of the commutating pole. This net corresponds to the remaining part of the mmf of the commutating pole F_{cp}.

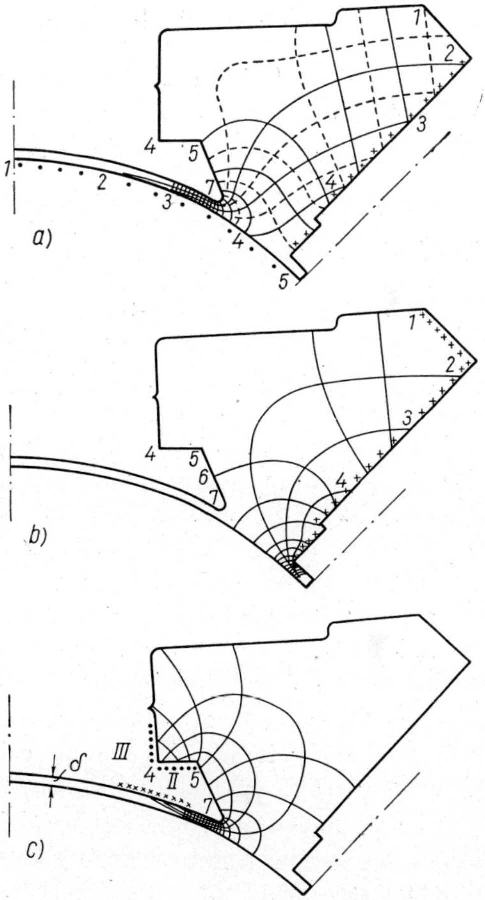

Fig. 7-2

Part of the flange of the main pole reaching into the interpolar space has been neglected in constructing the above nets (see Figs. 6-4a and 6-4b where this salient part is omitted), because this part exerts a relatively small influence upon the flux distribution and is usually highly saturated with leakage fluxes.

The nets so constructed yield, together with Eq. (6-18), the permeance of the leakage fluxes crossing the different fields of the pole shoe.

The leakage flux $\Phi'_{\sigma\mathrm{I}}$ entering the pole shoe between points 5-7 can be determined, on the side where the effect of the mmf F_{cp} has the same direction as that of F_e, with the following equation, on the analogy of the formula (6-19) and of the possibility of superposing leakage fluxes,

$$\Phi'_{\sigma\mathrm{I}} = (V_{0m} + V_a)\,\lambda_{\mathrm{I}} + F_a\,\lambda'_{\mathrm{I}} + F_{cp}\,\lambda'' \tag{7-1}$$

The value of the leakage flux entering the pole shoe between points 4-5* is

$$\Phi'_{\sigma\mathrm{II}} = (V_{0m} + V_0)\,\lambda_{\mathrm{II}} + F_a\,\lambda'_{\mathrm{II}} + F_{cp}\,\lambda''_{\mathrm{II}} \tag{7-2}$$

In the interpolar spaces where the mmfs F_a and F_{cp} are opposed to $F_e = V_{0m} + V_a$ (Fig. 7-3), the pertaining leakage fluxes are

$$\Phi'_{\sigma\mathrm{IV}} = (V_{0m} + V_a)\,\lambda_{\mathrm{I}} - F_a\,\lambda'_{\mathrm{I}} - F_{cp}\,\lambda''_{\mathrm{I}} \tag{7-3}$$

and

$$\Phi'_{\sigma\mathrm{V}} = (V_{0m} + V_a)\,\lambda_{\mathrm{II}} - F_a\,\lambda'_{\mathrm{II}} - F_{cp}\,\lambda'_{\mathrm{II}} \tag{7-4}$$

Here λ_{I}, λ'_{I}, λ''_{I} are the permeances of the flux entering the shoe in the section 5-7 obtained from the potential net (Figs. 1-14, 7-2a and 7-2b), and λ_{II}, λ'_{II}, λ''_{II} are the pertaining permeances of the flux entering the shoe in the section 4-5.

Let us investigate how the results obtained change if the leakage fluxes are determined not for the shoe type of Fig. 1-13, but for that of Fig. 1-12a.

This shoe should be divided into parts as shown in Fig. 7-4 so that point 5 should lie midway between points 4 and 7 and $e = d$. Otherwise the determination of the leakage flux is analogous to the previous method applied to the corresponding field configuration.

The formulae (7-1) to (7-4) for leakage fluxes are derived without taking into account the effect of the potential drops V_{pv} along the different sections of the pole shoe (Fig. 7-3).

Their influence on the leakage flux $\Phi'_{\sigma\mathrm{I}}$ can be expressed in the form of an imaginary flux of opposite sense λ'''_{I} $(V_{pv\mathrm{III}} + V_{pv\mathrm{II}} + 0.5V_{pv\mathrm{I}})$ (Fig. 7-3), and the effect upon $\Phi'_{\sigma\mathrm{II}}$, by an imaginary flux of opposite direction λ'''_{II} $(V_{pv\mathrm{III}} + 0.5V_{pv\mathrm{II}})$ where λ'''_{I} and λ'''_{II} represent the corresponding values of permeance.

* Points 4 and 5 are situated in the middle of the curve.

The values λ_{I}''' and λ_{II}''' can be taken from the potential net of Fig. 7-2c. In constructing the potential net the potential differences $V_{pv\mathrm{III}}$ and $V_{pv\mathrm{II}}$ have been substituted by an mmf of a corresponding surface distribution where, for the sake of simplicity, it has been assumed that $V_{pv\mathrm{III}} = V_{pv\mathrm{II}}$ and the influence of 0.5 $V_{pv\mathrm{I}}$ upon λ_{I}''',

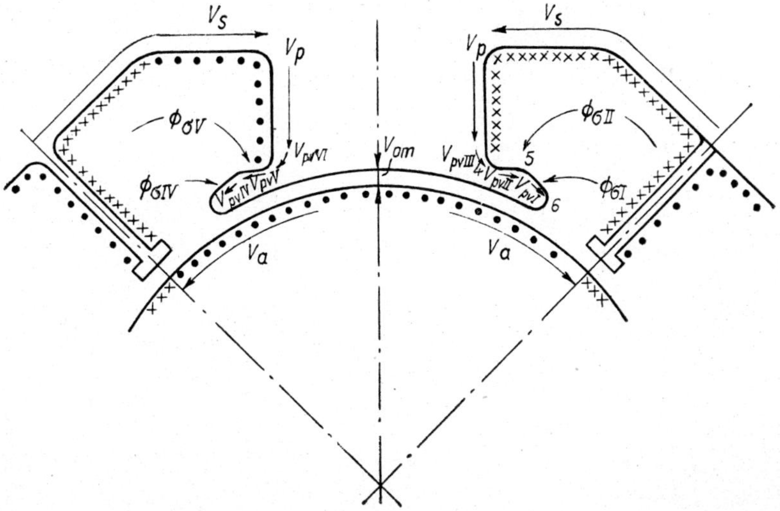

Fig. 7-3

as well as the influence of the magnitudes 0.5 $V_{pv\mathrm{I}}$ and 0.5 $V_{pv\mathrm{II}}$ upon λ_{II}''' have been neglected.

An examination of the potential net in Fig. 7-2c shows that the flux in the section 4-5 does not leave the shoe, as is the case in section 5-7, but passes from part II of the shoe through the air into part III. In the following, this flux will be looked upon as part of the total flux of the pole shoe passing from part II into part III, not through the iron but through the air.

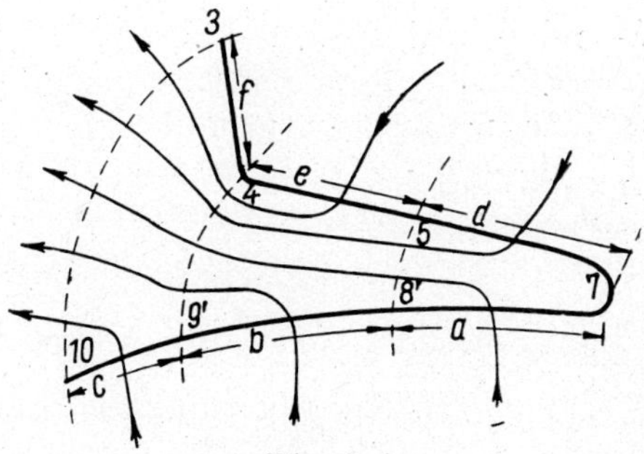

Fig. 7-4

This flux will, therefore, be neglected in determining leakage fluxes, i.e. it will be assumed that $\lambda_{\mathrm{II}}'' = 0$.

Thus, by taking into account the potential drop in the shoe, we obtain the final equations for leakage fluxes (Fig. 7-3) as

$$\Phi_{\sigma\mathrm{I}} = \Phi'_{\sigma\mathrm{I}} - \lambda'''_{\mathrm{I}} (V_{pv\mathrm{III}} + V_{pv\mathrm{II}} + 0.5\, V_{pv\mathrm{I}}) \tag{7-5}$$

$$\Phi_{\sigma\mathrm{II}} = \Phi'_{\sigma\mathrm{II}} \tag{7-6}$$

$$\Phi_{\sigma\mathrm{IV}} = \Phi'_{\sigma\mathrm{IV}} - \lambda'''_{\mathrm{I}} (V_{pv\mathrm{VI}} + V_{pv\mathrm{V}} + 0.5\, V_{pv\mathrm{IV}}) \tag{7-7}$$

$$\Phi_{\sigma\mathrm{V}} = \Phi'_{\sigma\mathrm{V}} \tag{7-8}$$

where $V_{p\nu\mathrm{VI}}$, $V_{p\nu\mathrm{V}}$, $V_{p\nu\mathrm{IV}}$ are the potential differences along the other shoe (see Fig. 7-3).

7-2. Approach to the Practical Determination of Leakage Fluxes Passing through the Pole Shoes without Regard to Saturation

On the basis of the theoretical considerations in section 7-1 the leakage fluxes passing through the pole shoe, disregarding the potential drop along it, can be determined as follows:

1. From the potential net of the field created by the mmf of the exciting winding (Fig. 1-14), determine the number $n_{t\mathrm{I}}$, and $n_{t\mathrm{II}}$ of line of force tubes crossing sections 5-7 and 4-5, and the number $m_{e\mathrm{I}}$, and $m_{e\mathrm{II}}$ of elements constituting each tube over this section. Using Eq. (6-18) compute λ_{I} and λ_{II}.

2. From the potential net of the field created by the mmf of the armature and by that part of the mmf of the commutating pole (Fig. 7-2a) which compensates it, determine $n'_{t\mathrm{I}}$ and $m'_{e\mathrm{I}}$ for the section 5-7 and $n'_{t\mathrm{II}}$ and $m'_{e\mathrm{II}}$ for the section 4-5, and compute λ'_{I} and λ'_{II} with Eq. (6-18).

3. From the potential net of the field created by the remaining part of the mmf of the commutating pole (Fig. 7-2b), determine $n''_{t\mathrm{I}}$ and $m''_{e\mathrm{I}}$ for the section 5-7 and $n''_{t\mathrm{II}}$ and $m''_{e\mathrm{II}}$ for the section 4-5, and compute λ''_{I} and λ''_{II} with Eq. (6-18).

4. Using Eqs. (7-1) to (7-4) compute $\Phi'_{\sigma\mathrm{I}}$, $\Phi'_{\sigma\mathrm{II}}$, $\Phi'_{\sigma\mathrm{IV}}$ and $\Phi'_{\sigma\mathrm{V}}$.

Let us now apply this method to a practical example.

Example. 82. Determine the leakage fluxes $\Phi'_{\sigma\mathrm{I}}$, $\Phi'_{\sigma\mathrm{II}}$ $\Phi'_{\sigma\mathrm{IV}}$ and $\Phi'_{\sigma\mathrm{V}}$ entering the pole shoe of a DPE—340 type motor during a one-hour current of $I = 250$ A.

The permeances of the leakage fluxes over sections 5-7, and 4-5 can be read from the potential net of Figs. 1-14, 7-2a and 7-2b:

$$\lambda_{\rm I} = 0.4\,\pi\,\frac{3}{4}\,30.5 = 28.6 \text{ M/A}$$

$$\lambda'_{\rm I} = 0.4\,\pi\,\frac{3}{7}\,30.5 = 16 \text{ M/A}$$

$$\lambda''_{\rm I} = 0.4\,\pi\,\frac{1}{4}\,30.5 = 9.5 \text{ M/A}$$

$$\lambda_{\rm II} = 0.4\,\pi\,\frac{1}{4}\,30.5 = 9.5 \text{ M/A}$$

$$\lambda'_{\rm II} = 0 \qquad \lambda''_{\rm II} = 0$$

According to the calculation table of the motor DPE—340, $V_{0m} = 14{,}300$ A, $V_a = 470$ A, $F_a = 10{,}650$ A. Though the calculated value $F_{cp} = 1{,}000$ A, the actual mmf of the commutating pole is 550 A greater than the computed one.

In this motor, however, between the yoke and the body of the commutating pole there is an additional air gap (a packing of non-magnetic material) in which the computed potential drop is 1,500 A. Thus the additional mmf of 550 A should be proportionally distributed between the two gaps. The actual mmf between the armature and the commutating pole is thus

$$F_{cp} = \frac{1{,}000 + 1{,}500 + 550}{1{,}000 + 1{,}500} \cdot 1{,}000 = 1{,}220 \text{ A}$$

By substituting V_{0m}, V_a, F_a and F_{cp} into Eqs. (7-1) to (7-4), we obtain the following values for the leakage fluxes (with the potential drop along the pole shoes neglected): $\Phi'_{\sigma\rm I} = 600{,}000$ M, $\Phi'_{\sigma\rm II} = 140{,}000$ M, $\Phi'_{\sigma\rm IV} = 240{,}000$ M and $\Phi'_{\sigma\rm V} = 140{,}000$ M.

Example. 83. Determine the leakage fluxes $\Phi'_{\sigma\rm I}$, $\Phi'_{\sigma\rm II}$, $\Phi'_{\sigma\rm IV}$ and $\Phi'_{\sigma\rm V}$ entering the pole shoes of a DMP—151 type motor at a demand of $A = 441$ A/cm.

The calculation table yields $V_{0m} = 7{,}400$ A, $F_a = 5{,}870$ A, $F_{cp} = 1{,}600$ A and $V_a = 370$ A.

From the potential nets (but slightly differing from those in Figs. 1-14, 7-2a and 7-2b, and therefore not represented separately) we have the permeances of the leakage fluxes pertaining to sections 5-7 and 4-5 as follows:

$$\lambda_{\mathrm{I}} = 0.4\,\pi \frac{3}{4} 41.2 = 39 \text{ M/A}$$

$$\lambda'_{\mathrm{I}} = 0.4\,\pi \frac{3}{4} 41.2 = 39 \text{ M/A}$$

$$\lambda''_{\mathrm{I}} = 0.4\,\pi \frac{2}{4} 41.2 = 26 \text{ M/A}$$

$$\lambda_{\mathrm{II}} = 0.4\,\pi \frac{3}{8} 41.2 = 19 \text{ M/A}$$

$$\lambda'_{\mathrm{II}} = 0 \qquad \lambda''_{\mathrm{II}} = 0$$

By substituting the values V_{0m}, V_a, F_a and F_{cp} into the formulae (7-1) to (7-3), and neglecting the potential drops along the pole shoes, we obtain the leakage fluxes as $\Phi'_{\sigma\mathrm{I}} = 574{,}000$ M, $\Phi'_{\sigma\mathrm{II}} = 147{,}000$ M, $\Phi'_{\sigma\mathrm{IV}} = 32{,}000$ M and $\Phi'_{\sigma\mathrm{V}} = 147{,}000$ M.

7-3. Replacing the Pole Shoe by Several Series-Connected Ferromagnetic Bodies

In order to replace the pole shoe by a body more convenient for further computation, it is necessary to divide it expediently into several parts. The boundaries of the parts may be selected, for instance, to coincide with the equipotential lines through points 5 and 4 (Fig. 7-1c). Since at points 5 and 4 the density of the flux passing through the shoe is substantially greater than that of the leakage fluxes perpendicular to the surface of the iron, the effect of the latter upon the direction of the equipotential lines can be neglected and these can be assumed as perpendicular to the surface of the shoe at points 5and 4. This assumption yields the following angles:

$$\varepsilon_4 = 135° \text{ and } \varepsilon_5 = \frac{1}{2} \sphericalangle 4-5-6 \sphericalangle$$

At points 8 and 9 the direction of the equipotential lines will be determined not only by the density of the flux passing along the shoe but also by that of the fluxes perpendicular to its surface (e. g. $B_{\delta 9}$ at point 9). Consequently, the angles ε_8 and ε_9 of the equipotential lines enclosed with the surface 8-9 (Fig. 7-1c) are determined by the ratio of the resultant flux density to the flux density in the air gap at the given points (e. g. B_9 and $B_{\delta 9}$).

Nevertheless, the course of further computation can be simplified materially if we proceed from the following considerations.

Let us suppose that the boundary between part II and part III, passing through point 4, has been drawn, not in the form of the equipotential line 4-9, but as part of the periphery 4-9′ (Fig. 7-1c) intersecting the boundary of the pole shoe at an angle of 90°.

Point 9 (Fig. 7-1c) would thereby be shifted to point 9′ (Figs. 6-4 and 7-1c) which would mean the decrement of the flux passing from the armature into the shoe between points 6 and 9′. This would, however, involve a decrease also in the length of the line 4-9, i. e. in the value of the cross-section Q_{II}, whence the flux density at this point would undergo a very slight change only. The situation would be similar along the boundary 5-8 between parts I and II, determining the cross-section Q_{I}.

The sum of the potential drops along the shoe, in the case of the above-mentioned substitutions, practically does not change because the section by which part I decreases is added to part II, and the section by which part II decreases is, in turn, added to part III.

In part III pertaining to the body of the pole, a substantial potential drop ensues since it is crossed not only by the flux passing from the pole shoe into the body of the pole but also by the flux entering part III through the air gap.

The body of the pole can be regarded practically as unsaturated. The position of the periphery 3-10 (Figs. 7-1a, 6-4 and 7-4) separating part III from the body of the pole can be determined on the strength of the following considerations:

We are concerned with part III only inasmuch as a great potential drop, due to great flux densities, is created along it. If the flux density in section 3-10, which should be denoted by Q_{III}, is much smaller than in Q_{II}, because for instance Q_{III} is twice as large as Q_{II}, then only a small potential drop will be created beyond the line 3-10, which can therefore be neglected.

Thus, for determining the line 3-10, we obtain the condition $Q_{\text{III}} = 2Q_{\text{II}}$. Accordingly, points 3 and 10 should be located so that the periphery at both terminal points should be perpendicular to the lines bounding the surface of the iron, and its length, twice the length of the line 4-9.′

If there is a ferromagnetic flange on the main pole (Fig. 6-4), the cross sections Q_I, Q_{II} and Q_{III} can be determined on the basis of the following considerations.

If the flange reaches all over the contour line 3-4-5, its cross-section will be considered at all points, i. e. the lengths of lines 10-3, 9′-4 and 8′-5 determined, as seen in Fig. 6-4a with regard to the width of the flange. The part of the flange protruding into the interpolar space (i. e. to the right of point 5 in Fig. 6-4) is neglected.

If the flange occupies part of the contour line 3-4-5, then its cross-section should be considered only at those points (for instance, at point 5 in Fig. 6-4b) where it bears against the iron sheets.

If the shoe has a layer 10-9′-8′-6-7-10 (Fig. 6-4a) filled with half the amount of iron as compared to its remaining part, then only the part 10-9′-8′-6-5-4-3 should be considered to be the shoe, because the reluctance of the layer 10-9′-8′-6-7-10 is computed with the method explained on p. 145, i. e. together with the reluctance of the teeth in the slot region and the air gap. In this connection the lengths of sections a, b and c in Fig. 6-4a on the contour line 10-9′-8′-6 are determined, whereas the cross-sections Q_I and Q_{II} are taken from points 4 and 5 to points 9′ and 8′ on the line 10—6.

By dividing the pole shoe into three parts I, II, III (see Fig. 6-4) and measuring the distances y_I, y_{II} and y_{III} from the pole centre to the middle of sections a, b and c, the potential differences acting in the said points between the contour line 10-9′-8′ and the bottom of the slot in the rotor can be determined if the values V_{pv} are neglected:

$$V'_{0yI} = V_{0m} + y_I\, A \tag{7-10}$$

$$V'_{0yII} = V_{0m} + y_{II}\, A \tag{7-11}$$

$$V'_{0yIII} = V_{0m} + y_{III}\, A \tag{7-12}$$

With the help of these values we can determine the fluxes

$$\Phi'_{yI} = B'_{\delta I}\, al \tag{7-13}$$

$$\Phi'_{yII} = B'_{\delta II}\, bl \tag{7-14}$$

$$\Phi'_{yIII} = B'_{\delta III}\, cl \tag{7-15}$$

that would pass through sections a, b and c of the pole shoe if there were no potential drop along their parts I, II and III. The flux densities $B'_{\delta\mathrm{I}}$, $B'_{\delta\mathrm{II}}$ and $B'_{\delta\mathrm{III}}$ can here be determined nomographically from the values $V'_{0y\mathrm{I}}$, $V'_{0y\mathrm{II}}$ and $V'_{0y\mathrm{III}}$.

Since along parts I, II and III of the pole shoe the potential differences $V_{pv\mathrm{I}}$, $V_{pv\mathrm{II}}$ and $V_{pv\mathrm{III}}$ prevail (Fig. 7-1a), the fluxes crossing the sections a, b and c, i.e. $\Phi_{y\mathrm{I}}$, $\Phi_{y\mathrm{II}}$ and $\Phi_{y\mathrm{III}}$ will be smaller than $\Phi'_{y\mathrm{I}}$, $\Phi'_{y\mathrm{II}}$ and $\Phi'_{y\mathrm{III}}$. These fluxes can be determined nomographically on the basis of the following potential differences:

$$V_{0y\mathrm{I}} = V_{0m} + Ay_{\mathrm{I}} - (V_{pv\mathrm{III}} + V_{pv\mathrm{II}} + 0.5\,V_{pv\mathrm{I}}) \tag{7-16}$$

$$V_{0y\mathrm{II}} = V_{0m} + Ay_{\mathrm{II}} - (V_{pv\mathrm{III}} + 0.5\,V_{pv\mathrm{II}}) \tag{7-17}$$

$$V_{0y\mathrm{III}} = V_{0m} + Ay_{\mathrm{III}} - 0.5\,V_{pv\mathrm{III}} \tag{7-18}$$

The values of flux densities in the sections 5-8′, 4-9′ and 3-10 can be computed by means of the following formulae:

$$B_{\mathrm{I}} = \frac{\Phi_{\sigma\mathrm{I}} + \Phi_{y\mathrm{I}}}{Q_{\mathrm{I}}} \tag{7-19}$$

$$B_{\mathrm{II}} = \frac{\Phi_{\sigma\mathrm{I}} + \Phi_{\sigma\mathrm{II}} + \Phi_{y\mathrm{I}} + \Phi_{y\mathrm{II}}}{Q_{\mathrm{II}}} \tag{7-20}$$

$$B_{\mathrm{III}} = \frac{\Phi_{\sigma\mathrm{I}} + \Phi_{\sigma\mathrm{II}} + \Phi_{y\mathrm{I}} + \Phi_{y\mathrm{II}} + \Phi_{y\mathrm{II}}}{Q_{\mathrm{III}}} \tag{7-21}$$

Part I of the pole shoe has a configuration in which the cross-sectional area proportionally increases along the path of the fluxes $\Phi_{\sigma\mathrm{I}}$ and $\Phi_{y\mathrm{I}}$ toward the cross-section 5-8′. Assuming a uniform flux distribution over the surface of part I of the shoe, the total flux crossing part I, when passing from the air into the shoe, will grow linearly, whence the flux density along the whole section I remains approximately constant.

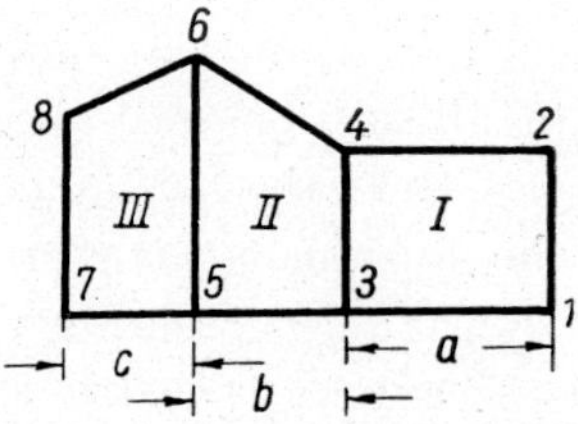

Fig. 7-5

In part II the flux increases toward the section 4-9′, while the cross-sectional area of the shoe decreases. Thus no great error is incurred by assuming that the flux density along part II increases linearly.

In part III the flux increases toward the section 3-10, but the cross-sectional area of the shoe grows even to a greater extent. We may therefore assume that the flux density along this part will decrease linearly.

The theoretical distribution of flux density along the pole shoe is represented in Fig. 7-5, where the ordinates correspond to the flux density at the given points of the shoe.

In chapter 3 the series-connected ferromagnetic bodies were replaced by an equivalent body by assuming a constant flux passing through these bodies.

In this case there is a diminishing flux passing through parts I, II and III of the pole shoe because fluxes Φ_y and Φ_σ enter the side walls.

Nevertheless, parts I, II and III (Fig. 7-1a) can be transformed into equivalent bodies I′, II′, and III′ (Fig. 7-1b) which are crossed by a flux of constant magnitude. For this purpose the actual shoe (Fig. 7-1a) having the contour 7-5-4-3 should be replaced by an equivalent shoe with the contour 7-5′-4-3′ (Fig. 7-1b) so that the cross-section Q_{I} should increase as

$$k_{\mathrm{I}} = \frac{\Phi_{\sigma\mathrm{I}} + \Phi_{\sigma\mathrm{II}} + \Phi_{y\mathrm{I}} + \Phi_{y\mathrm{II}}}{\Phi_{\sigma\mathrm{I}} + \Phi_{y\mathrm{I}}} \tag{7-22}$$

and the cross-section Q_{III} should decrease as

$$k_{\mathrm{III}} = \frac{\Phi_{\sigma\mathrm{I}} + \Phi_{\sigma\mathrm{II}} + \Phi_{y\mathrm{I}} + \Phi_{y\mathrm{II}}}{\Phi_{\sigma\mathrm{I}} + \Phi_{\sigma\mathrm{II}} + \Phi_{y\mathrm{I}} + \Phi_{y\mathrm{II}} + \Phi_{y\mathrm{III}}} \tag{7-23}$$

If a constant flux $\Phi_{\sigma\mathrm{I}} + \Phi_{\sigma\mathrm{II}} + \Phi_{y\mathrm{I}} + \Phi_{y\mathrm{II}}$ will pass through such an equivalent shoe (Fig. 7-1b), then the flux density distribution in all sections will be similar to that in Fig. 7-5.

Here the values in Eqs. (7-22) and (7-23) depend, according to the formulae (7-5), (7-6), (7-16) to (7-18), upon the values $V_{p\nu\mathrm{III}}$, $V_{p\nu\mathrm{II}}$ and $V_{p\nu\mathrm{I}}$ not yet known.

Yet by realizing that, if the values $V_{p\nu}$ change, the changes in the fluxes $\Phi_{\sigma\mathrm{I}}$, $\Phi_{\sigma\mathrm{II}}$, $\Phi_{y\mathrm{I}}$, $\Phi_{y\mathrm{II}}$ and $\Phi_{y\mathrm{III}}$ affect both the numerator and the denominator of the formula (7-23) in the same sense, we find that the change in the value $V_{p\nu}$ hardly affects the values k_{I} and k_{III}. In other words, the above-mentioned transformation of the bodies I, II and III into the bodies I′, II′ and III′ can be regarded, without appreciable error, as valid for any value $V_{p\nu\mathrm{III}}$, $V_{p\nu\mathrm{II}}$ and $V_{p\nu\mathrm{I}}$.

It follows that the values k_I and k_{III} may be computed according to the following formulae

$$k_I = \frac{\Phi'_{\sigma I} + \Phi'_{\sigma II} + \Phi'_{yI} + \Phi'_{yII}}{\Phi'_{\sigma I} + \Phi'_{yI}} \tag{7-24}$$

$$k_{III} = \frac{\Phi'_{\sigma I} + \Phi'_{\sigma II} + \Phi'_{yI} + \Phi'_{yII}}{\Phi'_{\sigma I} + \Phi'_{\sigma II} + \Phi'_{yI} + \Phi'_{yII} + \Phi'_{yIII}} \tag{7-25}$$

where it is assumed that $V_{pvI} = 0$, $V_{pvII} = 0$ and $V_{pvIII} = 0$.

Thus the dimensions of parts I′, II′ and III′ of the equivalent shoe, crossed by a constant flux equal to $\Phi'_{\sigma I} + \Phi'_{\sigma II} + \Phi'_{yI} + \Phi'_{yII}$, can be computed.

Having thus transformed the actual shoe (Fig. 7-1a) into an equivalent one (Fig. 7-1b), the method outlined in chapter 3 can be applied, i.e. the problem of determining the magnetic relations in the pole shoe can be reduced to the problem of determining the reluctance of several series-connected ferromagnetic bodies through which a constant flux passes having the value $\Phi'_{\sigma I} + \Phi'_{\sigma II} + \Phi'_{yII} + \Phi'_{yII}$.

By the aid of the flux densities prevailing in the individual cross-sections (Fig. 7-5), the pertaining values ϱ and γb_0 can readily be computed for any of these bodies:

$$\varrho_I = \frac{\overline{1-2}}{\overline{3-4}} = 1 \tag{7-26}$$

$$\varrho_{II} = \frac{B_{II}}{B_I} = \frac{Q_I}{Q_{II}} k_I \tag{7-27}$$

$$\varrho_{III} = \frac{B_{II}}{B_{III}} = \frac{Q_{III}}{Q_{II}} k_{III} \tag{7-28}$$

for section I′

$$\gamma b_{0I} = \frac{Q_I}{l} k_I \tag{7-29}$$

for section II′

$$\gamma b_{0II} = \gamma b_{0I} \tag{7-30}$$

for section III′

$$\gamma b_{0III} = \frac{Q_{III}}{l} k_{III} \tag{7-31}$$

The above applies also to the pole shoe of Fig. 7-4 and, *per analogiam*, also to the pole shoes to the left of the pole centre.

7-4. *Approach to the Replacement of the Pole Shoe by Several Series-Connected Ferromagnetic Bodies*

On the strength of the theoretical proofs expounded in section 7-3, the following method can be applied to replace the pole shoe by three series-connected ferromagnetic bodies.

1. Determine lines 5-8′ and 4-9′ as parts of the peripheries crossing respectively the points 5 and 4, and intersecting the surfaces bounding the pole shoe at an angle of 90°.

2. Determine line 3-10 as part of the periphery intersecting the surface of the pole shoe at an angle of 90°, if the length of the arc 3-10 is twice the length of arc 4-9′.

3. Determine a, b, c, e and f (Fig. 6-4), the mean heights h_{I}, h_{II} and h_{III} of bodies I′, II′ and III′, the distances y_{I}, y_{II} and y_{III} between the centers of sections a, b, c from the axis of the pole and the cross-sections Q_{I}, Q_{II} and Q_{III} as the products of the lengths of the equipotential lines 5-8′, 4-9′, 3-10 by γl.

4. Compute according to the method of section 6-9, the flux densities $B'_{\delta\text{I}}$, $B'_{\delta\text{II}}$ and $B'_{\delta\text{III}}$ in the gap at distances y_{I}, y_{II} and y_{III}, obtained by neglecting $V_{pv\text{I}}$, $V_{pv\text{II}}$ and $V_{pv\text{III}}$ and determine fluxes $\Phi'_{y\text{I}}$, $\Phi'_{y\text{II}}$ and $\Phi'_{y\text{III}}$ by the formulae

$$\Phi'_{y\text{I}} = B'_{\delta\text{I}}\ al \tag{7-32}$$

$$\Phi'_{y\text{II}} = B'_{\delta\text{II}}\ bl \tag{7-33}$$

$$\Phi'_{y\text{III}} = B'_{\delta\text{III}}\ cl \tag{7-34}$$

5. Determine the values k_{I} and k_{III} with Eqs. (7-24) and (7-25).

6. Compute the factors ϱ_{I}; ϱ_{II} and ϱ_{III} with Eqs. (7-26) and (7-28) and the values $\gamma b_{0\text{I}}$, $\gamma b_{0\text{II}}$ and $\gamma b_{0\text{III}}$ with Eqs. (7-29) to (7-31).

The other, less saturated, pole shoe can be replaced in the same way.

Example 84. Replace the saturated pole shoe of the traction motor DPE—340 by three series-connected ferromagnetic bodies.

Having divided the pole shoe by three equipotential lines 5-8′, 4-9′ and 3-10 (Fig. 6-4a) we obtain the following geometrical parameters characterizing the individual parts: $y_{\text{I}} = 14.6$ cm, $y_{\text{II}} = 12$

cm, $y_{\mathrm{III}} = 8.8$ cm, $a = 2.8$ cm, $b = 2.8$ cm, $c = 3.3$ cm (the values are corrected to the armature periphery); $e = 2.5$ cm, $f = 15$ cm, $h_{\mathrm{I}} = 3.3$ cm, $h_{\mathrm{II}} = 2.8$ cm, $h_{\mathrm{III}} = 3$ cm, $Q_{\mathrm{I}} = 98$ cm^2, $Q_{\mathrm{II}} = 86$ cm^2, $Q_{\mathrm{III}} = 172$ cm^2. The values $B'_{\delta\mathrm{I}} = 12{,}300$ G, $B'_{\delta\mathrm{II}} = 12{,}200$ G, $B'_{\delta\mathrm{III}} = 12{,}000$ G for $V_{0m} = 14{,}300$ A and $A = 428$ A/cm are calculated in Exs. 81 and 79 while the leakage fluxes $\Phi'_{\sigma\mathrm{I}} = 600{,}000$ M and $\Phi'_{\sigma\mathrm{II}} = 140{,}000$ M in Ex. 82.

With these data we can compute the fluxes $\Phi'_{y\mathrm{I}} = 1.05 \cdot 10^6$ M, $\Phi'_{y\mathrm{II}} = 1.04 \cdot 10^6$ M and $\Phi'_{y\mathrm{III}} = 1.2 \cdot 10^6$ M and determine the factors $k_{\mathrm{I}} = 1.72$ and $k_{\mathrm{III}} = 0.7$ with Eqs. (7-24) and (7-25).

As a result we obtain the parameters characterizing the individual ferromagnetic bodies: $\varrho_{\mathrm{I}} = 1.0$, $\varrho_{\mathrm{II}} = 1.96$, $\varrho_{\mathrm{III}} = 1.42$, $\gamma l b_{0\mathrm{I}} = 168$ cm^2 $= \gamma l b_{0\mathrm{II}}$ and $\gamma l b_{0\mathrm{III}} = 120$ cm^2.

Example 85. Replace the saturated pole shoe of a traction motor DMP—151 by three series-connected ferromagnetic bodies.

The division of the pole shoe by three equipotential lines (Fig. 6-4b) yields the following geometrical parameters characterizing the individual parts: $y_{\mathrm{I}} = 9.4$ cm, $y_{\mathrm{II}} = 7.2$ cm, $y_{\mathrm{III}} = 5.1$ cm, $a = 2.5$ cm, $b = 2.1$ cm, $c = 2.1$ cm (the values from y_{I} to c have been corrected to armature periphery); $e = 2.6$ cm, $f = 1$ cm, $h_{\mathrm{I}} = 2.8$ cm, $h_{\mathrm{II}} = 2.2$ cm, $h_{\mathrm{III}} = 1.8$ cm, $Q_{\mathrm{I}} = 106$ cm^2, $Q_{\mathrm{II}} = 71$ cm^2, $Q_{\mathrm{III}} = 142$ cm^2. Let us proceed from the values $V_{0m} = 7{,}400$ A and $A = 441$ A/cm. For the point corresponding to $y_{\mathrm{I}} = 9.4$ cm, we obtain $(V_0/h)_{\mathrm{I}} = 2{,}900$ A/cm, $\delta_{\mathrm{I}} = 0.8$ cm, $k_{c\mathrm{I}} = 1.14$ and $\overline{OF} = 28{,}300$ G. With the straight line for $\tan\beta = 1.6$ and with the curve for $\varrho = 1.467$ we find the point C and determine section $\overline{MC} = 18{,}700$ G, whence

$$B'_{\delta\mathrm{I}} = 18{,}700 \frac{1.98 \cdot 0.95}{3.4} = 10{,}400 \text{ G}$$

For the point corresponding to $y_{\mathrm{II}} = 7.2$ cm we obtain $(V_0/h)_{\mathrm{II}} = 2{,}600$ A/cm, $\delta_{\mathrm{II}} = 0.6$ cm, $k_{c\mathrm{II}} = 1.18$ and $\overline{OF} = 33{,}000$ G. Then we determine nomographically the section $\overline{MC} = 19{,}000$ G, whence $B'_{\delta\mathrm{II}} = 10{,}500$ G.

For the point corresponding to $y_{\mathrm{III}} = 5.1$ cm, we obtain $(V_0/h)_{\mathrm{III}} = 2{,}450$ A/cm, $\delta_{\mathrm{III}} = 0.5$ cm, $k_{c\mathrm{III}} = 1.2$ and $\overline{OF} = 36{,}400$ G. Then we determine nomographically the section $\overline{OF} = 19{,}350$ G, whence $B'_{\delta\mathrm{III}} = 10{,}700$ G. We compute $\Phi'_{y\mathrm{I}} = 1.07 \cdot 10^6$ M, $\Phi'_{y\mathrm{II}} = 0.91 \cdot 10^6$ M and $\Phi'_{y\mathrm{III}} = 0.925 \cdot 10^6$ M.

Considering the leakage fluxes $\Phi'_{\sigma I} = 574{,}000$ M and $\Phi'_{\sigma II} = 147{,}000$ M obtained in Ex. 83, we compute the factors $k_I = 1.64$ and $k_{III} = 0.745$ with Eqs. (7-24) and (7-25).

Finally we have the parameters characterizing the individual ferromagnetic bodies: $\varrho_I = 1$, $\varrho_{II} = 2.44$, $\varrho_{III} = 1.49$, $\gamma l b_{0I} = 174$ cm$^2 =$ $= \gamma l n_{0II}$ and $\gamma l b_{0III} = 105$ cm^2.

7-5. The Assessment of the Possibility of Neglecting the Saturation of the Pole Shoe and the Approximate Determination of the Potential Drop in It

Before determining the degree of saturation of the pole shoe it seems expedient to examine whether or not the potential drops V_{pvIII}, V_{pvII} and V_{pvI} can be neglected.

If these values were found to equal zero, then the flux passing through the bodies I′, II′ and III′ would be

$$\Phi'_{pv} = \Phi'_{\sigma I} + \Phi'_{\sigma II} + \Phi'_{yI} - \Phi'_{yII} \tag{7-35}$$

Should the V_{pvIII}, V_{pvII} and V_{pvI} values turn out to be more than zero, then the flux Φ'_{pv} decreases to

$$\Phi_{pv} = \Phi_{\sigma I} + \Phi_{\sigma II} + \Phi_{yI} + \Phi_{yII} \tag{7-36}$$

Consequently, in the case of saturation the value Φ_{pv} is always less than Φ'_{pv} and the magnitudes V_{pvI}, V_{pvII} and V_{pvIII} required can never be higher than the potential drops produced in the bodies I′, II′ and III′ by flux Φ'_{pv}.

Thus if the said potential drops (to be determined by the nomographic method) for flux Φ'_{pv} have a small value, the magnitudes V_{pvI}, V_{pvII} and V_{pvIII} can readily be neglected.

If such a preliminary assessment shows that the deliberately increased potential drops due to the flux Φ'_{pv} acting through the shoe must not be neglected, it is advisable to make another assessment on the basis of another assumption yielding a much lower value for V_{pv} yet somewhat higher than in reality. It should be taken into account that in connection with the high saturation in the section 4-9′, part of the flux Φ'_{pv} in the form of a parallel flux Φ_{par} passes from part II′ into part III′ through the air, parallel to the ferromagnetic bodies II′ and III′ (Fig. 7-6).

Parts II′ and III′ may be connected into a resultant body characterized by the values ϱ_{res}, h_{res} and γb_{0res}.

By assuming for the sake of simplicity, that the potential drops V_{pvIII} and V_{pvII} are distributed along the parts II′ and III′ uniformly, no great error is committed if we say that the flux Φ_{par} creates a uniform density and is due to the mean potential difference

$$\frac{V_{pvIII} + V_{pvII}}{2}$$

acting along the centre line

$$\frac{e+f}{2}\,\frac{\pi}{4}$$

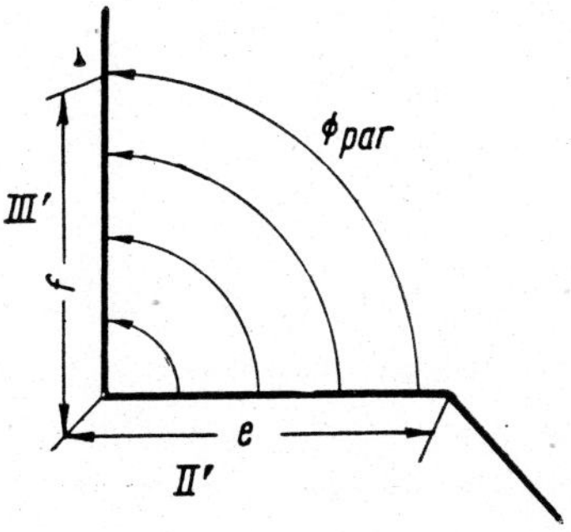

Fig. 7-6

(Fig. 7-6). Then its value is

$$\Phi_{par} = \frac{\dfrac{e+f}{2}\,\dfrac{0.4\,\pi(V_{pvIII} + V_{pvII})}{2}}{\dfrac{e+f}{8}\pi}\,l = 0.4\,\pi\,\frac{V_{pvIII} + V_{pvII}}{e+f}\,\frac{2}{\pi}\,(e+f)l \qquad (7\text{-}37)$$

Since

$$\frac{V_{pvIII} + V_{pvII}}{e+f}$$

differs but slightly from the mean field strength of parts II′ and III′, the presence of the parallel flux Φ_{par} may be taken into account as if there were a slot of a width of

$$b_{par} = \frac{2}{\pi}(e+f) \qquad (7\text{-}38)$$

between parts II′ and III′.

Thus we have reduced the problem of evaluating the magnetic relations in parts II′ and III′ to the problem of replacing two series-connected regions of tooth and parallel slot by a resultant body.

The first region has a tooth characterized by b_{0II}, ϱ_{II}, h_{II} and a slot b_{par} wide and having a factor ζ_{II} to be determined by the magnitude of ϱ_{II} from Fig. 4-5. The second tooth is characterized by b_{0III}, ϱ_{III}, h_{III} and has a slot b_{par} wide and with a factor ζ_{III} to be determined by ϱ_{III}.

According to the method expounded in section 5-3 the resultant body characterized by h_{res}, $b_{0\text{res}}\gamma l$ and ϱ_{res} can readily be determined with these values.

For flux Φ_t crossing the bodies II′ and III′, it is expedient to choose flux Φ'_{pv} because the potential drops due to them in the different bodies are known. True enough, sometimes flux Φ'_{pv} is considerably in excess of Φ_{pv} and it may occur that the mean field strengths due to Φ'_{pv} are to be found beyond the limits of the nomogram. In such cases it is advisable to choose some smaller value for flux Φ_t.

Let us assume that the potential drops due to Φ_t in the bodies II′ and III′ have the magnitude of V_{II} and V_{III}. Then on curve $\varrho = 1.44$ we obtain the abscissa $\overline{LC}$ for the ordinate

$$\frac{V_{\text{II}} + V_{\text{III}}}{h_{\text{II}} + h_{\text{III}}}$$

whence

$$b_{0\text{res}}\,\gamma\, l = \frac{\Phi_t}{\overline{LC}} \tag{7-39}$$

According to the method of section 4-6 (Eq. 4-43 and considering Eq. 7-38), the mean field strength $V'_{\text{II}}/h_{\text{II}}$ in the body II' can be determined for flux $\Phi_\tau = \Phi'_{pv}$ on curve ϱ_{II} and on the straight line

$$\tan\beta_{\text{II}} = \frac{0.8\,(e+f)}{\gamma\, b_{0\text{II}}}\,\zeta_{\text{II}} \tag{7-40}$$

and the mean field strength $V_{\text{III}}/h_{\text{III}}$ in the body III' on curve ϱ_{III} and on the straight line

$$\tan\beta_{\text{III}} = \frac{0.8\,(e+f)}{\gamma b_{0\text{III}}}\,\zeta_{\text{III}} \tag{7-41}$$

Then on curve $\varrho = 1.44$ we determine the abscissa $(\overline{LC})'$ for the ordinate

$$\frac{V'_{\text{II}} + V'_{\text{III}}}{h_{\text{II}} + h_{\text{III}}}$$

and compute

$$\tan\beta_{\text{res}} = \frac{\dfrac{\Phi_\tau}{b_{0\text{res}}\,\gamma\, l} - (\overline{LC'})}{\dfrac{V'_{\text{II}} + V'_{\text{III}}}{h_{\text{II}} + h_{\text{III}}}} \tag{7-42}$$

Thus, in the form of the curve ϱ_{res} and straight line tan β_{res} (Fig. 7-7,) we have found the geometry of all possible relations between the flux Φ_{pv} obtained by considering the saturation in the shoe, and the pertaining values

$$\frac{V_{pv\text{III}} + V_{pv\text{II}}}{h_{\text{III}} + h_{\text{II}}}$$

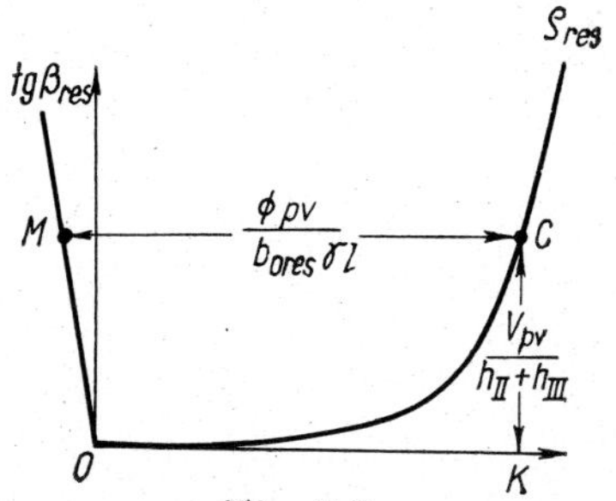

Fig. 7-7

By denoting $V_{pv\text{III}} + V_{pv\text{II}} = V_{pv}$ we find that a value

$$\frac{V_{pv}}{h_{\text{III}} + h_{\text{II}}}$$

corresponds to the ordinate of any point on curve ϱ_{res} (Fig. 7-8), and a value of

$$\frac{\Phi_{pv}}{l\gamma b_{0\text{res}}}$$

to the horizontal section $\overline{MC}$. At the same time we set a new upper limit for the values V_{pv} closer to the real value than the potential drops obtained in the case of Φ_t without considering the paralysing effect of Φ_{par}. These new limit values of V'_{III}, V'_{II} and V'_{I} are due to

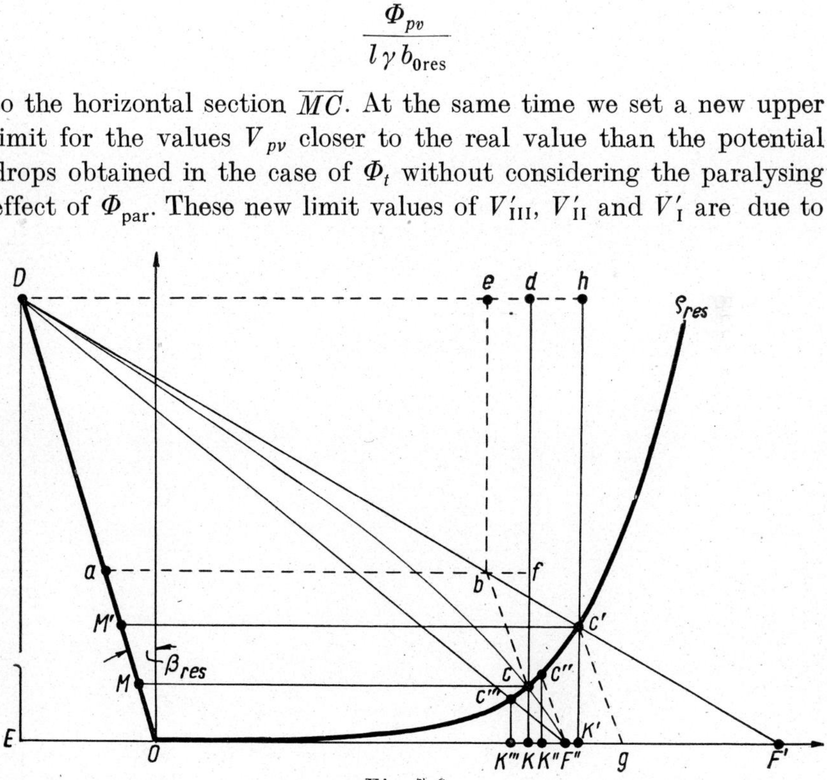

Fig. 7-8

flux Φ'_{pv} which cannot be less than Φ_{pv} whence $V_{pv\text{III}}$, $V_{pv\text{II}}$ and $V_{pv\text{I}}$ cannot be higher than those. Here V'_{I} is the potential drop along the body I′ computed earlier. On the other hand the values V'_{III} and V'_{II} must be smaller than V_{III} and V_{II} obtained with the help of flux Φ_t, because the parallel-connected air gap has a paralysing effect. Thus it may happen that while V_{III} and V_{II} can by no means be neglected, the values V'_{III} and V'_{II} are so small that the potential drops $V_{pv\text{III}}$, $V'_{pv\text{II}}$ and $V'_{pv\text{I}}$ in the shoe may be neglected.

Let us assume that the values V'_{III}, V'_{II} and V'_{I} cannot be neglected and therefore the values $V_{pv\text{III}}$, $V_{pv\text{II}}$ and $V_{pv\text{I}}$ must be determined.

The first step is to find out how these potential drops can be determined at a given value V_{pv}.

By replacing the actual shoe by an equivalent tooth and slot we have determined the potential drops V'_{III} and V'_{II} created along the parts III′ and II when crossed by the flux

$$\Phi_\tau = \Phi'_{pv} \tag{7-43}$$

With an increase of the flux passing through the shoe, the values $V_{pv\text{III}}$, $V_{pv\text{II}}$ and $V_{pv\text{I}}$ may be asumed to grow approximately equally, i.e. their relation changes comparatively little.

Then without incurring the danger of serious errors we may say that

$$V_{pv\,\text{III}} : V_{pv\,\text{II}} : V_{pv\,\text{I}} = V'_{\text{III}} : V'_{\text{II}} : V'_{\text{I}} \tag{7-44}$$

It follows that $V_{pv\text{III}}$, $V_{pv\text{II}}$ and $V_{pv\text{I}}$ can be computed by the formulae

$$V_{pv\,\text{I}} = \psi_{\text{I}}\, V_{pv} \tag{7-45}$$

$$V_{pv\,\text{II}} = \psi_{\text{II}}\, V_{pv} \tag{7-46}$$

$$V_{pv\,\text{III}} = (1 - \psi_{\text{II}})\, V_{pv} \tag{7-47}$$

where

$$\psi_{\text{I}} = \frac{V'_{\text{I}}}{V'_{\text{II}} + V'_{\text{III}}} \tag{7-48}$$

and

$$\psi_{\text{II}} = \frac{V'_{\text{II}}}{V'_{\text{II}} + V'_{\text{III}}} \tag{7-49}$$

In other words, if the actual value V_{pv} could be determined, also the values $V_{pv\text{I}}$, $V_{pv\text{II}}$ and $V'_{pv\text{III}}$ would be obtained with about the same degree of accuracy.

The position of point C on curve $\varrho_{r\,s}$ having an ordinate V_{pv} may be determined approximately on the strength of the following considerations.

Disregarding the potential drops in the region of tooth and slot of the armature, the following fluxes are found to enter the pole shoe:

$$\Phi_{y\,\mathrm{I}} = \frac{V_{0m} + y_{\mathrm{I}} A - V_{pv}(1 + 0.5\,\psi_{\mathrm{I}})}{\delta_{\mathrm{I}}\, k_{c\mathrm{I}}}\, a \cdot 0.4\,\pi\, l \tag{7-50}$$

$$\Phi_{y\,\mathrm{II}} = \frac{V_{0m} + y_{\mathrm{II}} A - V_{pv}(1 - 0.5\,\psi_{\mathrm{II}})}{\delta_{\mathrm{II}}\, k_{c\,\mathrm{II}}}\, b \cdot 0.4\,\pi\, l \tag{7-51}$$

$$\Phi_{\sigma\mathrm{I}} = \Phi'_{\sigma\mathrm{I}} - (1 + 0.5\,\psi_{\mathrm{I}})\,\lambda_{\mathrm{I}}'''\, V_{pv} \tag{7-52}$$

$$\Phi_{\sigma\mathrm{II}} = \Phi'_{\sigma\mathrm{II}} \tag{7-53}$$

wherefore the following equation is valid:

$$\frac{\Phi_{pv}}{b_{0res}\,\gamma\, l} = C_1 - C_2 \frac{V_{pv}}{h_{\mathrm{II}} + h_{\mathrm{III}}} \tag{7-54}$$

where

$$C_1 = \left[\left(\frac{V_{0m} + y_{\mathrm{I}} A}{\delta_{\mathrm{I}}\, k_{c\mathrm{I}}}\, a + \frac{V_{0m} + y_{\mathrm{II}} A}{\delta_{\mathrm{II}}\, k_{c\mathrm{II}}}\, b\right) 0{,}4\,\pi\, l + \Phi'_{\sigma\mathrm{I}} + \Phi'_{\sigma\mathrm{II}}\right] \frac{1}{b_{0\,\mathrm{res}}\,\gamma\, l} \tag{7-55}$$

and

$$C_2 = (h_{\mathrm{II}} + h_{\mathrm{III}}) \times$$

$$\times \left[\left(\frac{1 + 0.5\,\psi_{\mathrm{I}}}{\delta_{\mathrm{I}}\, k_{c\mathrm{I}}}\, a + \frac{1 - 0.5\,\psi_{\mathrm{II}}}{\delta_{\mathrm{II}}\, k_{c\mathrm{II}}}\, b\right) 0.4\,\pi\, l + (1 + 0.5\,\psi_{\mathrm{I}})\,\lambda_{\mathrm{I}}'''\right] \frac{1}{b_{0\,\mathrm{res}}\,\gamma\, l} \tag{7-56}$$

Thus, beside the known relation between Φ_{pv} and V_{pv} in the form of curve $\varrho_{r\,s}$ and the straight line $\tan \beta_{\mathrm{res}}$ (Fig. 7-8), we have obtained another relation between these very values in the form of Eq. (7-54) which can also be expressed graphically.

On the straight line $\tan \beta_{\mathrm{res}}$ point D (Fig. 7-8) is determined so that the ordinate of $\overline{DE}$ should equal C_1/C_2 and, on the axis of the abscissa, point F' so that the abscissa of $\overline{DF'}$ should equal B_1. Thus it can readily be seen that for any point C on the straight line DF' whose ordinate is

$$\frac{V_{pv}}{h_{\mathrm{I}} + h_{\mathrm{II}}}$$

the horizontal distance from the straight line DO is $\Phi_{pv}/b_{0\mathrm{res}}\gamma_1$.

It follows that point C', where the straight line DF' and curve ϱ_{res} intersect, yields the solution for the task of determining Φ_{pv} and V_{pv} which would be obtained by neglecting the potential drops in the region of tooth and slot of the armature.

Thus the section $\overline{C'K'}$ would correspond to the potential drop along the shoe, and section $\overline{C'h}$ to the potential drop in the air gap.

In reality flux Φ_{pv} passes also through the region of tooth and slot of the armature, whence its actual magnitude will correspond not to section $\overline{M'C'}$ but to section $\overline{MC}$. Then the actual magnitude V_{pv} will correspond to the section $\overline{CK}$ and the potential drop in the air gap to the value $df = \overline{eb}$. The horizontal distance $\overline{ab}$ of point b from the straight line OD will equal $\overline{MC}$, i.e. $Cb \| OD$. Thus the part fC of the potential drop is spent in the region of tooth and slot of the armature.

If curve DCF'' could be determined in such a way that the vertical distance between any point on it and the straight line Dh should correspond to the total potential drop due to flux Φ_{pv} in the air gap and in the region of tooth and slot of the armature, and the horizontal distance from line DO, to flux Φ_{pv}, then the intersection of this curve and of curve ϱ_{res} would yield point C characterizing the actual values Φ_{pv} and V_{pv}.

For the time being, only two points of this curve are known. One of them — point D — can be obtained if $\Phi_{pv} = 0$. The other one — point F'' — corresponds to flux Φ_{pv} obtained by computing the potential drop in the region of tooth and slot of the armature and in the air gap and by neglecting the potential drop along the shoe, i.e. to flux Φ'_{pv}.

The other points of curve DF'' are not yet known, whence point C is not known either.

We can, however, find two limiting points between which point C will lie.

According to the above, point C' may serve as the upper limit. In addition to this, we have earlier computed a point, as a limiting one, whose abscissa is $\Phi'_{pv}/b_{0res}\gamma l$ and whose ordinate is

$$\frac{V'_{\text{III}} + V'_{pv}}{h_{\text{III}} + h_{\text{II}}}$$

Since $\Phi'_{pv}/b_{0res}\gamma l = \overline{OF''}$, the said point C'' is obtained as the point of intersection of curve ϱ_{res} and the straight line $F''C''$ parallel to OD.

The ordinate of point C'' must always be greater than the ordinate of point C because the distance $\overline{MC}$ necessarily increases with the increment of sections $\overline{df}$ and $\overline{fC}$, i.e. point C must lie to the left from C''.

Since the horizontal distance of point C'' from line OD is

$$\overline{OF''} = \frac{\Phi'_{pv}}{b_{0\,\mathrm{res}}\,\gamma\, l} \tag{7-57}$$

its ordinate is

$$\frac{V'_{\mathrm{III}} + V'_{\mathrm{II}}}{h_{\mathrm{III}} + h_{\mathrm{II}}}$$

computed earlier as the upper limit for point C.

The question arises, which of the points C'' and C' lies closer to the actual point C.

As shown in Fig. 7-8, this depends on the degree of saturation of the teeth in the armature.

In the case of high saturation, point F'' lies to the left from point g obtained by the intersection of the straight line $C'g$ parallel to OD and of the axis of the abscissa, whence point C'' lies to the left from, and lower than, point C'. In the case of low saturation, point F'' lies to the right from point g, whence point C' lies to the left from and lower than, point C''.

It is therefore expedient to determine the ordinate $\overline{CK'}$ nomographically (as explained above), to compare it with the known magnitude $V'_{pv}/b_{0\,\mathrm{res}}\,\gamma l$ and to select the smaller one as the upper limit

$$\frac{V_{pv\max}}{h_{\mathrm{II}} + h_{\mathrm{III}}}$$

for point C.

The lower limit

$$\frac{V_{pv\min}}{h_{\mathrm{II}} + h_{\mathrm{III}}}$$

for point C can be determined on the strength of the following considerations.

Since with the increase of $\overline{MC}$ the section $\overline{fC}$, corresponding to the potential drop in the region of tooth and slot of the armature, must increase more rapidly than section $\overline{df}$, corresponding to the potential drop in the air gap, the curve DF'' must have an upward convexity. It follows that by plotting a straight line between points D and F'', then point C''' where it intersects the curve ϱ_{res} will necessarily lie to the left from, and lower than, point C, i.e.

$$\overline{C''' K'''} = \frac{U_{pv\min}}{h_{II} + h_{III}} \tag{7-58}$$

Obviously, for computations requiring no high degree of accuracy, the mean value may be assumed as

$$V_{pvm} = 0.5\,(V_{pv\max} + V_{pv\min}) \approx V_{pv} \tag{7-59}$$

7-6. Approach to Assessing the Possibility of Neglecting the Saturation of the Pole Shoe and of Determining Approximately the Potential Drop in It

A) A rough estimation of the possibility of neglecting values V_{pvIII}, V_{pvII} and V_{pvI}

1. Proceeding from Eqs. (7-10) and (7-11), determine nomographically the values $B'_{\delta I}$ and $B'_{\delta II}$. Then compute Φ'_{pv} with Eqs. (7-1), (7-2), (7-13), (7-14) and (7-35).

2. On curve ϱ_I determine nomographically the ordinate V_I/h_I for the abscissa $\Phi_t/b_{0I}\gamma l = \Phi'_{pv}/b_{0I}\gamma l$.

3. On curve ϱ_{II} determine nomographically the ordinate V_{II}/h_{II} for the abscissa $\Phi_t/b_{0II}\gamma l = \Phi'_{pv}/b_{0II}\gamma l$.

4. On curve ϱ_{III} determine nomographically the ordinate V_{III}/h_{III} for the abscissa $\Phi_t/b_{0III}\gamma l = \Phi'_{pv}/b_{0III}\gamma l$.

If V_{III}, V_{II} and V_I are small compared to the potential differences V'_{0yIII}, V'_{0yII} and V'_{0I} acting at points y_{III}, y_{II} and y_I, then V_{pvIII}, V_{pvII} and V_{pvI} may be neglected.

B) A more accurate estimation of the possibility of neglecting values V_{pvIII}, V_{pvII} and V_{pvI}

1. If the above estimation reveals that V_{III}, V_{II} and V_I are not small enough to be neglected, then on curve $\varrho_{res} = 1.44$ the abscissa $\overline{LC}$ is determined for the ordinate

$$\frac{V_{III} + V_{II}}{h_{III} + h_{II}}$$

and compute $b_{0res}\gamma l$ with Eq. (7-39). If V_{III} and V_{II} are found too great for the nomographic method, then their determination is repeated according to points 3 and 4 in *A)* with a lower value of Φ_t.

2. Determine b_{par} with Eq. (7-38) and ζ_{II} and ζ_{III} in Fig. 4-5 for ϱ_{II} and ϱ_{III}.

3. Compute tan β_{II} and tan β_{III} with Eqs. (7-40) and (7-41).

4. On curve ϱ_{II} and the straight line tan β_{II} determine, according to section 4-6, the ordinate V'_{II}/h_{II} for $\Phi_t/b_{0res}\gamma l = \Phi'_{pv}/b_{0II}\gamma l$, and on curve ϱ_{III} and the straight line tan β_{III} the ordinate V'_{III}/h_{III} for $\Phi_\tau/b_{0res}\gamma l = \Phi'_{pv}/b_{0res}\gamma l$. The value V_I/h_I in *A)*1 is used as V'_I/h'_I. If V'_{III}, V'_{II} and V'_I are small compared to V'_{0yI} and V'_{0yII}, then V_{pvIII}, V_{pvII} and V_{pvI} can be neglected.

C) The approximate determination of V_{pvIII}, V_{pvII} and V_{pvI}

1. If the estimation made in point *B)* reveals that V'_{III}, V'_{II} and V'_I cannot be neglected, then the abscissa $(\overline{LC})'$ should be determined on curve $\varrho_{res} = 1.44$ for the ordinate

$$\frac{V'_{III} + V'_{II}}{h_{III} + h_{II}}$$

and tan β_{res} computed with Eq. (7-42).

2. Compute ψ_I and ψ_{II} with Eqs. (7-48) and (7-49).

3. Compute C_1 and C_2 with Eqs. (7-55) and (7-56).

4. Compute point F' on the axis of the abscissae to obtain its abscissa $\overline{OF}' = C_1$, and point D on the straight line tan β_{res} to obtain its ordinate equal to C_1/C_2. Thus, find nomographically the point C' where the straight line DF' and curve ϱ_{res} intersect.

Collate the ordinate of point C' to

$$\frac{V'_{III} + V'_{II}}{h_{III} + h_{II}}$$

and choose the smaller value for the upper limit

$$\frac{V_{pv\max}}{h_{III} + h_{II}}$$

5. On the axis of the abscissa determine point F'' in such a way as to obtain its abscissa $\overline{OF}'' = \Phi'_{pv}/b_{0res}\gamma l$.

Determine nomographically point C''' where curve ϱ_{res} and the straight line $\overline{DF''}$ intersect, and choose the ordinate of point C''' to be the lower limit

$$\frac{V_{pv\min}}{h_{\text{II}} + h_{\text{III}}}$$

6. Compute $V_{pv} = V_{pvm}$ with Eq. (7-59).

7. Compute $V_{pv\text{III}}$, $V_{pv\text{II}}$ and $V_{pv\text{I}}$ with Eqs. (7-45) to (7-47) on the basis of V_{pv}.

For determining the potential drops $V_{pv\text{VI}}$, $V_{pv\text{V}}$ and $V_{pv\text{IV}}$ (Fig. 7-3) in the less saturated opposite shoe, the same procedure is repeated with the indices I, II and III replaced by the indices IV, V and VI.

Example 86. Estimate the values $V_{pv\text{III}}$, $V_{pv\text{II}}$ and $V_{pv\text{I}}$ in a highly saturated pole shoe of a DPE—340 type traction motor with $V_{0m} = 14{,}300$ A and $A = 428$ A/cm. The geometrical dimensions of the region of tooth, slot and air are those in Ex. 71.

According to the results of Ex. 84, compute $\Phi'_{pv} = \Phi_t = 2.83 \cdot 10^6$ M. On curve $\varrho_{\text{I}} = 1$, with this flux, we obtain the ordinate 90 A/cm for the abscissa 16,800 G, i.e. $V_{\text{I}} = V'_{\text{I}} = 300$ A/cm; on curve $\varrho_{\text{II}} = 1.96$ the ordinate 3,400 A/cm for the abscissa 16,800 G, i.e. $V_{\text{II}} = 9{,}500$ A, and on curve $\varrho_{\text{III}} = 1.42$ the ordinate 5,600 A/cm for the abscissa 23,500 G, i.e. $V_{\text{III}} = 16{,}800$ A.

Thus the magnitudes V_{III}, V_{II} and V_{I} are not to be neglected.

On curve $\varrho_{\text{res}} = 1.44$, determine the abscissa $\overline{LC} = 22{,}000$ G for the ordinate

$$\frac{26{,}300}{2.8 + 3} = 4{,}500 \text{ A/cm}$$

and compute $b_0 \gamma l_{\text{res}} = 2.83 \cdot 10^6/22{,}000 = 129$. For $\varrho_{\text{II}} = 1.96$ on Fig. 4-5 we find the factor $\zeta_{\text{II}} = 3.1$ and for $\varrho_{\text{II}} = 1.42$, the factor $\varrho_{\text{III}} = 1.49$ and compute.

$$\tan \beta_{\text{II}} = \frac{0.8\,(2.5 + 1.5)}{168}\, 3.1 \cdot 30.5 = 1.76$$

and

$$\tan \beta_{\text{III}} = \frac{0.8\,(2.5 + 1.5)}{120}\, 1.49 \cdot 30.5 = 1.09$$

On curve ϱ_{II} and the straight line $\tan \beta_{\text{II}}$ determine the ordinate 1,450 A/cm for the abscissa 16,800 G, i.e. $V'_{\text{II}} = 4{,}100$ A, and on the straight line tan β_{III} and curve ϱ_{III}, the ordinate 2,850 A/cm for the abscissa 23,500 G, i.e. $V'_{III} = 8{,}500$ A.

It is again found that V'_{II} and V'_{III} cannot be neglected.

Let us now estimate the values V_{pvIII}, V_{pvII} and V_{pvI}.

On curve $\varrho_{res} = 1.44$ determine the abscissa $\overline{LC''} = 19{,}300$ G for the ordinate

$$\overline{C''\,K''} = \frac{4{,}100 + 8{,}500}{5.8} = 2{,}180 \text{ A/cm}$$

Compute

$$\tan \beta_{res} = \frac{22{,}000 - 19{,}300}{2{,}180} = 1.24$$

$$\psi_1 = \frac{300}{4{,}100 + 8{,}500} = 0.024$$

and

$$\psi_2 = 0.33 \text{ and } C_1 = 50{,}000 \text{ G}.$$

From Fig. 7-2c we have $\lambda'''_{I} = 0.4\,\pi \cdot 3.5 \cdot 30.5/4 = 33.5$ M/A and $\lambda'''_{II} = 0$ and then compute $C_2 = 13.46$ G cm/A.

On the straight line tan $\beta_{res} = 1.24$ determine point D with the ordinate 3,730 A/cm and point F' with the 50,000 G on the axis of the abscissa. According to section 6-2, determine point C' where the straight line DF' and the curve $\varrho_{res} = 1.44$ intersect as well as its ordinate $\overline{C'K'} = 2{,}120$ A/cm. Since the ordinate $\overline{C''K''} = 2{,}180$ A/cm, the value 2,120 A/cm is selected for the upper limit V_{pvmax}/h_{res}. Take the section $\overline{OF'} = 22{,}000$ G and determine point C''' where the straight line $\overline{DF''}$ and curve $\varrho_{res} = 1.44$ intersect. The ordinate of this point $\overline{C'''K'''} = V_{pvmin}/h_{res} = 740$ A/cm. This yields the approximate value

$$V_{pvm} = 5.8\,\frac{740 + 2{,}120}{2} = 8{,}300 \text{ A}$$

whence $V_{pvI} = 0.024 \cdot 8{,}300 = 200$ A, $V_{pvII} = 0.33 \cdot 8{,}300 = 2{,}750$ A and $V_{pvIII} = 5{,}550$ A.

Example 87. Estimate V_{pvIV}, V_{pvV} and V_{pvVI} in a less saturated shoe of a traction motor DPE—340 with $V_{0m} = 14{,}300$ A, and $A = 428$ A/cm. In Ex. 81, we have the flux density $B_\delta = 9{,}050$ G for $y_I = -14.6$ cm, and $B_\delta = 9{,}050$ G for $y_{II} = -12$ cm, whence $\Phi_{-14.6} = 780{,}000$ M and $\Phi_{-12} = 820{,}000$ M.

In Ex. 82, the values $\Phi'_{\sigma\text{IV}} = 240{,}000$ M and $\Phi'_{\sigma\text{V}} = 140{,}000$ M have been calculated, whence $\Phi'_{pv} = 1.98 \cdot 10^6$ M. With this flux we obtain the ordinate $C''K'' = 330$ A/cm for the abscissa $\Phi'_{pv}/129 = 15{,}300$ G on curve $\varrho_{\text{res}} = 1.44$.

By assuming, according to Ex. 86, that $\psi_{\text{I}} = 0.024$ and $\psi_{\text{II}} = 0.33$, compute $C_1 = 22{,}300$ G. Since, according to Ex. 86, $C_2 = 13.4$, $C_1/C_2 = 1{,}670$ A/cm. On the straight line $\tan \beta_{\text{res}} = 1.24$, determine point D with the ordinate 1,670 A and on the axis of the abscissa point F' with the abscissa 22,300 G. The ordinate of point C' where the straight line DF' and curve ϱ_{res} intersect will be $\overline{C'K'} = 440$ A/cm, whence $\overline{C''K''} = 330$ A/cm is chosen for the upper limit.

By connecting point F'' (with the abscissa 15,300 G) and point D, we obtain $\overline{C'''K'''} = 130$ A/cm. The value V_{pv} will be approximately equal to $V_{pvm} = 5.8 \cdot 460/2 = 1{,}330$ A, whence, in the same manner as with Eqs. (7-45) to (7-47), $V_{pv\text{IV}} = \psi_1 V_{pv} = 32$ A, $V_{pv\text{V}} = \psi_2 V_{pv} = 440$ A and $V_{pv\text{VI}} = (1 - \psi_{\text{II}}) V_{pv} = 890$ A.

Example 88. Estimate $V_{pv\text{III}}$, $V_{pv\text{II}}$ and $V_{pv\text{I}}$ in a more saturated shoe of a traction motor DMP—151 with $V_{cm} = 7{,}400$ A and $A = 441$ A/cm. The geometrical parameters are selected as in Ex. 75.

According to the results in Ex. 85, $\Phi'_{pv} = 2.8 \cdot 10^6$ M. On curve $\varrho_{\text{I}} = 1$ we obtain the ordinate 60 A/cm for the abscissa 16,100 G, i.e. $V'_{\text{I}} = 150$ A, and on curve $\varrho_{\text{II}} = 2.44$, an ordinate beyond the limits of the nomogram, for the abscissa 16,100 G.

This shows that the values V_{pv} cannot be neglected. For the determination of V_{II} and V_{III} let us examine a smaller flux Φ_t, i.e. choose it equal to $2.1 \cdot 10^6$ M. With this flux we have, on curve $\varrho_{\text{II}} = 2.44$, the ordinate 1,600 A/cm for the abscissa 12,000 G, i.e. $V_{\text{II}} = 3{,}600$ A, and on curve $\varrho_{\text{III}} = 1.49$ the ordinate 3,000 A/cm for the abscissa 20,000 G, i.e. $V_{\text{III}} = 5{,}400$ A.

On curve $\varrho_{\text{res}} = 1.44$ we obtain $\overline{LC} = 19{,}400$ G for the ordinate 9,000/4 A/cm, whence $b_{0\text{res}} \gamma l = 108$ cm².

According to Fig. 4-5, we shall have for $\varrho_{\text{II}} = 2.44$ the factor $\zeta_{\text{II}} = 4.6$ and for $\varrho_{\text{III}} = 1.49$ the factor $\zeta_{\text{III}} = 1.67$. Then we compute

$$\tan \beta_{\text{II}} = \frac{0.8\,(2.6 + 1)\,4.6}{174}\,41.2 = 3.2$$

and

$$\tan \beta_{\text{III}} = \frac{0.8\,(2.6 + 1)\,1.67}{105}\,41.2 = 1.88$$

Choose $\Phi_\tau = \Phi'_{pv} = 2.8 \cdot 10^6$ M and determine the ordinate 1,350 A/cm for the abscissa 16,100 G on the straight line $\tan \beta_{II}$ and curve ϱ_{II}, i.e. $V'_{II} = 3{,}000$ A, and the ordinate 3,350 A/cm for the abscissa 26,700 G on the straight line $\tan \beta_{III}$ and curve ϱ_{III}, i.e. $V'_{III} = 6{,}000$ A.

It is again found that V'_{II} and V'_{III} cannot be neglected.

Let us next estimate V_{pvIII}, V_{pvII} and V_{pvI}. On curve $\varrho_{res} = 1.44$ determine the section $\overline{CL} = 19{,}500$ G for the ordinate $\overline{C''K''} =$ $= 2{,}380$ A/cm and

$$\tan \beta_{res} = \frac{\dfrac{2{,}800{,}000}{108} - 19{,}500}{2{,}380} = 2.75$$

Compute $\psi_I = 0.017$ and $\psi_{II} = 0.325$ and determine the permeabilities $\lambda_I''' = 52$ M/A and $\lambda_{II}''' = 0$ from the figure of the field.

Compute $C_1 = 36{,}000$, $C_2 = 12$ and the ratio $C_1/C_2 = 3{,}000$ A/cm.

On the straight line $\tan \beta_{res} = 2.75$, determine point D with the ordinate 3,000 A/cm and on the axis of the abscissa point F' with the abscissa 36,000 G and find nomographically the ordinate $\overline{C'K'} =$ $= 1{,}200$ A/cm. Since $\overline{C''K''} = 2{,}380$ A/cm,

$$\frac{V_{pv\max}}{h_{II} + h_{III}} = 1{,}200 \text{ A/cm}$$

will be chosen for the upper limit.

Determine the section $\overline{OF''} = 25{,}900$ G and the nomogram will yield

$$\overline{C'''K'''} = \frac{V_{pv\min}}{h_{II} + h_{III}} = 800 \text{ A/cm}$$

Considering the upper limit and the lower limit, compute $V_{pvm} =$ $= 4{,}000$ A, whence $V_{pvI} = 70$ A, $V_{pvII} = 1{,}300$ A and $V_{pvIII} = 2{,}700$ A.

Example 89. Estimate V_{pvIV}, V_{pvV} and V_{pvVI} in a less saturated shoe of a traction motor DMP—151 with $V_{0m} = 7{,}400$ A and $A =$ $= 441$ A/cm.

At point $y = -9.4$ cm, we have $V_0/h = 830$ A/cm and $\overline{OF} =$ $= 8{,}100$ G, whence the nomographic determination yields $B'_{\delta IV} =$ $= 4{,}500$ G and $\Phi'_{yIV} = 465{,}000$ M.

At point $y = -7.2$ cm, we have $V_0/h = 1{,}080$ A/cm and $\overline{OF} = 13{,}600$ G, whence the nomographic determination yields $B'_{\delta V} = 7{,}400$ G and $\Phi'_{yV} = 630{,}000$ M.

From Ex. 83 we have $\Phi'_{\sigma IV} = 32{,}000$ M and $\Phi'_{\sigma V} = 147{,}000$ M, whence $\Phi'_{pv} = 1.27 \cdot 10^6$ M. The section $\overline{C''K''} = 30$ A/cm can be obtained nomographically as the ordinate of point C'' on curve $\varrho = 1.44$ for which $\Phi'_{pv}/108 = 11{,}700$ G.

It follows that the values V_{pvIV}, V_{pvV} and V_{pvVI} can be neglected without further computation.

Example 90. Estimate $V_{pvI} = V_{pvIV}$, $V_{pvII} = V_{pvV}$ and $V_{pvIII} = V_{pvVI}$ in the pole shoe of a motor type DMP—151 with $V_{0m} = 7{,}400$ A and at no load. For point $y = \pm 9.4$, $V_0/h = 1{,}870$ A/cm is valid and $\overline{OF} = 18{,}300$ G, whence we obtain nomographically $\overline{MC} = 15{,}500$ G and $B'_{\delta I} = 8{,}650$ G.

In point $y_2 = \pm 7.2$ cm, we have $V_0/h = 1{,}870$ A/cm, $\overline{OF} = 23{,}600$ G, $\overline{MC} = 16{,}850$ G and $B'_{\delta II} = 9{,}300$ G.

The individual fluxes will have the following values: $\Phi'_I = 890{,}000$ M, $\Phi'_{II} = 800{,}000$ M, $\Phi'_{\sigma I} = (7{,}400 + 370) \cdot 39 = 303{,}000$ M and $\Phi'_{\sigma II} = 147{,}000$ M.

On curve $\varrho = 1.44$ and the straight line $\tan \beta_{res} = 2.75$ we find the ordinate $\overline{C''K''} = 1{,}050$ A/cm of point C'', whose horizontal distance from the straight line $\overline{OD}$ is 19,600 G.

Compute $C_1 = 24{,}000$ G and $C_2 = 12$ G cm/A, as well, as the ratio $C_1/C_2 = 2{,}000$ A/cm. For point D with the ordinate 2,000 A/cm, and for point F' with the abscissa 25,900 G the nomogram yields point C' whose ordinate is $\overline{C'K'} = 600$ A/cm.

Since $600 < 1{,}050$, choose

$$\frac{V_{pv\max}}{h_{II} + h_{III}} = 600 \text{ A/cm}$$

for the upper limit and determine $\overline{OF''} = 19{,}600$ G. By applying points D and F'' we obtain nomographically point C''' with the ordinate

$$\overline{C'''K'''} = \frac{V_{pv\min}}{h_{II} + h_{III}} = 350 \text{ A/cm}$$

As a result we have $V_{pv} \approx 1{,}900$ A, whence $V_{pvI} = V_{pvIV} \approx 30$ A, $V_{pvII} = V_{pvV} \approx 610$ A and $V_{pvIII} = V_{pvVI} \approx 1{,}290$ A.

Some 15 per cent of V_{0m} is thus found to be spent in the pole shoe of the DMP—151 type motor even at no load.

7-7. Theoretical Considerations Underlying the Accurate Determination of the Potential Drop in the Pole Shoe

Let us assume that the total potential drop V_{pv} in the pole shoe is V_{pvm}, obtained in the previous section as the mean value between the lower limit and the upper limit.

By using Eqs. (7-45) to (7-47), (7-16) and (7-17) we can thus compute $V_{0y\mathrm{I}}$ and $V_{0y\mathrm{II}}$ and determine nomographically fluxes $\Phi_{y\mathrm{I}}$ and $\Phi_{y\mathrm{II}}$. Having then determined, with Eqs. (7-52) and (7-53), the

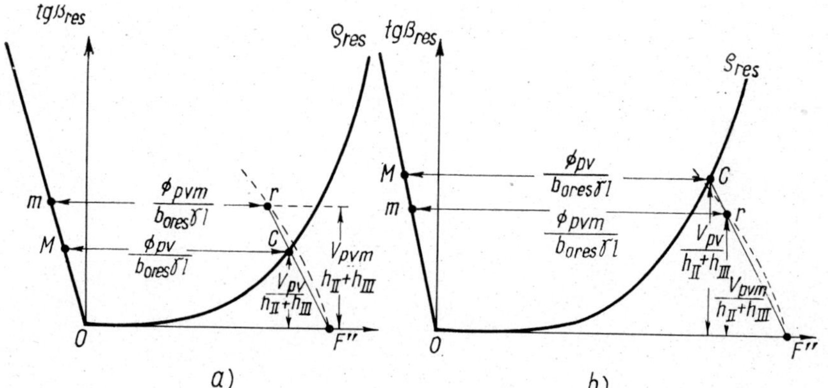

Fig. 7-9

fluxes $\Phi_{\sigma\mathrm{I}}$ and $\Phi_{\sigma\mathrm{II}}$, we can use the formula (7-36) for computing the total flux Φ_{pv} pertaining to V_{pvm} wherefore it will be denoted Φ_{pvm}.

If we have found the exact value

$$\frac{V_{pv}}{h_{\mathrm{II}} + h_{\mathrm{III}}}$$

then the value $\Phi_{pvm}/b_{\mathrm{ores}}\gamma l$, computed as described above, must be equal to the horizontal distance between curve ϱ_{res} and point m (Fig. 7-9) with the ordinate

$$\frac{V_{pvm}}{h_{\mathrm{II}} + h_{\mathrm{III}}}$$

Let it be assumed, however, that point r thus obtained (Fig. 7-9a) is not on curve ϱ_{res} but to the left of it. Since point r lies on curve

DF'' (Fig. 7-8), it will be found to lie to the left of, and higher than, the point of intersection of DF'' in Fig. 7-9 (dotted) and of curve ϱ_{res}, whence the actual magnitude V_{pv} will be less than V_{pvm}.

Since, however, curve rF'' differs but slightly from the straight line rF'', we are still on the safe side in the case in question if we assume that the point of intersection of the straight line rF'' and of curve ϱ_{res} is the point C required whose ordinate is

$$\frac{V_{pv}}{h_{II} + h_{III}}$$

Yet if point r lies to the right of curve ϱ_{res} (Fig. 7-9b), it will be found to lie to the right of, and lower than, the point of intersection of curve DF'' (dotted in Fig. 7-9b) and of curve ϱ_{res}, i.e. $V_{pv} > V_{pvm}$. In this case, too, it may be assumed without the danger of significant errors that point C whose ordinate is

$$\frac{V_{pv}}{h_{II} + h_{III}}$$

coincides with the point of intersection of the straight line rF'' and curve ϱ_{res}.

7-8. Approach to the Determination of the Potential Drop in the Pole Shoe with an Exact Method

On the strength of the considerations expounded in section 7-7, the exact method for the determination of V_{pvI}, V_{pvII} and V_{pvIII} and, in a similar manner, of V_{pvIV}, V_{pvV} and V_{pvVI} is as follows:

1. With Eqs. (7-45) to (7-47), (7-16) and (7-17) compute V_{0yI} and V_{0yII} for y_I and y_{II} respectively, assuming for V_{pv}

$$V_{pvm} = \frac{V_{pv\max} + V_{pv\min}}{2}$$

Then $\Phi_{\sigma Im}$ and $\Phi_{\sigma IIm}$ are computed with Eqs. (7-5) and (7-6).

2. Compute the sections $(\overline{OF})_{Im}$ and $(\overline{OF})_{IIm}$ for y_I and y_{II} respectively and determine nomographically Φ_{yIm} and Φ_{yIIm} according to the method of 6-9.

3. Compute $\Phi_{pvm} = \Phi_{yIm} + \Phi_{yIIm} + \Phi_{\sigma Im} + \Phi_{\sigma IIm}$

4. Determine point r with the ordinate

$$\frac{V_{pvm}}{h_{\rm II} + h_{\rm III}}$$

and with the abscissa

$$\frac{\Phi_{pvm}}{b_{0\rm res}} - \tan \beta_{\rm res} \frac{V_{pvm}}{h_{\rm II} + h_{\rm III}}$$

5. If point r lies on curve $\varrho_{\rm res}$, then $V_{pv} = V_{pvm}$.

6. If point r does not lie on curve $\varrho_{\rm res}$, then the exact value of V_{pv} is obtained by multiplying the ordinate of the point of intersection of the straight line rF'' and curve $\varrho_{\rm res}$ by $h_{\rm II} + h_{\rm III}$.

7. Use Eqs. (7-45) to (7-47) for computing from V_{pv} the exact values $V_{pv\rm I}$, $V_{pv\rm II}$ and $V_{pv\rm III}$.

Example 91. Determine the exact values $V_{pv\rm I}$, $V_{pv\rm II}$ and $V_{pv\rm III}$ in the pole shoe of a DMP—151 type motor for $V_{0m} = 7{,}400$ A and $A = 441$ A/cm.

Proceed from $V_{pvm} = 4{,}000$ A, $V_{pv\rm I} = 70$ A, $V_{pv\rm II} = 1{,}300$ A and $V_{pv\rm III} = 2{,}700$ A obtained in Ex. 88 on the basis of approximative determination. For $y_{\rm I} = 9.4$ cm we get the following values: $(V_0/h)_{\rm I} = 1{,}910$ A/cm, $(\overline{OF})_{\rm I} = 18{,}600$ G, $\varrho = 1.467$, $\tan\beta = 1.6$, $B_\tau = 15{,}500$ G (nomographically), $B_\delta = 8{,}550$ G and $\Phi_{y\rm Im} = 880{,}000$ M.

For $y_{\rm II} = 7.2$ cm, we shall have $(V_0/h)_{\rm II} = 1{,}800$ A/cm, $(\overline{OF})_{\rm II} = 22{,}500$ G, $B_\tau = 16{,}600$ G, $B_\delta = 9{,}250$ G and $\Phi_{y\rm IIm} = 810{,}000$ M.

Compute $\Phi_{\sigma\rm Im} = 574{,}000 - 4{,}030 \cdot 52 = 368{,}000$ M, $\Phi_{\sigma\rm IIm} = 147{,}000$ M, $\Phi_{pvm} = 2{,}200{,}000$ M, the ratio $\Phi_{pv}/b_{0\rm res}\gamma l = 20{,}300$ G and the section $\overline{ML} = 2.75 \cdot 4{,}000/4 = 2{,}750$ G. The abscissa of point r is 17,250 G and its ordinate is 1,000 A/cm. This point lies quite close to curve $\varrho_{\rm res} = 1.44$, whence $V_{pv} = 4{,}000$ A, $V_{pv\rm I} = 70$ A, $V_{pv\rm II} = 1{,}300$ A and $V_{pv\rm III} = 2{,}700$ A.

Example 92. Determine the exact values $V_{pv\rm I}$, $V_{pv\rm II}$ and $V_{pv\rm III}$ in the pole shoe of a DPE—340 type motor for $V_{0m} = 14{,}300$ A and $A = 428$ A/cm.

Proceed from the values $V_{pv} = 8{,}300$ A, $V_{pv\rm I} = 200$ A, $V_{pv\rm II} = 2{,}750$ A and $V_{pv\rm III} = 5{,}550$ A obtained in Ex. 86 by approximation.

For $y_{\rm I} = 14{,}6$ cm, we have $(V_0/h)_{\rm I} = 1{,}810$ A/cm, $(\overline{OF})_{\rm I} = 37{,}500$ G, $\tan\beta = 1.58$, $\varrho = 1.44$, $\gamma b_0 = 1.94$ cm, $B_\tau = 18{,}700$ G, $B_\delta = 10{,}200$ G, $\Phi_{y\rm Im} = 870{,}000$ M (see Ex. 74).

For $y_{II} = 12$ cm, we have $(V_0/h)_{II} = 2{,}000$ A/cm, $(\overline{OF})_{II} =$ 38,500 G, $\tan\beta = 1.58$, $\varrho = 1.44$, $\gamma b_0 = 1.93$, $B_\tau = 19{,}000$ G, $B_\delta = 10{,}300$ G, and $\Phi_{yIIm} = 880{,}000$ M (see Ex. 74).

Use Eq. (7-5) for computing $\Phi_{\sigma Im} = 600{,}000 - 8{,}300 \cdot 1.012 \cdot$ $\cdot\, 33.5 = 320{,}000$ M, $\Phi_{\sigma IIm} = 140{,}000$ M, $\Phi_{pvm} = 2{,}180{,}000$ M, $\Phi_{pvm}/129 = 16{,}900$ G and the section $\overline{ML} = 1.24 \cdot 8{,}300/5.8$. The abscissa of point r is 15,200 G and its ordinate is 1,430 A/cm. By connecting it with point F'' whose abscissa is 22,000 G (Ex. 86), we obtain point C where line $F''r$ and curve ϱ_{res} with the ordinate 1,000 A/cm intersect. Thus $V_{pv} = 5{,}800$ A, $V_{pvI} = 140$ A, $V_{pvII} = 1{,}940$ A, and $V_{pvIII} = 3{,}860$ A.

Example 93. Determine V_{pvI}, V_{pvII} and V_{pvIII} in the shoe of a DMP—151 type motor for $V_{0m} = 7{,}400$ A and $A = 0$ (no load).

Proceed from $V_{pv} = 1{,}900$ A, $V_{pvI} = 30$ A, $V_{pvII} = 610$ A and $V_{pvIII} = 1{,}290$ A obtained on the basis of Ex. 90.

For $y_I = 9.4$ cm we have $(V_0/h)_I = 1{,}400$ A/cm, $(\overline{OF})_I = 13{,}600$ G, $\varrho = 1.467$, $\tan\beta = 1.6$, $B_\tau = 13{,}150$ G, $B_\delta = 7{,}300$ G and $\Phi_{yIm} =$ 750,000 M.

For $y_{II} = 7.2$ cm, we have $(V_0/h)_{II} = 1{,}500$ A/cm, $(\overline{OF})_{II} =$ $= 18{,}800$ G, $B_\tau = 15{,}300$ G, $B_\delta = 8{,}350$ G and $\Phi_{yIIm} = 720{,}000$ M.

Compute $\Phi_{\sigma Im} = 204{,}000$ M, $\Phi_{\sigma IIm} = 147{,}000$ M, $\Phi_{pvm} =$ $= 1{,}820{,}000$ M, $\Phi_{pvm}/108 = 16{,}900$ G and the section $\overline{ML} = 2.75 \cdot$ $\cdot\, 1{,}870/4 = 1{,}400$ G. The abscissa of point r is 15,000 G and its ordinate is 470 A/cm.

The straight line connecting points r and F'' (abscissa 19,600 G; see Ex. 90) intersects curve $\varrho_{res} = 1.44$ at point C (ordinate 400 A/cm), i. e. $V_{pv} = 1{,}600$ A, $V_{pvI} = 30$ A, $V_{pvII} = 470$ A and $V_{pvIII} = 1{,}130$ A.

7-9. Checking the Degree of Accuracy of the Method Adopted for Determining the Potential Drop in the Shoe

The method expounded in section 7-8 for the determination of point C is based on the assumption that the straight line rF'' practically coincides with the corresponding part of curve DF''. The position of point C could be determined even more exactly. For this purpose not only point r but also point s (Fig. 7-10a) should be found on curve DF''. The latter lies on the other side of curve ϱ_{res} but closer to it than F''. Then the point of intersection of curve ϱ_{res} and of the

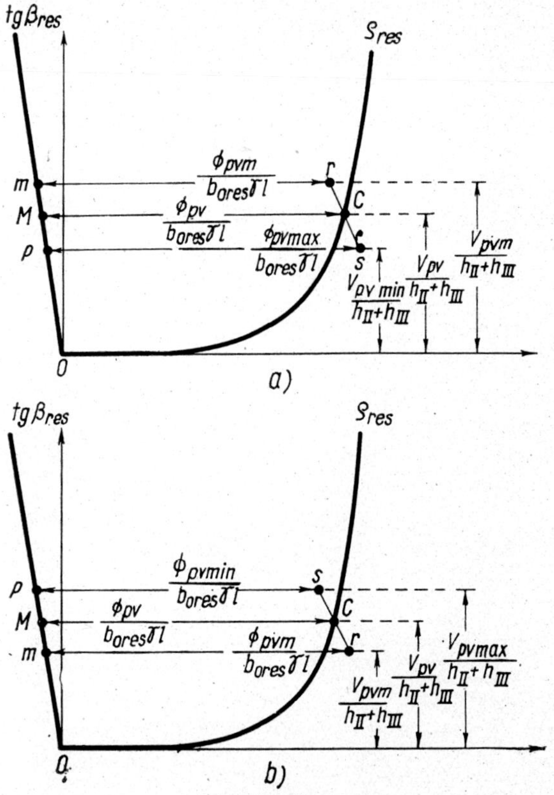

Fig. 7-10

straight line rs should be determined. If point s is to be located to the right of curve ϱ_{res}, its ordinate should be less than

$$\frac{V_{pv}}{h_{II} + h_{III}}$$

Such an ordinate is the value

$$\frac{V_{pv\min}}{h_{II} + h_{III}}$$

found in the previous section. The flux $\Phi_{pv\max} > \Phi_{pv}$, composed of $\Phi_{yI\max}$, $\Phi_{yII\max}$ and $\Phi_{\sigma I\max}$, $\Phi_{\sigma II\max}$, corresponds to it.

If point r lies to the right of curve ϱ_{res} (Fig. 7-10b), and it is necessary to position the point C more accurately, then the values

$\Phi_{y\mathrm{Imin}}$, $\Phi_{y\mathrm{IImin}}$, $\Phi_{\sigma\mathrm{Imin}}$ and $\Phi_{\sigma\mathrm{IImin}}$ pertaining to

$$\frac{V_{pv\max}}{h_{\mathrm{II}} + h_{\mathrm{III}}}$$

should be determined. These fluxes are always less than the actual ones. Thus $\Phi_{pv\min}/b_{0\mathrm{res}}\gamma l = \overline{ps}$ will be less than $\Phi_{pv}/b_{0\mathrm{res}}\gamma l$, i.e. point s will be found to lie to the left from curve ϱ_{res}. The point where this curve and the straight line rs intersect may be regarded as point C whose ordinate is

$$\frac{V_{pv}}{h_{\mathrm{II}} + h_{\mathrm{III}}}$$

Example 94. Determine point C for a DPE—340 type motor with $V_{0m} = 14{,}300$ A and $A = 428$ A/cm.

Since point r (Ex. 92) is on the left side of curve ϱ_{res}, we proceed from $V_{pv\min} = 4{,}300$ A obtained in Ex. 86.

For $y_{\mathrm{I}} = 14.6$ cm we have

$$\left(\frac{V_0}{h}\right)_{\mathrm{Imax}} = \frac{20{,}500 - 4{,}300 \cdot 1.012}{0.679} = 2{,}380 \text{ A/cm}$$

$(\overline{OF})_{\mathrm{Imax}} = 49{,}200$ A, $\tan\beta_{\mathrm{res}} = 1.58$, $\varrho_{\mathrm{res}} = 1.44$, $\gamma b_{0\mathrm{res}} = 1.94$ cm, $B_{\tau} = 20{,}300$ G, $B_{\delta} = 11{,}250$ G and $\Phi_{y\mathrm{Imax}} = 960{,}000$ M.

For $y_{\mathrm{II}} = 12$ cm we have

$$\left(\frac{V_0}{h}\right)_{\mathrm{IImax}} = \frac{19{,}440 - 4{,}300 \cdot 0.835}{6.29} = 2{,}520 \text{ A/cm}$$

$(\overline{OF})_{\mathrm{IImax}} = 48{,}600$ G, $\tan\beta_{\mathrm{res}} = 15.8$, $\gamma b_{0\mathrm{res}} = 1.93$ cm, $B_{\tau} = 20{,}450$ G, $B_{\delta} = 11{,}300$ G and $\Phi_{y\mathrm{IImax}} = 960{,}000$ M.

Compute the fluxes $\Phi_{\sigma\mathrm{Imax}} = 600{,}000 - 4{,}300 \cdot 1.012 \cdot 33.5 = 455{,}000$ M, $\Phi_{\sigma\mathrm{IImax}} = 140{,}000$ M, $\Phi_{pv\max} = 2{,}520{,}000$ M, $\Phi_{pv\max}/129 = 19{,}500$ G and $\overline{MC} = 1.24 \cdot 4{,}300/5.8 = 900$ G.

The abscissa of point s is 18,600 G and its ordinate is 740 A/cm.

The nomogram shows that point s lies almost exactly on the straight line rF''. This, in turn, reveals that the determination of point s is superfluous because the corresponding part of curve DF'' is in reality almost rectilinear.

Example 95. Determine point s pertaining to $V_{pv\min}$ for a DMP—151 type motor with $V_{0m} = 7{,}400$ A and $A = 441$ A/cm.

Proceed from $V_{pv\min} = 3{,}200$ A obtained in Ex. 88.

For $y_{\mathrm{I}} = 9.4$ cm we have $(V_0/h)_{\mathrm{Imax}} = 2{,}100$ A/cm, $(\overline{OF})_{\mathrm{Imax}} = 20{,}500$ G, $\varrho = 1.467$, $\tan\beta = 1.6$, $B_\tau = 16{,}250$ G, $B_\delta = 9{,}000$ G and $\Phi_{y\mathrm{Imax}} = 920{,}000$ M.

For $y_{\mathrm{II}} = 7.2$ cm we have $(V_0/h)_{\mathrm{IImax}} = 1{,}950$ A/cm, $(\overline{OF})_{\mathrm{IImax}} = 24{,}600$ G, $B_\tau = 17{,}000$ G, $B_\delta = 9{,}500$ G and $\Phi_{y\mathrm{IImax}} = 825{,}000$ M.

Compute $\Phi_{\sigma\mathrm{I}} = 574{,}000 - 3{,}030 \cdot 52 = 416{,}000$ M, $\Phi_{\sigma\mathrm{IImax}} = 147{,}000$ M, $\Phi_{pv\mathrm{max}} = 2{,}300{,}000$ M, $\Phi_{pv\mathrm{max}}/108 = 21{,}200$ G, and $\overline{ML} = 2.75 \cdot 800 = 2{,}200$ G.

The abscissa of point s is 19,000 G, its ordinate is 800 A/cm. On the other hand, the ordinate of point r (Ex. 91) is 1,000 A/cm, its abscissa being 17,250 G, whereas the abscissa of point F'' is 25,900 G (Ex. 88). This shows point s to lie exactly on curve rF''.

Exs. 94 and 95 show that the assumption, according to which part rF'' of curve DF'', underlying the method of section 7-8, is rectilinear, is correct and that any attempt at a more accurate determination of point s is superfluous.

7-10. Approach to the Determination of the Magnetic Relations in the Region of Tooth, Slot and Air Gap beneath the Saturated Pole Shoe

Having determined the potential drops along the individual parts of the pole shoe, we can find the potential difference acting upon the region of tooth, slot and air gap, at any arbitrary point.

This difference is obviously

$$V_{0y} = V_{0m} \pm yA - V_{pvy} \tag{7-60}$$

where V_{pvy} = the potential drop from point 10 (Figs. 7-1a, 7-1b and 7-4) to the point examined.

For the sake of simplicity it may be assumed that the potential drops along each part I′, II′, III′ of the shoe are distributed linearly.

Example 96. Find the distribution of the magnetic relations over the periphery of the armature in a DPE—340 type traction motor with due regard to the saturation of the pole shoes (Exs. 92 and 87) during a one-hour load ($A = 428$ A/cm, $V_{0m} = 14{,}300$ A).

In Ex. 79 the magnetic relations have been determined for points located at such distances as $y = -6$, $y = -3.5$, $y = -0$, $y = +3.5$ and $y = +6$ cm from the pole centre, for which the effect of the saturation of the shoes could be neglected. What we have to do now is to determine the magnetic relations at the following points:

$$y = +10.5 \text{ cm}, \; y = +13.5 \text{ cm}, \; y = +16.5 \text{ cm},$$
$$y = -10.5 \text{ cm}, \; y = -13.5 \text{ cm}, \; y = -16.5 \text{ cm}.$$

From Ex. 74 we have the following values for tan β_{res}, γb_{0res}, h_{res}, δ, k_c and ϱ:

For $y = \pm 10.5$ cm: tan $\beta_{res} = 1.58$, $\gamma b_{0res} = 1.92$ cm, $h_{res} = 6.09$ cm, $\delta = 0.63$ cm, $k_c = 1.18$, $\varrho_{res} = 1.44$.

For $y = \pm 13.5$ cm: tan $\beta_{res} = 1.58$, $\gamma b_{0res} = 1.935$ cm, $h_{res} = 6.54$ cm, $\delta = 0.63$ cm, $k_c = 1.18$, $\varrho_{res} = 1.44$.

For $y = \pm 16.5$ cm: tan $\beta_{res} = 1.58$, $\gamma b_{0res} = 1.95$ cm, $h_{res} = 7.16$ cm, $\delta = 0.63$ cm, $k_c = 1.18$, $\varrho_{res} = 1.44$.

Relying on these data we can determine the flux density in the air gap for each individual point (see Table 7-1)

TABLE 7-1

Distance from pole centre cm	$\frac{V_{0y}}{h_{res}}$ A/cm	Section $\overline{OF}$ G	V/h_{res} (nomographically) A/cm	B_τ (nomographically) G	B_δ G	V A
1	2	3	4	5	6	7
+ 10.5	2,460	46,200	1,310	20,000	10,900	8,000
± 13.5	2,200	44,000	1,240	19,700	10,800	8,100
± 16.5	2,140	46,500	1,260	19,800	10,950	9,000
— 10.5	1,470	27,500	550	17,200	9,400	3,350
— 13.5	1,100	22,000	320	15,800	8,700	2,090
— 16.5	830	18,000	150	14,650	8,100	1,080

Both parts of curve $B_\delta = f(y)$ (curve III) valid for the above ranges (positive and negative) are plotted in Fig. 6-11 together with curve $B_\delta = f(y)$ (middle part of curve I) related to the other (central) ranges for which the values have been computed in Ex. 79.

Example 97. Find the distribution of the magnetic field over the periphery of the armature of a DMP—151 type traction motor with due regard to the saturation of one pole shoe (Exs. 91 and 89) during a one-hour load ($V_{0m} = 7{,}400$ A, $A = 441$ A/cm).

In Ex. 78 we have found the magnetic relations of the points located at distances from $y = +3.48$ cm to $y = -12.18$ cm from the pole centre, for which the effect of the saturation in the shoe can be neglected. Determine now the magnetic relations at points $y = +5.22$ cm, $y = +6.95$ cm, $y = +8.7$ cm, $y = +10.44$ cm and $y = +12.19$ cm (Table 7-2).

TABLE 7-2

y cm	$\frac{V_{0y}}{h}$ A/cm	Section $\overline{OF}$ G	B_τ (nomographically) G	B_δ G	V A
1	2	3	4	5	6
5.22	2,040	29,800	18,000	10,000	3,270
6.96	1,800	24,000	16,850	9,250	2,090
8.7	1,850	20,000	16,000	8,900	1,460
10.44	2,020	15,900	14,600	8,100	710
12.18	2,210	6,900	6,900	3,800	0

Example 98. Find the distribution of the magnetic relations over the periphery of the armature of a DMP—151 type traction motor with due regard to the saturation of the pole shoes (Ex. 93) at no load ($V_{0m} = 7{,}400$ A, $A = 0$).

From Ex. 76 we have the values of the magnetic relations for the points located at distances $y = 0$, $y = +1.74$ cm, $y = \pm 3.48$ cm

TABLE 7-3

y cm	$\frac{V_{0y}}{h}$ A/cm	Section $\overline{OF}$ G	B_τ G	B_δ G	V A
1	2	3	4	5	6
± 5.22	1,720	25,200	16,900	9,400	2,200
± 6.96	1,500	20,000	15,700	8,800	1,400
± 8.7	1,410	15,200	14,360	8,000	480
± 10.44	1,400	11,000	10,700	5,950	120
± 12.18	1,400	4,350	4,350	2,400	0

from the pole. Determine now the magnetic relations for points $y = \pm 5.22$ cm, $y = \pm 6.96$ cm, $y = \pm 8.7$ cm, $y = \pm 10.44$ cm and $y = \pm 12.18$ cm (Table 7-3).

Example 99. Determine the effect of armature reaction on the flux of excitation in a DMP—151 type machine with $V_{0m} = 7{,}400$ A and $A = 441$ A/cm.

Add up all the values B_τ obtained for each of the thirteen points of Exs. 78 and 97, as well as all the values B_τ obtained for each of the identical points in Exs. 76 and 98.

The quotient of these sums, i.e. in this case $103{,}400/115{,}480 = 0.9$ shows the decrease of the magnetic flux of the machine at load if the value V_{0m} is given.

The distribution curves $B_\tau = f(y)$ and $V = f(y)$ are obtained in a similar way for the regime of enhanced excitation in a DK—103A type traction motor. The curves are shown in Fig. 6-12 by dotted lines.

Relying on curve $B_\delta = f(y)$ we can construct the distribution curve of the potential differences e_k along the commutator between two neighbouring commutator segments. In order to do so, it is necessary to compute the electromotive force e due to the flux density B_δ in one conductor. Here curve $e = f(y)$ will obviously differ from curve $B_\delta = f(y)$ in no more than the scale of the ordinate axis. Then add graphically the values e for all series-connected conductors of one section with regard to the enlarging or reduction of the pitch of the armature winding. Curve $e_k = f(y)$ thus obtained for the DK—103A type traction motor, corresponding to curve $B_\delta = f(y)$* shown in Fig. 6-12 by a dotted line, is plotted in Fig. 7-11.

7-11. The General Application of the Results Obtained in Chapter 7 to other Electrical Machines

The nomographic method for determining the magnetic potential drop in the pole shoe is not only the solution of an extremely difficult and hitherto unsolved problem, but is at the same time a contribution to the final development of a system of nomographic methods enabling us, as was explained in chapter 6, to determine all magnetic parameters in the whole active layer of the machine.

* See note on p. 169.

The necessity of such an additional development of this system depends on the degree of saturation in the pole shoe. As shown by the previous examples, considerable error may be committed by neglecting the saturation in certain cases, particularly in case of d.c. machines. That is why the method expounded in chapter 7 was developed with due regard to the configurations used in d.c. machines and to the magnetic phenomena occurring in them.

In much the same way, as it was explained in section 6-10, the method developed in chapter 6 in connection with the example

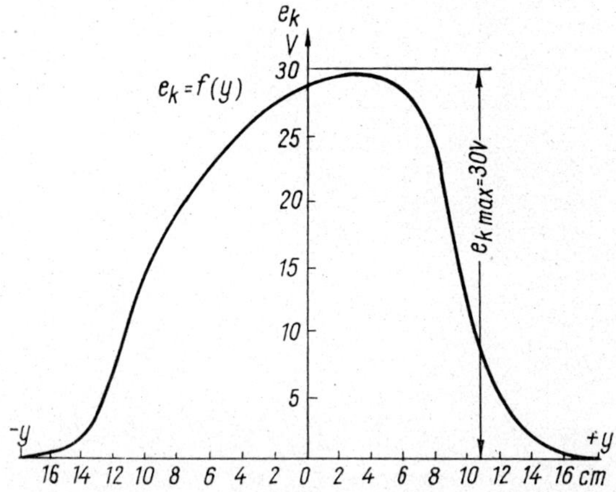

Fig. 7-11

of the standard d. c. machines and applied to other electrical machines can be used also to solve the similar problems of chapter 7. Indeed the methods of computing the potential drops in the pole shoes can, in principle, be also applied to other electrical machines with similar pole shoes, if the assumptions concerning the ordinary d.c. machines in this chapter are modified and generalized correspondingly.

In other electrical machines the distribution of the leakage fluxes passing through the pole shoes will, obviously, differ either on account of the different form of the air gaps or because of the different potential distribution. (An example of the latter is the absence of the commutating poles or the simultaneous occurrence of the quadrate (cross) and direct armature ampere-turns beside the field ampere-turns, etc.) The basic idea of sections 7-1 and 7-2, i. e. that the leakage fluxes should first be determined from the potential relations obtained by neglecting the potential drops in the pole shoes, applies in these cases also. As to the replacement of the pole shoes by several series-connected ferromagnetic bodies, the results obtained in sections 7-3 and 7-4 remain valid in principle. The sole difference to take into account is that the values $V'_{0y\mathrm{I}}$, $V'_{0y\mathrm{II}}$ and $V'_{0y\mathrm{III}}$ should not be computed from Eqs. (7-10), (7-11) and (7-12) but according to the actual potential distribution, i.e. with regard to the direct and quadrature fluxes actually acting at points at distances of y_{I}, y_{II} and y_{III}.

The same applies to section 7-5 and 7-6 as well. Should the estimate of the potential drops in the pole shoes prove them to be negligible, the magnetic relations in the active layer should be determined according to section 6-10. Should the potential drop not prove negligible, the computation should be undertaken according to sections 7-7 and 7-8, and the distribution of potentials, underlying the nomographic determination of the relations in the active layer according to section 6-10, should be corrected in accordance with the potential drop.

The system of nomographic methods developed in this book can be used for a rapid yet exact determination, in any electrical machine, of the influence of the configuration of the air gap, of the pole shoes and of the teeth in the rotor and the stator, both at no load and under load. For any arbirrary point of the armature periphery the electromotive forces induced by the different fluxes, the distribution of the electrical potential, the electromagnetic forces, the different kinds of losses, the elactromagnetic energy, etc. can be determined,

CHAPTER EIGHT

NOMOGRAPHIC METHOD FOR DETERMINING TRANSVERSE SLOT FLUXES DUE TO THE SATURATION OF THE TEETH

8-1. The Law of Induction Distribution of the Transverse Slot Flux along the Height of the Tooth

Let us first examine the character of the induction distribution of the transverse slot fluxes along the height of the teeth and then consider the relation between the transverse fluxes of the different slots.

The distribution of the density of the transverse slot flux, with different potential distribution in the tooth, can be studied on the basis of the following considerations.

Let us take two extreme cases.

In the first case (Fig. 8-1a) $a = 1$ for the teeth, whence the field strength H_{x1} due to flux Φ_{t1} in tooth no. 1 is uniform throughout the length of the tooth. The field strength in tooth no. 2 is usually set up by another flux Φ_{t2} and has the magnitude H_{x2}. The induction of the transverse slot flux, crossing teeth 1 and 2, is

$$\frac{0.4\,\pi}{b} \int_{0}^{x} (H_{x1} - H_{x2})\, dx$$

and, with the growing value of x, increases linearly along the straight line AB (Fig. 8-2a) from zero to

$$\overline{CB} = \overline{AD} = \frac{0.4\,\pi}{b} (V_1 - V_2)$$

In the second case (Fig. 8-1b) the teeth have a profile almost never occurring in practice, characterized by $a = 0.15$. When fluxes Φ_{t1} and Φ_{t2} traverse the minimum cross-section of these teeth, a very high field strength is set up which, with the increase of x, rapidly diminishes until zero. Owing to this, the potential differences V_1 and V_2 will occur in practice in such regions only as are very close to the minimum cross-section. Consequently, the transverse slot flux density

$$\frac{0.4\,\pi}{b}\int_{0}^{x}(H_{x1}-H_{x2})\,dx$$

will attain the value

$$\overline{AD}=\frac{0.4\,\pi}{b}\,(V_1-V_2)$$

quite close to the bottom of the slot, and will have a constant value $\overline{AD}=\overline{CB}$ along almost the whole height of the teeth.

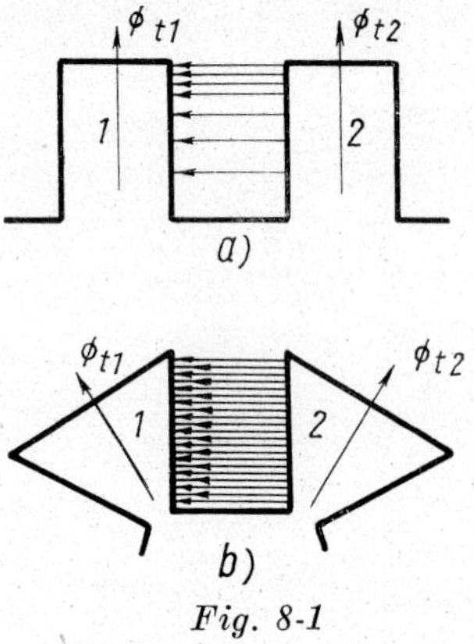

Fig. 8-1

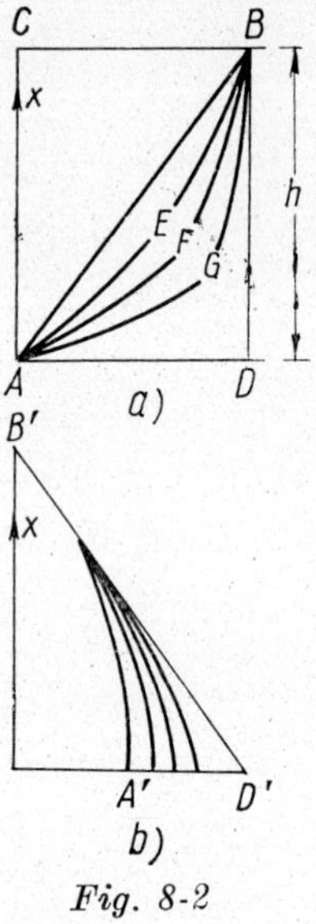

Fig. 8-2

While the tooth fluxes Φ_{t1} and Φ_{t2} change their value (Fig. 8-1a), the rectilinear distribution of the transverse flux density will be maintained though the gradient of the straight line AB will be altered.

With the changes in the value of the tooth fluxes Φ_{t1} and Φ_{t2} (Fig. 8-1b) it may be assumed that the whole potential drop is concentrated, as before, around the minimum cross-section. The density of the transverse slot flux may, therefore, be assumed to be constant along the entire height of the slot and to have a somewhat different value $\overline{AD}=\overline{CB}$.

It may thus be presumed with fair accuracy that the density of the transverse slot flux along the entire height, for both tooth configurations examined, will maintain its character, at least approximately, even if the flux changes. For teeth with parallel walls the transverse slot flux density will be distributed according to the law $Z = Z_{\max} x/h$, and for the teeth with $a = 0.15$, according to the law $Z = Z_{\max}$ where $Z_{\max}$ is the maximum flux density.

If this thesis holds for both extreme cases within a wide range of tooth configuration, no serious error is incurred by assuming that for each tooth configuration, i.e. each possible ratio of the maximum and the minimum cross-section, there is a definite radial distribution of the transverse slot flux density, characterizing the individual teeth, and independent in practice of the magnetic demand of the tooth.

When deducing this thesis it was assumed that the tooth fluxes were constant along the height. In reality, affected by the transverse and longitudinal slot fluxes, the tooth flux will not be constant. This fact modifies the distribution of the field strength along the tooth. Nevertheless, by taking into account the consideration to follow, it will become obvious that the modification will not be a significant one.

For teeth with $a > 0.15$, the flux density is distributed according to one of the intermediate curves AEB, AFB, AGB (Fig. 8-2a). The flux density distribution is almost identical with the distribution along teeth with parallel walls.

By introducing

$$Z_1 = \frac{0.4\,\pi}{b} \int_0^x (H_{x1} - H_{x2})\,dx \tag{8-1}$$

$$Z_2 = 0.4\,\pi \int_0^x (H_{x2} - H_{x3})\,dx \tag{8-2}$$

and

$$\Delta Z = Z_1 - Z_2 \tag{8-3}$$

the difference of transverse slot fluxes entering and leaving the tooth is obtained, according to Eq. (1-8), as

$$\Delta \Phi_x = l \int_x^h \Delta Z\,dx \tag{8-4}$$

If $a = 1$,

$$\Delta \Phi_x = l \int_x^h \Delta Z_{max} \frac{x}{h} dx = \frac{(h^2 - x^2)\, l}{2\, h} \Delta Z_{max} \tag{8-5}$$

$$\Delta Z_{max} = Z_{1max} - Z_{2max} \tag{8-6}$$

The distribution of $\Delta\Phi_x$ along the height for this case is represented by the curve $B'A'$ (Fig. 8-2b).

For the other extreme case

$$\Delta \Phi_x = l \int_x^h \Delta Z_{max}\, dx = \Delta Z_{max}(h - x)\, l \tag{8-7}$$

but the distribution of $\Delta\Phi_x$ along the height corresponds to the straight line $B'D'$ (Fig. 8-2b). The intermediate curves (Fig. 8-2b) lying between $B'A'$ and $B'D'$ will correspond to the intermediate curves AEB, AFB and AGB (Fig. 8-2a) Thus, in the selected very wide range of different a factors (much wider than the range of tooth profiles used in electrical engineering) the laws of distribution of $\Delta\Phi_x$ along the height of the tooth differ but slightly from one another.

If we realize that the flux density distribution is but slightly affected even by greatly differing tooth forms, it becomes evident that the modification of the tooth fluxes due to the values $\Delta\Phi_x$ have no considerable effect upon the distribution of the transverse fluxes. (This refers not to their magnitude but to the character of the flux density distribution along the height of the slot.)

For given tooth form this permits us to assume that, on considering the effect of the values $\Delta\Phi_x$, the transverse slot fluxes are distributed again according to the above laws, i.e. that

$$Z = Z_{max}\, f_1\left(\frac{x}{h}, a\right) \tag{8-8a}$$

and that

$$\Delta Z = \Delta Z_{max}\, f_1\left(\frac{x}{h}, a\right) \tag{8-8b}$$

where $f_1(x/h,\ a)$ is a function characterizing the dependence of the radial of induction distribution of the transverse slot fluxes upon the configuration of the tooth.

The author's investigations concerning the quantitative relations between the form of the tooth and the induction distribution of transverse slot fluxes have yielded the function

$$\frac{Z}{Z_{\max}} = f_1\left(\frac{x}{h}, a\right)$$

in the form of curves (Fig. 8-3). Relying on these curves constructed for different values of a, we can determine the value Z at any arbitrary height x, if the corresponding value $Z_{\max}$ is known.

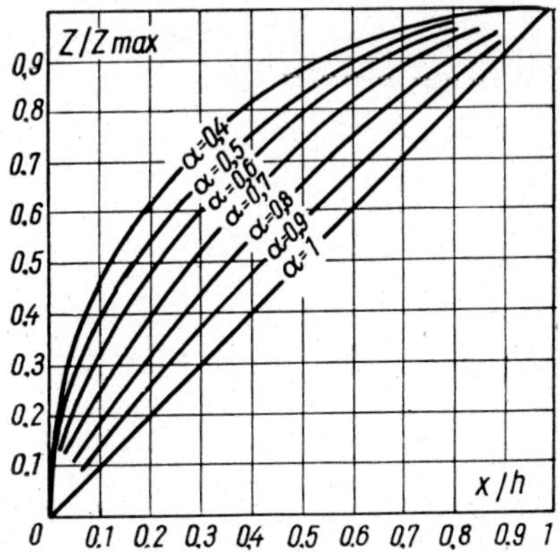

Fig. 8-3.

8-2. The Theoretical Foundation of the Nomographic Determination of the Correlation between the Transverse Fluxes in two Adjacent Slots and the Flux of the Tooth between Them

By introducing the notation

$$\int_{x/h}^{1} f_1\left(\frac{x}{h}, a\right) d\left(\frac{x}{h}\right) = f_2\left(\frac{x}{h}, a\right) \tag{8-9}$$

we obtain, instead of the formula (8-4), the equation

$$\Delta \Phi_x = lh\, \Delta Z_{\max} f_2\left(\frac{x}{h}, a\right) \tag{8-10}$$

Since $f_2(x/h, a)$ has an identical form for all teeth with a definite value a, the value of flux $\Delta\Phi_x$ passing through the tooth at a height x can be related to the maximum density $\Delta Z_{\max}$ of the transverse fluxes in the adjacent slots.

If the exact values V_1, V_2 V_3 etc. were known, the value $\Delta\Phi_x$ could be computed for any tooth with the formula

$$\Delta Z_{\max} = \frac{0.4\pi}{b}(V_1 - 2V_2 + V_3) \tag{8-11}$$

and with Eq. (8-10). Yet in our nomographic determination of V_n we have neglected the effect of the transverse slot fluxes, i. e. the values $\Delta\Phi_x$.

By considering the inaccuracy caused by neglecting $\Delta\Phi_x$, we would obtain, instead of V_1, V_2, V_3 etc., other values $V_1-\Delta V_1$, $V_2-\Delta V_2$, $V_3-\Delta V_3$ etc. where ΔV_1, ΔV_2, ΔV_3 etc. are the errors committed by neglecting the values $\Delta\Phi_x$. The negative sign of the members ΔV follows from the assumption that fluxes $\Delta\Phi_x$ unload the teeth.

Thus Eq. (8-10) for tooth 2 (whose flux $\Delta\Phi_x$ is denoted in this case by $\Delta\Phi_{x2}$) assumes the form

$$\Delta\Phi_{x2} = [V_1 - 2V_2 + V_3 - (\Delta V_1 - 2\Delta V_2 + \Delta V_3)]\frac{0.4\pi}{b}hl\cdot f_2\left(\frac{x}{h}, a\right) \tag{8-12}$$

In an analogous equation for the next tooth we should have the following unknown values: $\Delta\Phi_{x3}$ and ΔV_4 etc.. Consequently, in order to solve the above system of equations, we must find, for each tooth, a second formula relating the magnitudes $\Delta\Phi_x$ and ΔV.

In section 2-9 we have shown that the effect of the slot fluxes, closing through the minimum cross-section of the tooth, upon the potential difference due to the basic tooth flux can be taken into account in the form of a corresponding change of ϱ.

In this case we can proceed in much the same manner. If, for the sake of simplicity, the factor ϱ is assumed to be computed with the formula

$$\varrho = \frac{2}{3}\left(\frac{b_0}{b_2} + \frac{b_0}{b_1}\right) - \frac{1}{3} = \frac{2}{3}\left(\frac{B_2 + B_1}{B_0}\right) - \frac{1}{3} \tag{8-13}$$

obtained by transforming Eq. (2-7), and flux $\Delta\Phi_{x=0}$ appears in the smallest cross-section $b_2\gamma l$, while flux $\Delta\Phi_{x=h/2}$ appears in the mean cross-section $b_1\gamma l$, then the flux density B_2 will decrease by $\Delta\Phi_{x=0}/b_2\gamma l$ and the flux density B_1 by $\Delta\Phi_{x=h/2}/b_1\gamma l$. Thus the flux density B_0 remains unchanged, i.e. will be $\Phi_t/b_0\gamma l$.

It may therefore be presumed that ϱ has now a different value

$$\varrho' = \varrho - \Delta\varrho \tag{8-14}$$

and

$$\Delta\varrho = \frac{2}{3}b_0\left(\frac{\Delta\Phi_{x=0}}{b_2} + \frac{\Delta\Phi_{x=h/2}}{b_1}\right)\frac{1}{\Phi_t} \tag{8-15}$$

Flux $\Delta\Phi_{x=0}$ can be determined by computing $f_2(x/h, a)$ for $x = 0$ with Eq. (8-9) and flux $\Delta\Phi_{x=h/2}$ by computing $f_2(x/h, a)$ for $x = h/2$.

Thus the dependence of $\Delta\varrho$ on $Z_{\max}$ and on a can be expressed by the equation

$$\Delta\varrho = \frac{hl\,Z_{\max}}{2\,\Phi_t} f_3(a)\,, \tag{8-16}$$

where

$$f_3(a) = \frac{4}{3}\left\{\left[f_2\left(\frac{x}{h}, a\right)\right]_{x=0} \cdot \frac{b_0}{b_2} + \left[f_2\left(\frac{x}{h}, a\right)\right]_{x=h/2} \cdot \frac{b_0}{b_1}\right\} \tag{8-17}$$

Eq. (8-17) expresses the fact that at a given relation $hl\Delta Z_{\max}/2\Phi_t$ the value $\Delta\varrho$ depends on the spatial distribution of the transverse fluxes, i.e. on function a, and on the form of the tooth, that is, on the correlation of b_0, b_1 and b_2 which is also a function of a.

By integrating $f_1(x/h, a)$ (Fig. 8-3) according to x/h within the range x/h to 1, we can obtain f_2 $(x/h, a)$. If $x = 0$, we have the flux $\Delta\Phi_{x=0}$ passing through the smallest cross-section $b_2\gamma l$ of the tooth, and if $x/h = 1/2$, we obtain the flux $\Delta\Phi_{x=h/2}$ passing through the mean cross-section $b_1\gamma l$ when $lh\Delta Z_{\max} = 1$.

Finally we can obtain the flux density values $\Delta\Phi_{x=0}/b_2\gamma l$ and $\Delta\Phi_{x=h/2}/b_1\gamma l$ by which the flux densities B_2 and B_1 change owing to the effect of the transverse fluxes. The magnitude $\Delta\varrho$, pertaining to the condition $1 = hl\Delta Z_{\max}/2\Phi_t$, yields, according to Eq. (8-16), the required function $f_3(a)$ shown in Fig. 4-5.

Thus the computation of the transverse fluxes should be performed with the value ϱ':

$$\varrho' = \varrho - C_a \frac{\Delta Z_{\max}}{\Phi_t} \tag{8-18}$$

where

$$C_a = \frac{hl}{2} f_3(a) \tag{8-19}$$

i.e. depends on the dimensions of the teeth and the slots only.

If $\Delta Z_{\max} = 0$ (with the transverse fluxes neglected), then $\varrho' = \varrho$, and point C whose ordinate is V/h can readily be determined from the nomogram by using ϱ and $\Phi_\tau/b_0\gamma l$. If $\Delta Z_{\max} > 0$, the value V/h decreases to V'/h and ϱ to ϱ'.

With the decrement of V/h to V'/h the difference $V_0/h - V/h$ increases to $V_0/h - V'/h$ and flux Φ_τ to Φ_τ'. The increase of ϱ to ϱ' affects the magnetic condition of the tooth in the same manner as the decrease of factor a to a definite value a'. Since the factor ζ depends on a, the former also decreases to $\zeta - \Delta\zeta$.

The values V', Φ'_τ, ϱ', a', and $\zeta - \Delta\zeta$ are unknown for the time being, yet their correlation can readily be determined nomographically.

Let us assume that for $\Delta Z_{\max} = 0$ we have determined nomographically the value ζ, point D, curve ϱ, the straight line DF and

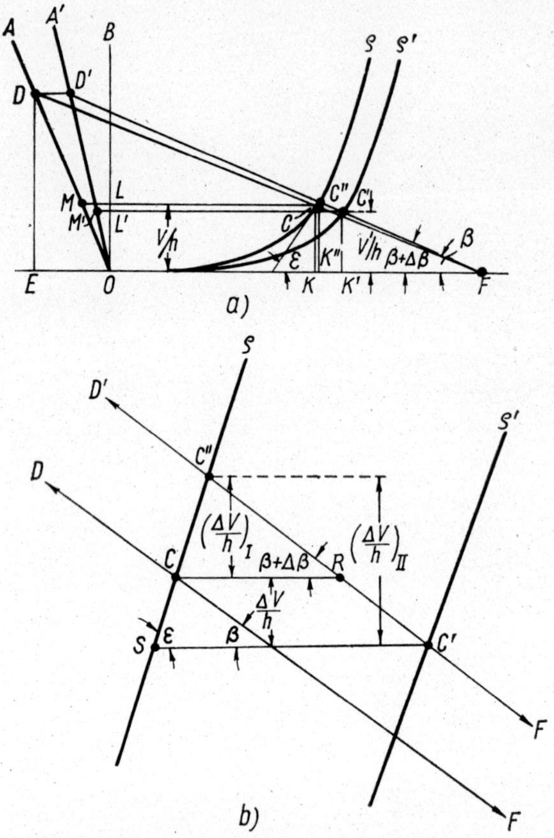

Fig. 8-4

point C, whereas $\overline{CK} = V/h$ and $\overline{MC} = \Phi_\tau/b_0\gamma l$ (Fig. 8-4a). If now $\Delta Z_{\max} > 0$, then these values undergo a change.

If $\zeta - \Delta\zeta$ and ϱ' were known, it would be easy to determine nomographically V'/h and $\Phi'_\tau/b_0\gamma l$. The only thing to do would be to find point D' with the ordinate V_0/h lying on the straight line OA' for which

$$\tan \sphericalangle A'OB = \frac{0.4\,\pi\, b(\zeta - \Delta\zeta)}{b_0\,\gamma} \tag{8-20}$$

and to find the curve for ϱ'. The ordinate $\overline{C'K'}$ of point C' where this curve intersects the straight line $D'F$ would then be V'/h, and the section $\overline{M'C'}$ would equal $\Phi_\tau/b_0\gamma l$.

The shift of point C to point C' can be calculated to take place in two steps. First the factor ζ alone changes to $\zeta - \Delta\zeta$ while ϱ remains unchanged, then ϱ changes to ϱ' with ζ' remaining constant (Figs. 8-4a and 8-4b).

Point C'' lying on curve ϱ and on the straight line $D'F$ would correspond to the values $\zeta - \Delta\zeta$ and ϱ. If we denote the difference of the ordinates $\overline{C''K''}$ and $\overline{CK}$ by $(\Delta V/h)_{\mathrm{I}}$, angle DFO by β, angle $D'FO$ by $\beta + \Delta\beta$, the angle, enclosed by the axis of the abscissae and the tangent to curve ϱ at point C, by ε and the point on the straight line $D'F$ with an ordinate equal to that of point C by R, then (neglecting the very small value $\Delta\beta$) we can write

$$\left(\frac{\Delta V}{h}\right)_{\mathrm{I}} = \frac{\overline{CR}}{\cot\varepsilon + \cot\beta} \tag{8-21}$$

If on curve ϱ we denote by S the point with an ordinate equal to that of point C', we can write $\overline{C'S} = \Delta\varrho K_\varrho$ where K_ϱ is constant because, with a definite difference of ordinates $\overline{C''K''}$ and $\overline{C'K'}$ section $\overline{C'S}$ is proportional to $\Delta\varrho$. Thus

$$\left(\frac{\Delta V}{h}\right)_{\mathrm{II}} = \frac{\overline{C'S}}{\cot\varepsilon + \cot\beta} = \Delta\varrho\,\frac{K_\varrho}{\cot\varepsilon + \cot\beta}$$

where $(\Delta V/h)_{\mathrm{II}}$ is the difference of the ordinates $\overline{C''K''}$ and $\overline{C'K'}$.

Section $\overline{DD'}$ equals

$$\frac{V_0}{h}\,0.4\,\pi\,\frac{b'\,\Delta\zeta}{b_0\,\gamma}$$

On the other hand, it may obviously be assumed that $\Delta\zeta/\Delta\varrho = d\zeta/d\varrho$. By denoting $d\zeta/d\varrho = K_\zeta$ we get

$$\overline{CR} = \overline{DD'}\,\frac{V/h}{V_0/h} = 0.4\,\pi\,\frac{b' K_\zeta \Delta\varrho}{b_0\,\gamma}\,\frac{V}{h}$$

By introducing $\Delta V/h$ for $V/h - V'/h$ we can write

$$\frac{\Delta V}{h} = \left(\frac{\Delta V}{h}\right)_{II} - \left(\frac{\Delta V}{h}\right)_{I} = \Delta \varrho N \tag{8-22}$$

where

$$N = \frac{1}{\cot \varepsilon + \cot \beta}\left[K_\varrho - \frac{0.4\pi b' K_\zeta V/h}{b_0 \gamma}\right] \tag{8-23}$$

Thus we obtain a linear relation between the unknown values $\Delta V/h$ and $\Delta \varrho$. Value N depends exclusively on such magnitudes as can be readily determined from the nomogram because all of them are related to point C which can be determined as explained in chapters 6 and 7 by neglecting the transverse fluxes.

The factor K_ζ can be determined from Fig. 4-5 and $\cot \beta$ from the equation

$$\cot \beta = \frac{\overline{OF} + \overline{OE}}{\overline{DE}} \tag{8-24}$$

The values $\cot \varepsilon$ and K_ϱ are determined directly from the nomogram (see section 8-3).

The relation obtained between $\Delta \varrho$ and $\Delta V/h$ (8-22) can be transformed, on the basis of Eqs. (8-14) and (8-18), into the relation between $\Delta Z_{\max}$ and $\Delta V/h$. Thus we get

$$\frac{\Delta V_m}{h} = \Delta Z_{\max m} \frac{C_a N_m}{\Phi_{tm}} \tag{8-25}$$

for the mth tooth and slot. When V_m/h changes to $V_m/h - \Delta V_n/h$, the values V/h of the other teeth also change under the influence of the transverse fluxes: for instance, V_{m-1}/h changes to $V_{m-1}/h - \Delta V_{m-1}/h$ and V_{m+1}/h to $V_{m+1}/h - \Delta V_{m+1}/h$. Therefore a second linear relation between $\Delta V_m/h$ and $\Delta Z_{\max m}$ can be established and $\Delta Z_{\max m}$ can be excluded by the aid of the formula

$$\Delta V_m = M_m[-V_{m-1} + 2V_m - V_{m+1} - (\Delta V_{m-1} + 2\Delta V_m - \Delta V_{m+1})] \tag{8-26}$$

where

$$M_m = \frac{0.4\pi C_a h N_m}{b \Phi_{tm}} \tag{8-27}$$

We can write as many such linear equations as the number of tooth pitches. They can be solved on the assumption that the values

$\Delta V/h$ equal zero at points where the tooth fluxes are insignificant, i.e. in the interpolar space.

Thus the hitherto unsolved problem of determining the intricate magnetic relations connected with the transverse slot fluxes has been reduced to a simple method, analogous to the one often used for computing complicated electric circuits.

8-3. Approach to the Practical Determination of Transverse Slot Fluxes

On the strength of the theoretical considerations expounded in sections 8-1 and 8-2, the following method can be used for determining the the values ΔV for all teeth and the values of density of the transverse slot fluxes at a height x in any slot:

1. Using the methods of sections 6-9 or 7-10 determine the points C_m and the values V_m and Φ_{tm} at distances y pertaining to the centres of subsequent teeth, and also the values $K_{\varrho m}$, $\cot \varepsilon_m$ and $\cot \beta_m$. The values $\cot \beta_m$ are obtained in G cm/A from Eq. (8-24) as the relation of the sum of the abscissae of points D_m and F_m pertaining to the tooth in question, to the ordinate of point D_m. The values $\cot \varepsilon_m$ are obtained as the inverse values of the derivatives of curve ϱ at points C_m in G cm/A. The values $x\,K_{\varrho n}$ in G are obtained by dividing the horizontal distance of points C_m from one of the closest curves by the difference of the pertaining factors ϱ.

2. According to the value a of the tooth, determine the values $f_3(a)$ and K_ζ from Fig. 4-5 and compute C_a with Eq. (8-19).

3. From the values K_ζ and the pertaining values V_n/h, $K_{\varrho m}$, $\cot \varepsilon_m$ and $\cot \beta_n$ find the values N_m according to Eq. (8-23).

4. From the values C_a and the pertaining values N_m and Φ_{tm} we obtain the values M_m with Eq. (8-27).

5. Write Eq. (8-26) for every tooth (for all indices m occurring).

6. Solve the system of equations of point 5 to obtain the values ΔV_m and $V_m - \Delta V_m$.

7. Find the maximum density of the transverse flux $Z_{\max m}$ of any slot at a height of $x=h$ by multiplying the difference between the values $V_m - \Delta V_m$ of both neighbouring teeth by $0.4\pi/b$.

8. Compute the density of the transverse slot flux Z_m at a height x in the same slot, multiplying $Z_{\max m}$ by $f_1(x/h)$ obtained according to Fig. 8-3 for a given a.

TABL

y cm	$\overline{DE}$ A/cm	$\overline{OF}$ G	$\overline{CK}$ A/cm	V A	$\overline{LC}$ G	Φ_t 10^6 M	cot ε G cm/A
1	2	3	4	5	6	7	8
+12.18	2,210	6,900	0	0	6,900	0.54	∞
+10.44	2,020	15,900	180	710	14,300	1.13	9.0
+ 8.7	1,850	20,000	370	1,460	15,400	1.20	3.8
+ 6.96	1,800	24,000	530	2,090	16,000	1.25	3.0
+ 5.22	2,040	29,800	830	3,270	16,700	1.31	2.6
+ 3.48	2,280	34,000	980	3,900	17,100	1.33	2.2
+ 1.74	2,060	30,900	830	3,300	16,700	1.31	2.6
0	1,870	28,000	690	2,740	16,400	1.27	3.0
— 1.74	1,680	25,000	540	2,150	16,000	1.25	3.0
— 3.48	1,480	22,200	390	1,540	15,500	1.20	3.5
— 5.22	1,280	19,000	220	960	14,900	1.15	9.6
— 6.96	1,100	14,800	90	360	13,300	1.03	26.0
— 8.7	900	9,900	10	40	9,700	0.76	∞
—10.44	700	5,600	3	10	5,400	0.42	∞
—12.18	500	1,600	0	0	1,600	0.12	∞

Example 100. Determine the mean density in part of the transverse slot fluxes due to the saturation of the teeth of a DMP—151 type machine under a load of $I = 300$ A acting upon the upper layer of the armature winding.

In Tables 6-3 and 7-2 we find the values of V and Φ_t computed for different points at a distance of 1.74 cm from one another.

Table 8-1 shows the magnetic relations determined for all these points according to the above method, as well as the pertaining values M.

The character of the change in V and M depending on y is shown in Fig. 8-5.

In order to compute the transverse slot fluxes due to the saturation of the teeth, we must know the values V and M pertaining to points lying at a distance of an entire tooth pitch from one another, i.e. 3.4 cm. Such are, for instance, the points lying at distances from the pole centre as shown in the second column of Table 8-2. The per-

8-1

cot β G cm/A	cot ε + +cot β G cm/A	K_ϱ G	K_ζ	N A/cm	$f_3(a)$	C_a cm^2	M
9	10	11	12	13	14	15	16
4.7	∞	—	3	0	2.13	174	0
9.5	18.5	6,800	3	340	2.13	174	0.188
12.0	15.6	7,300	3	400	2.13	174	0.2
14.0	17.0	7,400	3	340	2.13	174	0.173
16.3	18.9	7,500	3	270	2.13	174	0.125
16.5	18.7	7,500	3	240	2.13	174	0.11
16.5	19.1	7,500	3	260	2.13	174	0.12
16.5	19.5	7,500	3	270	2.13	174	0.129
16.5	19.5	7,400	3	300	2.13	174	0.15
16.5	20.0	7,300	3	310	2.13	174	0.16
16.4	26.0	6,800	3	230	2.13	174	0.123
15.1	41.1	6,400	3	150	2.13	174	0.085
12.5	∞	—	3	0	2.13	174	0
9.8	∞	—	3	0	2.13	174	0
4.7	∞	—	3	0	2.13	174	0

taining values V_m and M_m (see columns 3 and 4 of Table 8-2) can be determined from Fig. 8-5. Columns 5,6 and 7 can be used to compute the values $2V_m - V_{m-1} - V_{m+1}$ (see column 8) and to obtain the following system of equations:

$$\Delta V_1 = 0$$
$$\Delta V_3 = -0.19 \cdot 530 - 0.19 \ (2\Delta V_3 - \Delta V_1 - \Delta V_5)$$
$$\Delta V_5 = -0.17 \cdot 395 - 0.17 \ (2\Delta V_5 - \Delta V_3 - \Delta V_7)$$
$$\Delta V_7 = +0.11 \cdot 2{,}900 - 0.11 \ (2\Delta V_7 - \Delta V_5 - \Delta V_9)$$
$$\Delta V_9 = +0.129 \cdot 20 - 0.129 \ (2\Delta V_9 - \Delta V_7 - \Delta V_{11})$$
$$\Delta V_{11} = -0.16 \cdot 20 - 0.16 \ (2\Delta V_{11} - \Delta V_9 - \Delta\Delta V_{13})$$
$$\Delta V_{13} = -0.085 \cdot 770 - 0.085 \ (2\Delta V_{13} - \Delta V_{11} - \Delta V_{15})$$
$$\Delta V_{15} = 0$$

The solution of the system of equations yields the values ΔV_m in column 9 of Table 8-2.

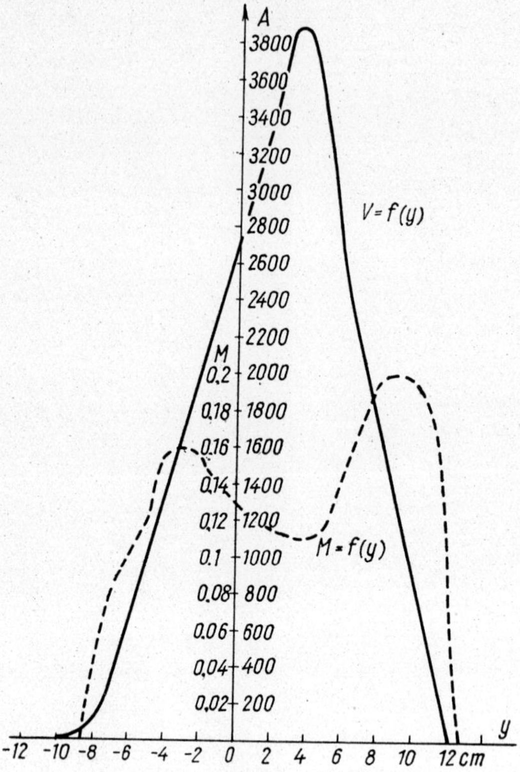

Fig. 8-5

TABLE 8-2

Point	y cm	V_m A	M_m	$2\ V_m$ A	V_{m-1} A	V_{m+1} A	$2\ V_m - V_{m-1} - V_{m+1}$ A	ΔV_m A
1	2	3	4	5	6	7	8	9
1	13.6	0	0	0	0	815	—815	0
3	10.2	815	0.19	1,630	0	2,160	—530	—77
5	6.8	2,160	0.17	4,320	815	3,900	—395	—27
7	3.4	3,900	0.11	7,800	2,160	2,740	+2,900	+262
9	0	2,740	0.129	5,480	3,900	1,560	+20	+28
11	—3.4	1,560	0.16	3,120	2,740	400	—20	—6
13	—6.8	400	0.085	800	1,560	10	—770	—56
15	—10.2	10	0	20	400	0	—380	0
17	—13.6	0	0	0	10	0	—10	0

The points calculated in Table 8-2 are denoted by the numbers 1, 3, 5 (see column 1). Let us perform the same computation for the intermediate points 2, 4, 6. . . to 16, i.e. for another position of the armature in which all teeth are shifted to the half of the tooth pitch. From Fig. 8-5 we obtain similarly the corresponding values V_m and M_m (see columns 3 and 4 of Table 8-3) and compute the values $2V_m - V_{m-1} - V_{m+1}$ (see column 8 in Table 8-3). The solution of the system of equations

$$\begin{aligned}
\Delta V_2 &= 0\\
\Delta V_4 &= -0.2 \cdot 410 - 0.2(2\Delta V_4 - \Delta V_2 - \Delta V_6)\\
\Delta V_6 &= +0.125 \cdot 1{,}885 - 0.125\,(2\Delta V_6 - \Delta V_4 - \Delta V_8)\\
\Delta V_8 &= +0.12 \cdot 1{,}055 - 0.12\,(2\Delta V_8 - \Delta V_6 - \Delta V_{10})\\
\Delta V_{10} &= +0.15 \cdot 25 - 0.15\,(2\Delta V_{10} - \Delta V_8 - \Delta V_{12})\\
\Delta V_{12} &= -0.123 \cdot 185 - 0.123\,(2\Delta V_{12} - \Delta V_{10} - \Delta V_{14})\\
\Delta V_{14} &= 0
\end{aligned}$$

yields the required values ΔV_m (column 9 in Table 8-3).

TABLE 8-3

Point	y cm	V_m A	M_m	$2V_m$ A	V_{m-1} A	V_{m+1} A	$2V_m - V_{-1} - V_{m+1}$ A	ΔV_m A
1	2	3	4	5	6	7	8	9
2	11.9	120	0	240	0	1,530	—1,290	0
4	8.5	1,530	0.2	3,060	120	3,350	—410	—30
6	5.1	3,350	0.125	6,700	1,530	3,285	+1,885	+198
8	1.7	3,285	0.12	6,570	3,350	2,165	+1,055	+122
10	—1.7	2,165	0.15	4,330	3,285	1,020	+25	+15
12	—5.1	1,020	0.123	2,040	2,165	60	—185	—17
14	—8.5	60	0	120	1,020	0	—900	0
16	—11.9	0	0	0	60	0	—60	0

The values $V_m - \Delta V_m$, i.e. the actual drops of potential along the height of the teeth (see column 3 in Table 8-4) can now be calculated for each point 1, 2, 3 to 16 according to columns 3 and 9 of Tables 8-2 and 8-3.

TABLE 8-4

Point	y cm	$V_m - \Delta V_m$ A	$V_{m+1} - \Delta V_{m+1} - (V_{m-1} - \Delta V_{m-1})$	Z_{max} G	Z_m G
1	2	3	4	5	6
1	13.6	0	120	100	94
2	11.9	120	892	790	700
3	10.2	892	1,440	1,270	1,120
4	8.5	1,560	1,295	1,145	1,010
5	6.8	2,187	1,592	1,410	1,250
6	5.1	3,152	1,451	1,290	1,140
7	3.4	3,638	11	10	9
8	1.7	3,163	— 926	— 820	—725
9	0	2,712	—1,013	— 900	—795
10	— 1.7	2,150	—1,146	—1,010	—895
11	— 3.4	1,566	—1,113	— 980	—865
12	— 5.1	1,037	—1,110	— 980	—865
13	— 6.8	456	— 977	— 860	—760
14	— 8.5	60	— 446	— 395	—350
15	—10.2	10	— 60	— 53	— 47
16	—11.9	0	— 10	— 9	— 8

As can be seen from Table 8-4, the values $V_m - \Delta V_m$ hardly differ from the values V_m (column 3 in Tables 8-2 and 8-3) obtained by the method of chapters 6 and 7, where the influence of the transverse slot fluxes on the magnetic relations of the teeth was not taken into account. Since the differences of the pertaining values of the flux density B_δ become even smaller, it can be assumed that these examples clearly demonstrate the correctness and the applicability of the method developed in chapters 6 and 7. Hence, the effect of the transverse slot fluxes can in practice always be neglected, except for the cases discussed in this chapter, where the values to be determined are exactly the transverse slot fluxes.

If the difference of the values $(V_{m+1} - \Delta V_{m+1}) - (V_{m-1} - \Delta V_{m-1})$ are computed for each mth point, we obtain the potential difference between the tops of the teeth neighbouring the slot pertaining to the given point (column 4 in Table 8-4). If these values are multiplied by $0.4\pi/1.42$ we obtain the values Z_{max} according to column 5 for the given slot. In order to determine the mean flux density of that part of the flux which passes through the upper layer of the winding, we proceed from the curves $f_1(x/h, a)$ of Fig. 8-3.

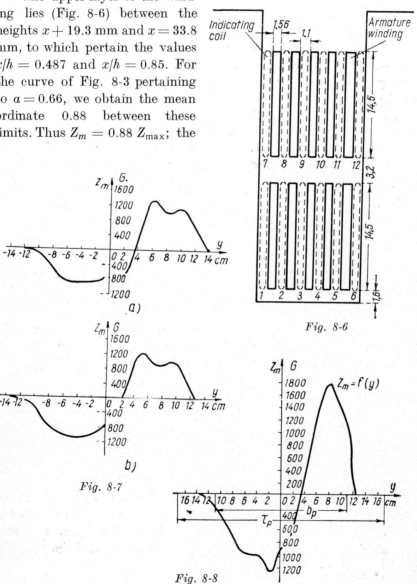

The upper layer of the winding lies (Fig. 8-6) between the heights $x + 19.3$ mm and $x = 33.8$ mm, to which pertain the values $x/h = 0.487$ and $x/h = 0.85$. For the curve of Fig. 8-3 pertaining to $a = 0.66$, we obtain the mean ordinate 0.88 between these limits. Thus $Z_m = 0.88\ Z_{max}$; the

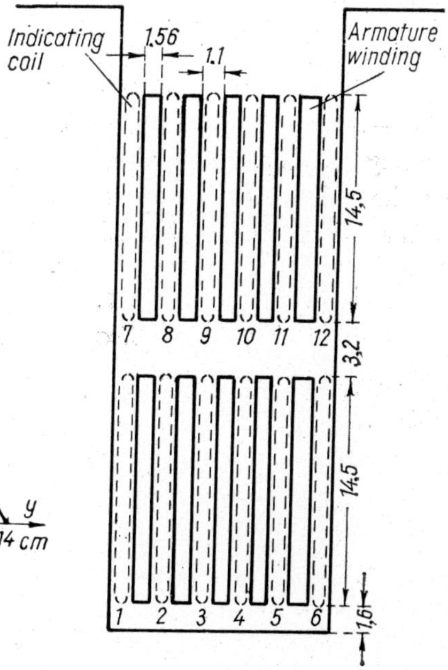

Fig. 8-6

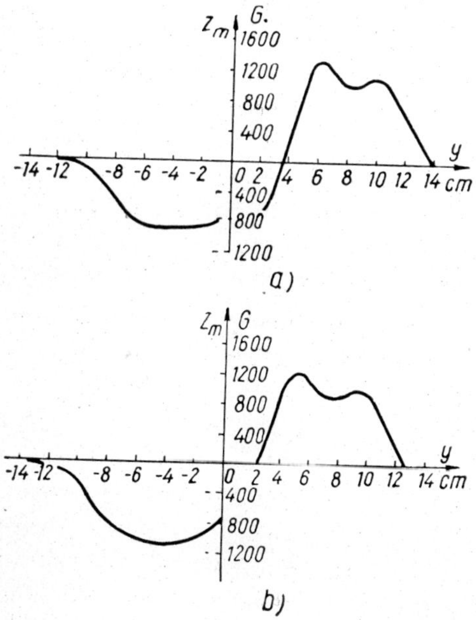

Fig. 8-7

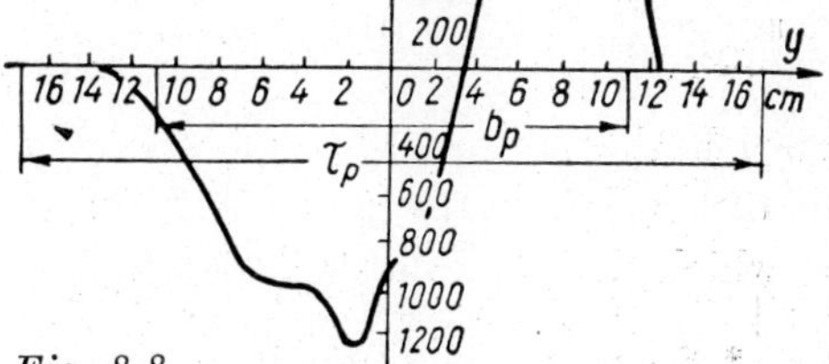

Fig. 8-8

corresponding results are compiled in column 6 of Table 8-4. *We have thus found a perfect solution of the hitherto unsolvable problem of determining the density of the transverse slot fluxes at any arbitrary height.*

The distribution of the induction Z_m over the armature periphery is shown in Fig. 8-7a.

The curve $Z_m = f(y)$ in Fig. 8-8,* showing the distribution of the mean density of the transverse slot fluxes in a traction motor of the DK—103A type in a field-amplifying regime can be obtained in an analogous way. The curve obtained with due regard to the saturation of the pole shoes corresponds to the curve of the distribution of the values V plotted in a dashed line in Fig. 6-12.

8-4. The Corroboration of the Theoretical Results by Experimental Data

With a view to checking the accuracy of the nomographic method developed above, the results obtained theoretically have been verified by collating them with the results of the extremely interesting experiments carried out in 1935 in the research section of the Kirov Factory "Dynamo". Carefully planned experiments have been performed with a DMP—151 type traction motor to find out the values and the distribution of the various slot fluxes.

In the course of these experiments the value of the transverse slot flux due to the saturation of the teeth was also examined. In one of the slots of the armature investigated the winding consisted of a thinner copper (1.56 mm) than the usual (1.81 mm), and twelve measuring loops were installed between the conductors (Fig. 8-6). The other part of the armature winding was of normal size. Thus, when the load current flowed through the armature winding and the excitation winding of the stator, transverse fluxes developed, part of which passed through the said loops. These fluxes (i.e. on another scale their mean density) were measured with a ballistic galvanometer by switching on and off the current.

These measurements were undertaken for cases when the slot was beneath the pole centre and also when at points 1.7, 3.4, 5.1, etc. cm distant from the pole centre in both directions, i.e. at points for which the values of flux density had been computed theoretically.

* See remark on page 169.

The columns of Table 8-5 show the values of the mean density of the transverse fluxes passing through loops 7 to 12 at a current $I = 300$ A, for which the nomographic computation had been performed. The different induction values for the different loops for each point can be explained by the fact that the slot flux measured by them comprises also the transverse components of that part of the longitudinal slot flux which turns toward the tooth walls in the slot (Fig. 1-4). This flux is distributed symmetrically to the axis of the slot, and in one half of the slot its direction coincides with the transverse flux examined, while in the other, it is opposed to it.

TABLE 8-5

Point	y cm	Mean induction of resultant transverse slot flux in the measuring circuit						Mean density of transverse flux	Mean density of transverse flux due to tooth saturation
		7	8	9	10	11	12		
1	2	3	4	5	6	7	8	9	10
1	+13.6	+1,120	+1,030	+1,000	+ 900	+ 760	+ 700	+ 920	— 80
2	+11.9	+1,080	+1,160	+1,240	+1,360	+1,400	+1,400	+1,280	+ 280
3	+10.2	+1,280	+1,400	+1,900	+2,100	+ 2,400	+2,500	+1,940	+ 940
4	+ 8.5	+1,160	+1,380	+1,700	+2,200	+2,480	+2,700	+1,900	+ 900
5	+ 6.8	+ 1,300	+1,440	+1,700	+2,100	+2,350	+2,600	+1,910	+ 910
6	+ 5.1	+1,500	+1,650	+2,000	+2,340	+2,760	+3,100	+2,210	+1,210
7	+ 3.4	+ 760	+1,000	+1,360	+1,900	+2,060	+2,640	+1,610	+ 610
8	+ 1.7	— 40	+ 250	+ 620	+1,000	+1,360	+1,650	+ 810	— 190
9	0	— 420	— 200	+ 120	+ 450	+ 800	+ 900	+ 280	— 720
10	— 1.7	— 660	— 450	— 160	+ 200	+ 700	+ 500	+ 40	— 960
11	— 3.4	— 780	— 470	— 200	+ 140	+ 500	+ 500	— 30	—1,030
12	— 5.1	— 780	— 580	— 300	+ 100	+ 380	+ 600	— 100	—1,100
13	— 6.8	— 500	— 360	— 100	+ 200	+ 450	+ 620	+ 50	— 950
14	— 8.5	— 140	0	+ 200	+ 560	+ 700	+ 860	+ 360	— 640
15	—10.2	+ 440	+ 530	+ 700	+ 880	+1,000	+1,080	+ 770	— 230
16	—11.9	+ 720	+ 730	+ 820	+ 900	+ 940	+1,000	+ 850	— 150
17	—13.6	+ 640	+ 660	+ 760	+ 860	+ 870	+ 900	+ 780	— 220

The influence of these fluxes on the results of the measurements can be eliminated by determining the mean value from the six measuring circuits pertaining to each distance y, whence we obtain the mean induction value of the transverse slot flux crossing the upper layer (column 9).

These magnitudes, however, comprise also the induction values of the transverse leakage flux in the slot due to currents in the armature coils. This flux density

$$\frac{0.4 \cdot 0.75 \cdot 300}{2 \cdot 1.42} \approx 1{,}000 \text{ G}$$

is identical in all slots (except for those lying close to the centre of the commutator zones). By computing this value from column 9 we obtain the required magnitude Z_n.

The values of Z_n obtained experimentally are shown in Fig. 8-7b. This curve is found to coincide almost exactly with the curve of Fig. 8-7a, obtained theoretically.

Though in practice, e.g. for the computation of losses caused by eddy currents due to transverse fluxes, the slight difference between these curves (Fig. 8-7) is insignificant, yet it is very instructive to analyze the causes of this difference. On closer inspection two interesting phenomena can be revealed.

The first thing that merits attention is the fact that the two curves are shifted in relation to one another along the axis of the abscissa (i.e. along the armature periphery). This is easily explained. As is evident from the report on the experiments, the machine investigated was coupled to another DMP—151 type machine in order to equalize the torques. Though both machines were mechanically braked, the inevitable difference between the torques might easily have somewhat displaced the armature examined along its periphery. This might have called forth the said shift along the axis of the abscissae between the curves in Fig. 8-7. Indeed, a certain displacement of the armature was observed during the experiment.

The other interesting phenomenon consists in the following: for the points to the right from the pole centre the values obtained experimentally are somewhat smaller than those obtained nomographically, while for the points lying to the left from the pole centre, the experimental values Z_m are somewhat higher than those obtained nomographically.

This phenomenon, too, can be made clear quite simply. Among the experiments described there was one in which normal excitation occurred, yet there was no current in the armature. Obviously, the transverse slot fluxes, due in this case to the saturation of the teeth, should be distributed symmetrically, owing to the symmetry of the configuration.

Nevertheless, as shown by Table 8-6, the values Z (column 8) obtained as mean values from the results of measuring circuits 7 to 12

TABLE 8-6

y cm	The mean induction of the resultant transverse slot flux in the measuring loop						The mean induction of the transverse slot flux due to the saturation of the teeth
	7	8	9	10	11	12	
1	2	3	4	5	6	7	8
15.3	0	0	0	0	0	0	0
13.6	0	0	0	0	0	0	0
11.9	— 50	0	+ 50	+ 100	+ 200	+ 250	+ 90
10.2	— 120	+ 50	+ 300	+ 550	+ 700	+ 850	+ 390
8.5	0	+ 250	+ 500	+ 800	+1,110	+1,400	+ 670
6.8	+ 280	+ 440	+ 700	+1,000	+1,300	+1,500	+ 870
5.1	+ 420	+ 600	+ 900	+1,200	+1,600	+1,800	+1,080
3.4	0	+ 200	+ 600	+ 950	+1,400	+1,600	+ 790
1.7	— 350	— 200	+ 150	+ 500	+ 800	+1,050	+ 320
0	— 800	— 500	— 250	+ 200	+ 500	+ 600	— 30
— 1.7	—1,060	— 800	— 500	— 100	+ 200	+ 400	— 310
— 3.4	—1,500	—1,000	— 700	— 300	0	+ 220	— 530
— 5.1	—1,900	—1,600	—1,250	— 850	— 500	— 200	—1,040
— 6.8	—1,800	—1,600	—1,300	—1,000	— 700	— 500	—1,150
— 8.5	—1,500	—1,300	—1,000	— 700	— 450	— 250	— 870
—10.2	—1,100	— 940	— 680	— 400	— 200	0	— 550
—11.9	— 400	— 350	— 300	— 200	— 100	0	— 230
—13.6	— 170	— 200	— 160	— 150	— 50	0	— 130
—15.3	— 60	0	— 60	— 50	— 50	0	— 40

(see columns 2 to 7) do not display this symmetry. Though the curve Z_m is not shifted in this case along the periphery (only because no torque occurred in this experiment), it can be revealed that the positive values are somewhat lower than the corresponding negative ones. In reality the mean value of all flux densities measured between $y = -15.3$ and $y = 0$ are -490 G, whereas their mean value between $y = 0$ and $y = 15.3$ equals $+420$ G. At no load this can be explained only by realizing that the magnetic system in the machine examined is, for some technical reasons, not strictly symmetrical. This phenomenon is confirmed also by the result of another experiment described in the same report.

The ordinates of the experimental curve of the longitudinal tooth fluxes (depending on the distance from the pole centre), plotted for the armature at no load but carrying the current of 300 A of the main winding, must be strictly symmetrical. In reality, however, the ordinates on the left side of the axis of the main pole proved to be greater than the ordinates of the points on the right side, lying at the same distance from the axis of the pole.

This symmetry of the magnetic system must manifest itself also under load, which makes it evident why in Fig. 8-7b the values Z_m on the right side of the pole centre are somewhat smaller and those on the left, somewhat greater, than those obtained nomographically.

In order to take into account the said symmetry of the magnetic system, the ordinates of the experimental curve in Fig. 8-7b within the range $y = 0$ to 15.3 should be multiplied by

$$\frac{490 \cdot 2}{490 + 420}$$

and in the range $y = 0$ to -153, by

$$\frac{420 \cdot 2}{490 + 420}$$

If, in order to evaluate the effect of the said shift of the armature, the experimental curve is correspondingly displaced to the right, it is found that the curves of Figs. 8-7a and 8-7b completely coincide in practice, i.e. the results of the nomographic computation coincide with those of the experiments with extreme accuracy.

As has been demonstrated, the distribution of the transverse slot fluxes is, in a high degree, dependent on the distribution of the other magnetic magnitudes and undergo considerable changes with the slightest change in the latter. Consequently, the exact coincidence of the results of the nomographic method with those of the experimental research shows that all the computations carried out so far, yielding the above results, attain a high degree of accuracy. Thus the curve in Fig. 8-7b can be regarded as the final experimental control of the entire system of the nomographic methods developed in this book. It has also been shown that such problems as have defied even the attempts at a theoretical solution by Dreyfus, can be solved rapidly and accurately with the help of simple instructions, without requiring particular qualification. All this goes to show the vast possibilites inherent in the nomographic method of computing complicated magnetic circuits.

CHAPTER NINE

THE EXACT NOMOGRAPHIC DETERMINATION OF LOSSES DUE TO EDDY CURRENTS AND HYSTERESIS IN THE ROTATING ELECTRICAL MACHINES

9-1. Theoretical Considerations Underlying the Nomographic Determination of Different Iron Losses

The overwhelming majority of the usually applied formulae for computing losses due to eddy currents in the teeth of the armature are based on the assumption that the flux density over the circumference of the armature is distributed sinusoidally and that the teeth have rectangular configurations, their form being

$$L_{et} = A_{et}\, B_{\max}^2 f^2 \quad [\text{W/kg}] \tag{9-1}$$

where

f = magnetization frequency in the armature,

A_{et} = constant depending on the quality, the thickness and the character of the treatment of the armature steel,

$B_{\max}$ = flux density in the mid-section of the tooth under the pole centre. The total flux of the slot pitch is assumed to pass through the tooth.

In reality, however, flux Φ_τ of the tooth pitch does not change sinusoidally, but according to a complicated curve. In addition, part of the flux crosses the slot connected in parallel to the tooth and is $0.4\pi\, H_x b' l$ at a height x. With respect to the eddy currents in the teeth, the error involved is small if we presume that the slot flux has a constant value

$$0.4\,\pi \frac{b' l}{h} \int_0^h H_x\, dx$$

throughout. This value equals Φ_s/ζ in which Φ_s can readily be determined from the nomogram (cf. chapter 4).

The flux density of the tooth at a distance x from the slot neck is

$$\left(\Phi_\tau - \frac{\Phi_s}{\zeta}\right)\frac{1}{b_x \gamma l}$$

Suppose that the actual distribution curve of this value over the armature periphery is divided into sections having a length Δy. Let this be so small as to permit the assumption that the flux density changes linearly during the time

$$\Delta T = \frac{\Delta y}{2 f \tau_p} \tag{9-2}$$

required for the transition from some nth section to an $(n+1)$th. Then the losses $L_{\Delta Tt}$ due to the eddy currents in the tooth during ΔT will be

$$L_{\Delta Tt} = C \int_0^h \left[\frac{\left(\Phi_\tau - \frac{\Phi_s}{\zeta}\right)_n - \left(\Phi_\tau - \frac{\Phi_s}{\zeta}\right)_{n+1}}{b_x \gamma l \Delta T}\right]^2 b_x \gamma l dx \tag{9-3}$$

where C = constant.

Considering further that the value

$$\int_0^h \frac{dx}{b_x \gamma l}$$

differs but slightly from

$$\frac{h(1+\varrho)}{2 b_0 \gamma l}$$

then Eq. (9-3) can be replaced by the formula

$$L_{\Delta Tt} = \frac{C b_0 \gamma l h(1+\varrho)}{2}\left[\frac{\left(\Phi_\tau - \frac{\Phi_s}{\zeta}\right)_n - \left(\Phi_\tau - \frac{\Phi_s}{\zeta}\right)_{n+1}}{\Delta T b_0 \gamma l}\right]^2 \tag{9-4}$$

Eq. (9-4) can be related to the magnitudes B_τ and B_s/ζ. Here the following circumstances should be taken into account.

In the previous chapter it has been presumed for the sake of simplicity that the values Φ_τ and Φ_s can be obtained by multiplying B_τ and B_s, taken for the middle of the tooth pitch, by $b_0 \gamma l$. The error here committed is negligible. Nevertheless, in certain conditions, this assumption may involve impermissible errors when determining the losses due to eddy currents in the teeth. This follows from the following considerations.

Suppose the flux density $B_\tau - B_s/\zeta$ changes considerably over the armature periphery. Then

$$\left[\frac{\left(B_\tau - \frac{B_s}{\zeta}\right)_n - \left(B_\tau - \frac{B_s}{\zeta}\right)_{n+1}}{\Delta T}\right]^2$$

will be extremely high, even if Δy and ΔT are chosen to be very low.

In the extreme case

$$\frac{\left(B_\tau - \frac{B_s}{\zeta}\right)_n - \left(B_\tau - \frac{B_s}{\zeta}\right)_{n+1}}{\Delta T} = \infty$$

Yet it is evident that the value

$$\frac{\left(\Phi_\tau - \frac{\Phi_s}{\zeta}\right)_n - \left(\Phi_\tau - \frac{\Phi_s}{\zeta}\right)_{n+1}}{\Delta T}$$

on which the losses at a given point depend, is a finite value, because flux $\Phi_\tau - \Phi_s/\zeta$ is, in fact, the integral of all values $(B_\tau - B_s)\zeta/\gamma l$ taken from section b_0. Thus, even if

$$\frac{d\left(B_\tau - \frac{B_s}{\zeta}\right)}{dy} = \infty$$

the flux $\Phi_\tau - \Phi_s/\zeta$ may change only during the time corresponding to the section of length b_0.

It follows that for exact calculation, the mean value

$$B'_\tau = \frac{1}{b_0} \int_{y-b_0/2}^{y+b_0/2} B_\tau \, dy \qquad (9\text{-}5$$

should be taken as $\Phi_\tau/b_0\gamma l$ pertaining to any arbitrary abscissa y.

The length of the integrated section is b_0. Similarly, the mean value

$$B'_s = \frac{1}{b_0} \int_{y-b_0/2}^{y+b_0/2} B_s \, dy \tag{9-6}$$

Thus, instead of Eq. (9-4), we get

$$L_{\Delta Tt} = \frac{C\, b_0 \gamma\, lh(1+\varrho)}{2} \left[\frac{\left(B'_\tau - \frac{B'_s}{\zeta}\right)_n - \left(B'_\tau - \frac{B'_s}{\zeta}\right)_{n+1}}{\Delta T} \right]^2 \tag{9-7}$$

The mean losses in one tooth will be

$$\frac{1}{k} \sum_1^k L_{\Delta Tt}$$

if k is the number of sections, into which the curve of the flux density distribution $B'_\tau - B'_s/\zeta = f(y)$ along one pole pitch is divided. If G_t is the weight of the steel of a tooth, the specific losses in W/kg will be

$$L_{et} = \frac{1}{G_t\, k} \sum_1^k L_{\Delta Tt} \tag{9-8}$$

If it is assumed, as has been done in deducting Eq. (9-1), that the flux density in the mid-section of the tooth of width b_1 changes according to the law

$$B_{\max} \sin \frac{\pi y}{\tau_p}$$

and that the tooth flux is equal in every cross section, then the flux density in the largest tooth cross-section equals

$$\frac{b_1}{b_0} B_{\max} \sin \frac{\pi y}{\tau_p}$$

For $\Delta T = 0$ we get, instead of Eq. (9-8), the formula

$$L_{et} = \frac{C}{G_t} b_0 \frac{b_1^2 (1+\varrho)}{2\, b_0^2} \gamma\, lh \frac{1}{\tau_p} \int_0^{\tau_p} \left(\frac{d\, B_{\max} \sin \frac{\pi y}{\tau_p}}{dt} \right)^2 dy = A_{et}\, B_{\max}^2 f^2 \tag{9-8a}$$

In the deduction of Eq. (9-1) it is also presumed that the tooth has parallel walls. In this case, i.e. when $\varrho = 1$ and $b_0 = b_1$, the formula (9-8a) yields the following expression

$$L_{et} = \frac{1}{G_t} C\, b_1 \gamma\, l h \frac{1}{\tau_p} \int_0^{\tau_p} \left(\frac{d\, B_{\max} \sin \frac{\pi y}{\tau_p}}{dt} \right)^2 dy \tag{9-8b}$$

Considering that, according to Eq. (9-2)

$$\frac{d\, B_{\max} \sin \frac{\pi y}{\tau_p}}{dt} = B_{\max} \cos \frac{\pi y}{\tau_p} \; \frac{d \frac{\pi y}{\tau_p}}{dt} = 2\pi f\, B_{\max} \cos \frac{\pi y}{\tau_p} \tag{9-9}$$

we obtain that

$$A_{et}\, B_{\max}^2 f^2 = \frac{1}{G_t} C\, b_1 \gamma\, l h\, 2\pi^2 f^2 B_{\max}^2 \tag{9-10}$$

Expressing

$$\frac{1}{G_t} C \gamma\, l h$$

by Eq. (9-10), we obtain, for the general case not Eq. (9-8) but the formula

$$L_{et} = \frac{A_{et}(1+\varrho)\, b_0}{4\pi^2 b_1 \Delta T^2} \; \frac{1}{k} \sum_1^k \left[\left(B'_\tau - \frac{B'_s}{\zeta} \right)_n - \left(B'_\tau - \frac{B'_s}{\zeta} \right)_{n+1} \right]^2 \tag{9-11}$$

Example 101. In Fig. 6-12 we find the curves $B_\delta = f(y)$ and $V = f(y)$ for a traction motor of type DK—103A in a condition of over-excitation, plotted for the case when the effect of saturation in the pole shoes is neglected (solid lines), and for the case when it is taken into account (dashed lines).

According to the data of V. A. Shilovski, who has undertaken the nomographic investigation of this motor, we have:

$b_0 = 1.93$ cm, $\varrho = 1.4$, $b_1 = 1.635$ cm, $h = 4.1$ cm, $f = 30$ Hz, $\tau_p = 34.6$ cm, $\tan \beta = 1.4$, $\tau_s = 3.21$ cm;

Δy is selected to equal 2 cm. Thus

$$\Delta T = 9.67 \cdot 10^{-4} \quad \text{and} \quad \frac{b_0(1+\varrho)}{4\pi^2 b_1 \Delta T^2} = 7.69 \cdot 10^4$$

$$B_\tau = B_\delta \frac{\tau_s}{y\, b_0} = 1.75\, B_\delta$$

and

$$B_s = \tan\beta \frac{V}{h} = \frac{1.4\,V}{4.1}$$

The computations necessary for the nomographic determination of the value

$$\sum_1^k \left[\left(B'_\tau - \frac{B'_s}{\zeta}\right)_n - \left(B'_\tau - \frac{B'_s}{\zeta}\right)_{n+1}\right]^2$$

are given in Table 9-1, based on the dashed curves $B_\delta = f(y)$ and $V = f(y)$ of Fig. 6-12.

TABLE 9-1

y cm	B_τ G	$\frac{B_s}{\zeta}$ G	$\left(B'_\tau - \frac{B'_s}{\zeta}\right)$ G	$\left[\left(B'_\tau - \frac{B'_s}{\zeta}\right)_n - \left(B'_\tau - \frac{B'_s}{\zeta}\right)_{n+1}\right]^2$ 10^6 G^2
1	2	3	4	5
−16	125	0	125	0.02
−14	875	0	1,000	0.77
−12	3,070	0	3,350	5.55
−10	8,750	10	8,650	28.2
− 8	13,100	40	12,900	18.2
− 6	14,800	110	14,700	3.24
− 4	15,500	200	15,300	0.36
− 2	16,100	280	15,820	0.27
0	16,600	370	16,230	0.17
+ 2	17,200	470	16,730	0.25
+ 4	17,500	570	16,930	0.04
+ 6	16,800	450	16,420	0.26
+ 8	15,800	260	15,440	0.96
+10	13,500	80	13,200	5.03
+12	4,430	0	5,050	66.7
+14	1,100	0	1,230	14.65
+16	125	0	125	1.22
				$\sum_1^{17} = 145.89$

On the basis of this value we get by applying Eq. (9-11) the following:

$$L_{et} = A_{et}\, 7.69 \cdot 10^4 \frac{145.89 \cdot 10^6}{17} = 6{,}600 \cdot 10^8\, A_{et} \;\; [\mathrm{W/kg}]$$

If L_{et} is computed with Eq. (9-1), then

$$L_{et} = A_{et}\; 19{,}600^2 \cdot 30^2 = 3{,}460 \cdot 10^8\; A_{et} \;\; [\mathrm{W/kg}]$$

provided we realize that under the pole centre $B_{\max} = 16{,}600\; b_0/b_1 = 19{,}600$ G.

Thus with the nomographic method we can find the additional losses which in our example constitute 91 per cent of those computed with the usual method, i.e. with Eq. (9-1).

TABLE 9-2

y	B_τ	$\frac{B_S}{\zeta}$	$\left(B'_\tau - \frac{B'_S}{\zeta}\right)$	$\left[\left(B'_\tau - \frac{B'_S}{\zeta}\right)_n - \left(B'_\tau - \frac{B'_S}{\zeta}\right)_n\right]^2$
cm	G	G	G	10^6 G^2
1	2	3	4	5
+ 4	17,500	570	16,930	0.04
+ 6	17,800	680	17,120	0.04
+ 8	17,800	680	17,000	0.02
+10	16,700	430	15,870	1.28
+12	5,800	40	6,560	87.00
+14	1,350	0	1,700	23.70
+16	320	0	320	1.00
				$\sum_{1}^{17}{}' = 171.01$

Table 9-2 refers to the case when the saturation of the pole shoes is neglected. For points lying further right from point $y = +\,4$ cm., i.e. where the saturation of the pole shoe has an influence, analogous computations have been performed. The value obtained is

$$L_{et} = A_{et}\, 7.69 \cdot 10^4 \frac{171.01}{17} = 7{,}730 \cdot 10^8\, A_{et} \;\; [\mathrm{W/kg}]$$

Instead of the very accurate formula (9-11) a simpler equation can be deduced which is sufficiently accurate for the overwhelming majority of the cases. This equation can be obtained on the strength of the following considerations.

If the values $B'_\tau - B'_s/\zeta$ are replaced by the values $B_\tau - B_s/\zeta$ increased losses due to the eddy currents are obtained, as has been pointed out above. If, however, Δy is chosen not to be less than b_0, no serious error can be committed in determining these losses. On the other hand, this error may be somewhat reduced by replacing the values $B_\tau - B_s/\zeta$ by somewhat lower values of $B_\tau - B_s = B_0$ which can easily be determined nomographically. Thus, instead of Eq. (9-11), we obtain

$$L_{et} = A_{et} \frac{(1+\varrho)\, b_0}{4\pi^2 b_1 \Delta T^2} \frac{1}{k} \sum_1^k (B_{0n} - B_{0n+1})^2 \tag{9-12}$$

The collation of the results of Ex. 101 with those of Ex. 102 (p. 249) shows that the simplified method for the nomographic computation of tooth losses due to eddy currents, with Eq. (9-12) is sufficiently accurate for practical purposes.

The losses due to hysteresis in the teeth are computed nowadays with formulae of the following shape:

$$L_{ht} = A_{ht} f B_{\max}^m \tag{9-13}$$

where

A_{ht} = constant,
$B_{\max}$ = maximum flux density in the centre of the tooth,
m = value of exponent.

If we find $B_{0\max}$ out of all values B_0, then according to Eq. (9-13) the value $B_{0\max} b_0/b_1$ will be $B_{\max}$ in Eq. (9-13):

$$L_{ht} = A_{ht} f \left(B_{0\max} \frac{b_0}{b_1} \right)^m \tag{9-14}$$

The losses due to eddy currents in the armature yoke can be determined on the strength of the following considerations.

Examine the part of a yoke, related to one tooth pitch. In the commutation zone the value of flux density in the yoke will be $\Phi/2b_a\gamma l$, where b_a is the width of the armature yoke. If the flux of the commutating pole is neglected, this flux density may be regarded as constant, provided the pertaining tooth is displaced within the range where $\Phi_\tau = 0$. On approaching the edge of the pole, the flux of the tooth pitch begins to increase, and during the further displacement of the tooth to the section Δy, the flux increases to some $\Phi_{\tau 1}$ value. Hence the flux density in the armature yoke decreases during ΔT, pertaining to Δy, by $\Phi_{\tau 1}/b_a \gamma l$ and losses, due to eddy currents, of the value $C'(\Phi_{\tau 1}/b_a \gamma l \Delta T)^2$ arise, where C' is a constant. If we choose $\Delta y \geq b_0$, then we may presume without incurring any serious error that $\Phi_{\tau 1} = B_{\delta 1} \Delta y l$, whence the losses will be

$$C' \left(\frac{B_{\delta 1} \Delta y}{\gamma b_a \Delta T} \right)^2$$

If the corresponding tooth is shifted under the nth section, the losses will be

$$L_{\Delta T a} = C' \left(\frac{B_{\delta n} 2 \tau_p f}{\gamma b_a} \right)^2 \qquad (9\text{-}15)$$

because

$$\frac{\Delta y}{\Delta T} = \frac{2 \tau_p}{T} = 2 \tau_p f \qquad (9\text{-}16)$$

Thus the mean specific losses in W/kg will be

$$L_{ea} = \frac{1}{G_{at} k} \sum_1^k L_{\Delta T a} \qquad (9\text{-}17)$$

where G_{at} = that part of the yoke which pertains to the tooth pitch.

The formulae usually applied for the computation of these losses have the shape

$$L_{ea} = A_{ea} f^2 B^2_{a\max} \qquad (9\text{-}18)$$

where

A_{ea} = constant,

$B_{a\max}$ = maximum flux density of the yoke, changing sinusoidally from the pole centre to the next pole centre.

With this assumption B_δ would change according to the law

$$B_{a\max} \frac{\gamma b_a \pi}{\tau_p} \sin \frac{\pi y}{\tau_p}$$

With regard to Eq. (9-15), the formula (9-17) could be written for $\Delta y \approx 0$ in the following form:

$$L_{ea} = \frac{C'}{\tau_p G_{at}} \int_0^{\tau_p} \left(\frac{B_{a\max} b_a \pi}{\tau_p} \frac{2 \tau_p f}{b_a} \sin \frac{\pi y}{\tau_p} \right)^2 dy \qquad (9\text{-}17a)$$

i. e.

$$L_{ea} = \frac{C' B^2_{a\max} f^2}{G_{at}} 2\pi^2 \tag{9-17b}$$

By equating Eq. (9-18) and Eq. (9-17b), for the general case we obtain, with due regard to (9-15), not Eq. (9-17) but

$$L_{ea} = A_{ea} f^2 2 \left(\frac{\tau_p}{\pi b_a}\right)^2 \sum_1^k \frac{B^2_{\delta n}}{\gamma^2} \frac{1}{k} \tag{9-19}$$

The other kind of steel losses can be obtained in a similar way. Let us investigate, for instance, the ways and means of determining the losses caused by eddy currents created under the pole by the tooth pulsations of flux density in the air gap.

These losses are usually computed with the formula

$$L_{ep} = A_{ep} B^2 \tag{9-20}$$

where

A_{ep} = constant depending on the configuration and rotation per minute,

B = mean radial component of flux density, assumed to be constant over the entire pole arc.

With the nomographic method it is easy to estimate in this formula the actual flux density distribution over the armature periphery. Since B, occurring in Eq. (9-20), recurs in the nomographic method as $B_\delta = B_\tau b_0 \gamma / \tau_s$, i.e. as value to be determined for each tooth pitch in the computation of a machine, we only have to compute the value

$$\frac{1}{k'} \sum_1^{k'} B^2_{\delta n}$$

where

k' = the number of sections pertaining to the pole arc, i.e.

$$k' = \frac{b_p}{\Delta y} \tag{9-21}$$

and to substitute it into Eq. (9-20) instead of B^2.

Thus we get

$$L_{ep} = A_{ep} \left(\frac{b_0 \gamma}{\tau_s}\right)^2 \frac{1}{k'} \sum_1^{k'} B^2_{\tau n} \tag{9-22}$$

9-2. *Approach to the Practical Determination of Different Iron Losses*

A) Losses due to eddy currents in the teeth

1. Proceed from one of the generally adopted formulae in the theory of electrical machines for the computation of losses due to eddy currents having the structure of Eq. (9-1) and compute therefrom the constant A_{et}.

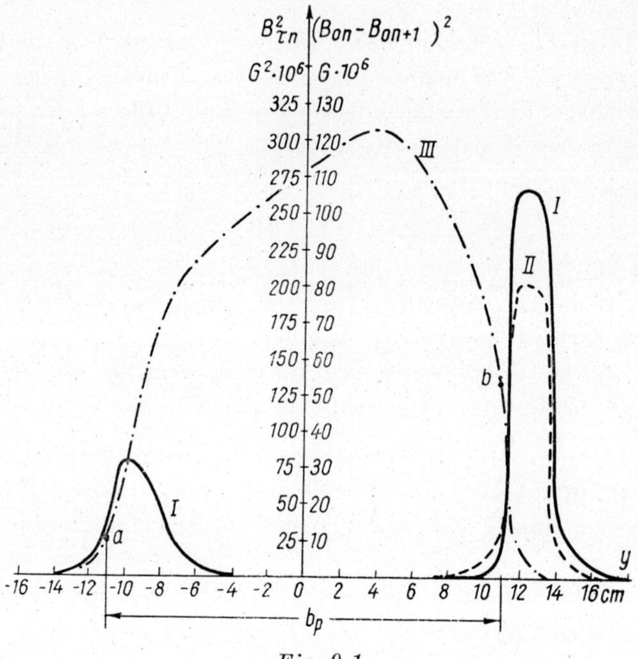

Fig. 9-1

2. According to the method of sections 6-9 and 7-10 construct a curve of flux density distribution in the maximum cross-section of the tooth along the pole pitch, i.e. curve $B_0 = f(y)$.

3. Determine the frequency of remagnetization f and, dividing the curve $B_0 = f(y)$ into k sections of Δy width, determine with Eq. (9-2) the value ΔT.

4. On the curve $B_0 = f(y)$ determine the values B_{0n}, pertaining to the chosen sections Δy, and compute with Eq. (9-12) the losses in the teeth due to eddy currents.

Example. 102. Table 9-3 contains the results of computations undertaken with Eq. (9-12). The starting point was the curve $B_0 = f(y)$ of Fig. 6-12*.

TABLE 9-3

y cm	Saturation in pole shoe neglected		Saturation in pole shoe taken into account	
	B_{0n} G	$(B_{0n}-B_{0n+1})^2$ 10^6 G^2	B_{0n} G	$(B_{0n}-B_{0n+1})^2$ 10^6 G^2
1	2	3	4	5
—16	125	0.02	125	0.02
—14	875	0.57	875	0.57
—12	3,070	4.83	3,070	4.83
—10	8,740	32.30	8,740	32.30
— 8	13,040	18.55	13,040	18.56
— 6	14,630	2.54	14,630	2.54
— 4	15,200	0.33	15,200	0.33
— 2	15,680	0.23	15,680	0.23
0	16,050	0.14	16,050	0.14
+ 2	16,500	0.20	16,500	0.20
+ 4	16,650	0.02	16,650	0.02
+ 6	16,780	0.02	16,120	0.28
+ 8	16,780	0	15,400	0.52
+10	16,050	0.53	13,380	4.10
+12	5,740	106.00	4,430	80.50
+14	1,350	19.40	1,100	11.10
+16	320	1.06	125	0.96
		$\sum_{1}^{17} = 186.74$		$\sum_{1}^{17} = 157.19$

In columns 2 and 3 the values B_{0n} and $(B_{0n} - B_{0n+1})^2$ are given for the case when the saturation of the pole shoe is neglected, in columns 4 and 5, for the case when it is taken into account. On Fig. 9-1, the curves I and II show the distribution of the values $(B_{0n} - B_{0n+1})^2$, i.e. the proportional values of losses due to eddy currents over the

* See note on p. 186.

armature periphery. Curve I corresponds to column 3, curve II, to column 5 of Table 9-3. As can be seen from these curves, eddy current losses occur actually under the edges of the pole only, whereas the bulk of losses is beneath the edge closest to the teeth in which we have the maximum flux density. The magnitude of specific losses with due regard to the saturation of the pole shoe will be obtained with the simplified method as being by 157.19/145.89 = 1.08 more than with the exact method (see Table 9-1).

If the saturation is neglected the difference will be 186.74/171.01 = = 1.09 (see Table 9-2).

B) Losses due to hysteresis in the teeth

1. Proceed from one of the generally adopted formulae for the computation of losses due to hysteresis in the teeth having a structure of the formula (9-13), and determine therefrom the constant A_{ht}.

2. On the curve $B_0 = f(y)$ we find $B_{0\max}$ and with Eq. (9-14) we compute the hysteresis losses.

C) Losses due to eddy currents in the armature yoke

1. Proceed from one of the generally adopted formulae for computing the losses due to eddy currents in the armature yoke having the structure of Eq. (9-18), and determine therefrom the constant A_{ea}.

2. With the method of sections 6-9 and 7-10 construct the curve of flux density distribution B_τ along the pole pitch, i.e. the curve $B_\tau = f(y)$, and divide it by k sections of Δy width.

On the curve $B_\tau = f(y)$ find the values $B_{\tau n}$ pertaining to the selected sections Δy, and compute with Eq. (9-19) the eddy current losses. In this formula the width of the armature yoke will be taken as b_a.

Example 103. Compute the difference between L_{ea} determined nomographically with Eq. (9-19) and L_{ea} determined with the usual method, i.e. with Eq. (9-18) in a DK—103A type machine in the case of over-excitation and with due regard to saturation in the pole shoe.

According to Table 9-1

$$\frac{1}{k}\sum_1^k B_\tau^2 = \frac{1}{17}\sum_1^{17} B_\tau^2 = \frac{25{,}962 \cdot 10^5}{17} = 1{,}525 \cdot 10^5$$

For $\tau_p = 34.6$ cm we obtain with Eq. (9-19)

$$L_{ea} = \frac{A_{ea} f^2}{b_a^2} 2 \left(\frac{34.6}{\pi}\right)^2 \cdot 1{,}525 \cdot 10^5 \left(\frac{b_0}{\tau_t}\right)^2 = 372 \cdot 10^8 \frac{A_{ea} f^2}{b_a^2} \left(\frac{b_0}{\tau_t}\right)^2$$

With Eq. (9-18) compute $B_{a\max} = \Phi/2b_a\gamma l$ where Φ is the flux of the pole pitch. In this case

$$\Phi = \sum_1^k B_\tau \Delta y \gamma l \left(\frac{b_0}{\tau_t}\right)$$

From Table 9-1

$$\sum_1^{17} B_\tau = 175{,}375$$

whence

$$B_{a\max} = \frac{175{,}375 \cdot 2\gamma l}{2 b_a \gamma l} \left(\frac{b_0}{\tau_t}\right) = \frac{175{,}375}{b_a} \left(\frac{b_0}{\tau_t}\right)$$

Thus, from Eq. (9-18) we have

$$L_{ea} = \frac{A_{ea} f^2}{b_a^2} 175{,}375^2 \left(\frac{b_0}{\tau_t}\right)^2 = 306 \cdot 10^8 \frac{A_{ea} f^2}{b_a^2} \left(\frac{b_0}{\tau_t}\right)^2$$

The magnitude of the losses due to eddy currents in the armature are actually greater by 20 per cent than that obtained with the usual methods. The curve $B_\tau^2 = f(y)$, whose area is proportional to the losses, is plotted in Fig. 9-1 as curve III.

D) Losses due to hysteresis in the armature

1. The usually applied formulae used for computing losses due to hysteresis yield accurate results because the value $B_{a\max} = \Phi/2b_a\gamma l$ in them is in reality the maximum of all the values B_a.

E) Losses due to eddy currents created in the pole by the pulsations of the flux density in the air gap

1. Proceeding from one of the generally adopted formulae for computing the said losses having the structure of Eq. (9-20), determine the constant A_{ep}.

2. Divide the part of the curve $B_\tau = f(y)$ beneath the pole arc into k' sections of Δy width and determine on it the values $B_{\tau n}$ pertaining to the chosen $\Delta y'$ values.

3. Compute with Eq. (9-22) the losses due to eddy currents.

Example 104. Compute the difference between L_{ep} determined nomographically with Eq. (9-22) and L_{ep} determined with the usually applied formula (9-20) in a DK—103A type machine for the case of pole over-excitation with due regard to the saturation of the pole shoe. We assume that $k' = 11$. Sum up from Table 9-1 the values B_τ^2 pertaining to the points from — 11 to + 11 cm, i.e. to the part of curve III in Fig. 9-1 which lies between points a and b. We get

$$\frac{1}{11}\sum_{1}^{11} B_\tau^2 = \frac{2{,}565 \cdot 10^6}{11} = 233 \cdot 10^6$$

Hence, according to Eq. (9-22)

$$L_{ep} = A_{ep}\left(\frac{b_0\gamma}{\tau_s}\right)^2 233 \cdot 10^6$$

According to Eq. (9-20) B is taken in the computation for that value of B_δ which occurs under the pole centre. From Table 9-1 this value can be read as 16,600 $b_0\gamma/\tau_s$.

Hence, according to Eq. (9-20), we get

$$L_{ep} = A_{ep}\left(\frac{b_0\gamma}{\tau_s}\right)^2 277 \cdot 10^6$$

The nomographic computation yields a loss less by 16 per cent than that obtained with the usually applied formulae, because owing to armature reaction and to saturation, the mean value of B_τ^2 is lower than $B_\tau^2 = 277 \cdot 10^6$ beneath the pole centre.

The application of the nomographic method permits the introduction into formulae relating to iron losses in electrical machine, of such factors as are characteristic both of the exact flux density distribution in the iron and of their influence upon the distribution of the iron losses. What is more, we can obtain, as for instance in Fig. 9-1, an accurate picture of the actual distribution of the losses, of the point where the values reach the maximum and of what the maximum value depends on. It is thus possible to study the relationship between the losses and the factors affecting them. This being so, the relationships can be made use of to reduce the losses.

The deduction of all formulae in this section are based on the assumption that the damping effect of the eddy currents can be neglected, which is allowable in case of sheet iron. The next section will be devoted to the creation of eddy currents whose damping effect must not be neglected.

9-3. Theoretical Consideration Underlying the Nomographic Determination of Losses Due to Eddy Currents in Copper Conductors

According to the usual method, the "additional copper losses" due to eddy currents are computed by dividing the flux density curve into harmonics. As mentioned in chapter 1, this method is rather inaccurate and fails to visualize the problem. In addition to this, by breaking up the curve of flux density distribution into harmonics, we are deprived of the possibility of determining the actual distribution of the eddy currents and of influencing it by changing the form of the machine parts in places where it would be most effective.

Thus, in order to avoid the method of harmonic analysis, the author has developed the following method for determining eddy currents in the copper conductors. This method is based on the system of nomograms and enables us to compute the magnitudes of these currents readily and with great accuracy, and to find their exact distribution, depending on the form and dimensions of the different parts of the machine.

Let us examine first the dependence of the eddy currents on the flux density responsible for them. Let it be assumed that a uniform magnetic flux, parallel to the plane of a plate along its length, penetrates this plate of infinite width, length and thickness d, consisting of some conductive substance. Any change in this flux in time creates eddy currents reacting to it and changing its magnitude and distribution both in time and in space.

Let us suppose that our plate is divided into elements of 1 cm length and dx height (Fig. 9-2).

Denoting the density of the eddy current in A/cm by $\jmath$ at a given place and the instantaneous value of the flux density by B, and considering that the magnetic permeability μ of the substance is constant, we get the equation

$$\frac{1}{\mu}\frac{dB}{dx} = -0.4\pi\jmath \qquad (9\text{-}23)$$

If, instead of a solid conductive substance, we have conductors separ-

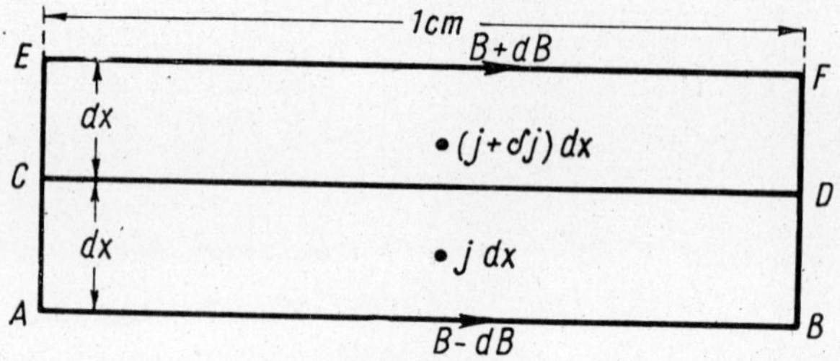

Fig. 9-2

ated from one another by an insulating layer, then instead of the density j, we can introduce the notion of mean density ja/b, where the factor a/b characterizes the decrease of the mean density of the eddy current on account of the uneven spatial distribution of the conductive substance.

In this case Eq. (9-23) will assume the following form

$$\frac{1}{\mu}\frac{dB}{dx} = -0.4\,\pi\frac{a}{b}j \tag{9-24}$$

By expressing dj/dx from Eq. (9-24), we obtain, on the strength of Maxwell's law, the following formula

$$\frac{d^2B}{dx^2} = \frac{\pi^2 T}{d^2}\frac{dB}{dt} \tag{9-25}$$

where

$$T = \frac{0.4\,a\,\lambda_e\,d^2\,\mu\,10^{-4}}{b\,\pi} \tag{9-26}$$

and λ_e = the specific electrical conductivity of the substance.

Let us assume that the solution B of the formula (9-25) can be expressed in the form of some function

$$B = B'(t) + B''(t, x) \tag{9-27}$$

where

B' = the original field,

B'' = the reaction of the eddy currents.

Since

$$\int_0^d j dx = 0 \tag{9-28}$$

we can write

$$B''(t,x) = \sum_{1}^{\infty} B''(t) \sin \frac{m \pi x}{d} \tag{9-29}$$

where m characterizes the number of harmonics to which the curve of flux density distribution $B''(t,x)$ is divided at the height x. Transforming Eqs. (9-29), (9-27) and (9-25), we obtain

$$\sum_{1}^{\infty} \left[T \frac{dB''(t)}{dt} + m^2 B''(t) \right] \sin \frac{m \pi x}{d} = - T \frac{dB'(t)}{dt} \tag{9-30}$$

Since

$$- T \frac{dB'(t)}{dt} = - T \frac{dB'(t)}{dt} \frac{4}{\pi} \sum_{1}^{\infty} \frac{1}{m'} \sin \frac{m' \pi x}{d} \tag{9-31}$$

where the number of m' characterizes the odd harmonics, we obtain

$$m = m' \tag{9-32}$$

i.e. the even harmonics are eliminated from the equation. Therefore

$$T \frac{dB''(t)}{dt} + m'^2 B''(t) = - \frac{4T}{\pi m'} \frac{dB'(t)}{dt} \tag{9-33}$$

The solution of this differential equation will be

$$B''(t) = e^{-\frac{m'^2(t-t_0)}{T}} \left[C - \frac{4}{\pi m'} \int_{t_0}^{t} \frac{dB'(t)}{dt} e^{\frac{m'^2(t-t_0)}{T}} dt \right] \tag{9-34}$$

The transformation of Eqs. (9-34), (9-32), (9-29), (9-27) and (9-24) yields

$$j = - \frac{10\,b}{a \pi \mu d} \sum_{1}^{\infty} e^{-\frac{m'^2(t-t_0)}{T}} \left[C \frac{m' \pi}{4} - \int_{t_0}^{t} \frac{dB'(t)}{dt} e^{\frac{m'^2(t-t_0)}{T}} dt \right] \cos \left(\frac{m' \pi x}{d} \right) \tag{9-35}$$

The first member in brackets of Eq. (9-35) obviously corresponds to the current that still exists at the moment $t = t_0$ as a result of the change in flux density in the preceding period, and diminishes under the effect of active resistance. The other member corresponds to the current that begins to increase again at the moment $t = t_0$ owing to new changes dB'/dt in flux density. This physical interpretation permits the use of a simple method of integration according to sections.

For this purpose let the curve of changes in time, $B'(t)$ be divided into a number of small sections k of width T_0 and assume dB'/dt to remain constant along each of these sections. Let us first presume that at $t_0 = 0$ there are no eddy currents. Thus the density of eddy currents at $t = T_0$ can be determined by the equation

$$j_{t=T_0} = \frac{10\,Tb\,\dfrac{dB'(t)}{dt}}{a\,\mu\pi\,d} \sum_1^{\infty} \frac{1}{m'^2} \left(1 - e^{-\frac{m'^2 T_0}{T}}\right) \cos \frac{m'\pi x}{d} \tag{9-36}$$

Let us first examine the fundamental wave of the eddy currents. Let j_{eff} be the density of a uniformly distributed current developing as much heat as the current of the fundamental wave. The magnitude of the wave of this current can be determined if $\cos \pi\, x/d$ in Eq. (9-36) is replaced by $1/\sqrt{2}$.

Let us introduce the expression

$$\frac{10\,bT}{\sqrt{2}\,a\,\pi\mu\,dT_0} = A \tag{9-37}$$

and denote $dB'(t)/dt$ at the moment $t = T_0$ by $\Delta B_{\text{I}}/T_0$, and at the moment $t = 2T_0$ by $\Delta B_{\text{II}}/T_0$, etc..

Thus for $t = T_0$ the density will be

$$j_{\text{effI}} = A\Delta B_{\text{I}}\,(1 - e^{-T_0/T}) \tag{9-38}$$

which corresponds to the first member of Eq. (9-35) and diminishes proportionally to $e^{-T_0/T}$. For the moment $t = 2T_0$ the value j_{effII} can be expressed in the form

$$\begin{aligned} j_{\text{effII}} &= A\,\Delta\,B_{\text{I}}(1 - e^{-T_0/T})\,e^{-T_0/T} + A\,\Delta\,B_{\text{II}}\,(1 - e^{-T_0/T}) = \\ &= j_{\text{effI}}\,e^{-T_0/T} + A\,\Delta\,B_{\text{II}}\,(1 - e^{-T_0/T}) \end{aligned} \tag{9-39}$$

If the expression j_{effI}, j_{effII} etc. are divided by $A\,(1 - e^{-T_0/T})$ and the "reduced current densities" thus obtained are denoted by

$$j_{\text{I}} = \frac{j_{\text{effI}}}{A\,(1 - e^{-T_0/T})} \tag{9-40a}$$

$$j_{\text{II}} = \frac{j_{\text{effII}}}{A\,(1 - e^{-T_0/T})} \tag{9-40b}$$

and so on, then we get the following equations

$$
\left.\begin{aligned}
j_{\mathrm{I}} &= \Delta B_{\mathrm{I}} + 0 \cdot \vartheta\,, \\
j_{\mathrm{II}} &= \Delta B_{\mathrm{II}} + j_{\mathrm{I}}\,\vartheta\,, \\
j_{\mathrm{III}} &= \Delta B_{\mathrm{III}} + j_{\mathrm{II}}\,\vartheta\,, \\
&\text{— — — — — — — —} \\
j_n &= \Delta B_n + j_{n-1}\,\vartheta\,, \\
j_{n+1} &= \Delta B_{n+1} + j_n\,\vartheta\,,
\end{aligned}\right\} \tag{9-41}
$$

where

$$\vartheta = e^{-T_0/T} \tag{9-42}$$

This is now a very simple method for determining the instantaneous value of the effective current density of the first harmonic.

Eq. (9-41) is based on the arbitrary assumption that at time $t_0 = 0$ the eddy current is zero. Yet if the magnetic flux changes periodically, there must needs occur some eddy current of density j_0 at the moment t_0, as obtained from Eq. (9-35) for $t = t_0$ and $m' = 1$.

If it is assumed that during the first half period this current decreases practically to zero (which is indeed the case with conductors correctly dimensioned), then the value j_0 can be determined by continuing the computation according to Eq. (9-41) until the moment kT_0, i.e. until the end of the half period and by computing the initial value j_0 from the final value j_k thus obtained, by means of the following formula

$$j_0 = -j_k \tag{9-43}$$

Thus, only the values j_{I}, j_{II} etc. should be added to the values $\vartheta\, j_0$, $\vartheta^2 j_0$ etc. to obtain the effect of the eddy current prevailing at the beginning of the half period. If the eddy currents are computed for cases when the changes in the flux are periodical, the conductors of the armature are properly dimensioned and the armature consists of sheets, then the said values $\vartheta\, j_0$, $\vartheta^2 j_0$ etc. should only be added to the first values j (because these reduce rapidly and very soon become zero). Thus the distribution of the eddy current densities in time can readily be found. The average losses due to eddy currents, related to unit space, can be determined by the formula

$$
\begin{aligned}
L_{ek} &= \frac{A^2(1-\vartheta)^2}{\lambda_e 10^4 k}\left[(j_{\mathrm{I}} + \vartheta j_0)^2 + (j_{\mathrm{II}} + \vartheta^2 j_0)^2 + \ldots + (j_k + \vartheta^k j_0)^2\right] = \\
&= \frac{A^2(1-\vartheta)^2}{\lambda_e 10^4 k} \sum_{n=1}^{n=k} (j_n + \vartheta^n j_0)^2
\end{aligned} \tag{9-44}
$$

which contains the reduced eddy current densities, etc. as well as the constant

$$\frac{A^2(1-\vartheta)^2}{\lambda_e 10^4 k}$$

We have hitherto examined only the fundamental wave of the eddy currents and neglected the influence of the upper harmonics. The determination of their influence requires no special computations because the above equations can be applied to any m'th harmonic with the sole difference that T/m'^2 is to be substituted into the formulae, instead of T.

Since, however, only odd harmonics occur in Eq. (9-35) and the losses due to the third harmonic will be rather insignificant, in correctly dimensioned armature conductors and at normal frequencies (i.e. with usual r.p.m.) the upper harmonics can be neglected and the losses computed with Eq. (9-44).

9-4. Approach to the Practical Determination of Losses Due to Eddy Currents in Copper Conductors

On the basis of the theoretical proofs expounded in section 9-3, the eddy current losses in copper conductors can be determined as follows:

1. Divide the curve of flux density distribution $B' = f(t)$ within the range of one period into $2k$ equal sections of width T_0 (where $T_0 = 1/2fk$) and determine the values $\Delta B_n = B_n - B_{n-1}$ as the differences of the ordinates of curve $B' = f(t)$ at the end and at the beginning of each section.

2. Determine T from Eq. (9-26), A from Eq. (9-37) and ϑ from Eq. (9-42). In these formulae

λ_e = specific electric conductivity of conductor
μ = permeability of conductor
d = height of conductor
a/b = coefficient of filling of the space by the conductor, e.g. the relation of the total width of the conductor to the width of the slot.

3. By using Eq. (9-41) determine j_{I}, j_{II} etc. which are proportional to the effective densities of the eddy currents at the times T_0, $2T_0$ etc.,

4. Add the values $\vartheta^n j_0$ to the computed values j_n where $j_0 = -j_k$, i.e. the reduced density of the eddy currents in the last kth section of the curve $B' = f(t)$.

5. Raise to the second power the values $j_n + \vartheta_n j_0$ and by using Eq. (9-44), determine the average losses due to eddy currents in the unit space of the conductor.

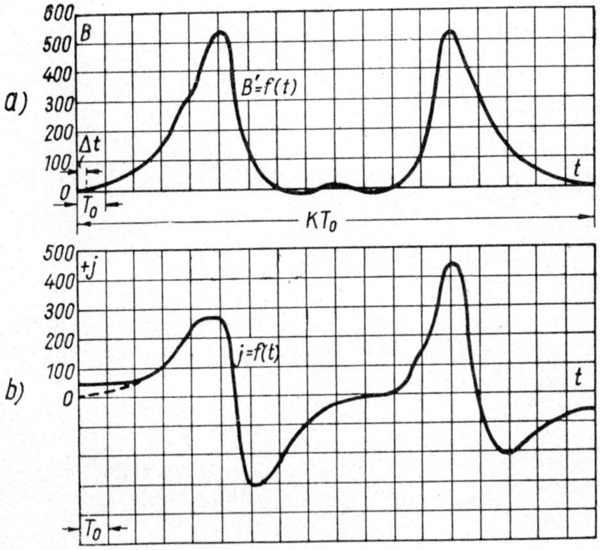

Fig. 9-3

Example 105. Let us assume that Fig. 9-3a corresponds to the curve of flux density distribution in time.

Compare the results obtained for eddy current losses by the method developed by the author and by the analytical computation method based on the analysis of the harmonics. For the curve in Fig. 9-3a we shall use the curve of the time distribution of the transverse slot fluxes over the armature periphery as suggested by Dreyfus in his work quoted in chapter 1.

Divide this curve into $k = 18$ equal sections and determine ΔB_{I}, ΔB_{II}, ΔB_{III} etc. as the differences of the ordinates of curve $B' = f(t)$ at the end and at the beginning of each section.

Compute the constants T, T_0 and ϑ etc. on the basis of the parameters $a/b = 10/14$, $f = 30$ Hz, $\lambda_e = 50$, $\mu = 1$, $d = 1.4$ cm, corresponding to the parameters given by Dreyfus:

$$T = 8.29 \cdot 10^{-4}$$

$$T_0 = \frac{1}{2 \cdot 30 \cdot 18} = 9.26 \cdot 10^{-6}$$

$$\vartheta = e^{-1.038} = 0.354$$

The values j_{I}, j_{II}, j_{III} etc. should be computed by means of Eq. (9-41) and the mean value

$$\frac{1}{k} \sum_{n=1}^{n=k} (j_n + \delta^n j_0)^2$$

should be determined (cf. Table 9-4). For j_0 we take the value $- j_{18}$.

The mean value is

$$\frac{1}{k} \sum_{n=1}^{n=k} (j_n + \vartheta^n j_0)^2 = \frac{6{,}001 \cdot 10^2}{18} = 33{,}300$$

The specific copper losses due to eddy currents can be computed with the following formula, if the fundamental wave alone is taken into account:

$$L_{ec} = 9.4 \cdot 10^{-6} \cdot 0.646^2 \cdot 33{,}300 \approx 0.131 \ \text{W/cm}^3$$

By breaking up the curve $B' = f(t)$ of Fig. 9-3a into 19 harmonic components and computing the losses due to each harmonic by using the usual method in his above-quoted work Dreyfus obtained the value $L = 0.135$ W/cm³. Thus the result obtained by means of the simple new method practically coincides with the magnitude of the specific losses computed with the complicated and cumbersome method of breaking up the curve of flux density distribution into its harmonic components. The new method enables us not only to determine the losses due to eddy currents but also to obtain the curve of distribution of eddy currents in time $j = f(t)$ (Fig. 9-3b) because the values in column 6 of Table 9-4 represent the current densities in the moments T_0, $2T_0$, $3T_0$ etc..

The possibility of determining this curve has a paramount practical and theoretical importance. First it gives an instructive picture of the effect of the form of the curve of flux density distribution upon

TABLE 9-4

n	ΔB_n G	ϑj_{n-1} A/cm²	$j_n = \Delta B_n + \vartheta j_{n-1}$ A/cm²	$\vartheta^n j_c$ A/cm²	$j_n + \vartheta^n j_0$ A/cm²	$(j_n + \vartheta^n i_0)^2 \cdot \frac{1}{100}$ A²/cm⁴
1	2	3	4	5	6	7
1	+26	0	+26	+20	+46	21
2	+38	+9	+47	+7	+54	29
3	+76	+17	+93	+2	+95	90
4	+192	+38	+225	+1	+226	507
5	+198	+80	+278	0	+278	770
6	—416	+98	—318	0	—318	1,010
7	—112	—113	—225	0	—225	507
8	—8	—80	—88	0	—88	78
9	+7	—31	—24	0	—24	6
10	—7	—9	—16	0	—16	3
11	+8	—6	+2	0	+2	0
12	+112	+1	+113	0	+113	128
13	+416	+40	+456	0	+456	2,085
14	—198	+162	—36	0	—36	13
15	—192	—13	—205	0	—205	420
16	—76	—72	—148	0	—148	219
17	—38	—52	—90	0	—90	81
18	—26	—32	—58	0	—58	34
						6,001
					$\sum_{n=1}^{18}$	$= 6{,}001 \cdot 10^2$

the magnitude and distribution of eddy currents. Secondly, it permits the exact computation of eddy currents when different flux changes due to different causes act simultaneously upon the armature conductors (cf. section 9-5).

9-5. *Approach to the Practical Determination of the Distribution of Different Eddy Currents in Copper Conductors and to the Computation of Losses Due to Them*

Let us first examine the practical method of determining the densities of eddy currents due to different kinds of slot fluxes.

A) Transverse slot flux between adjacent teeth, due to their saturation

As pointed out in chapter 7, the density of the transverse slot flux due to tooth saturation is distributed along the height of the slot according to some function AB (Fig. 9-4).

If the upper spatial harmonics of the flux density are neglected (as was done in sections 9-3 and 9-4), then the effective flux $KEDL$,

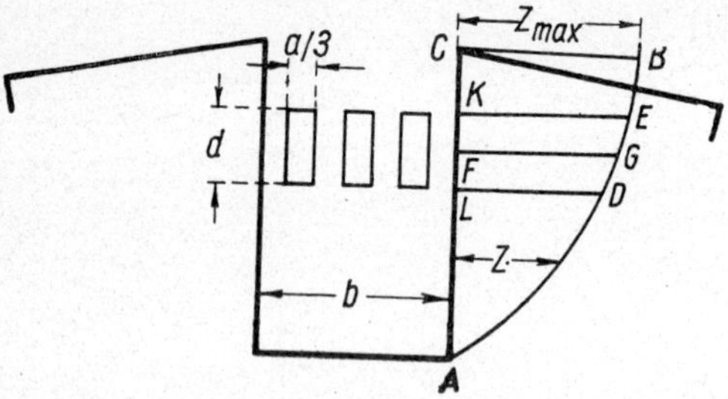

Fig. 9-4

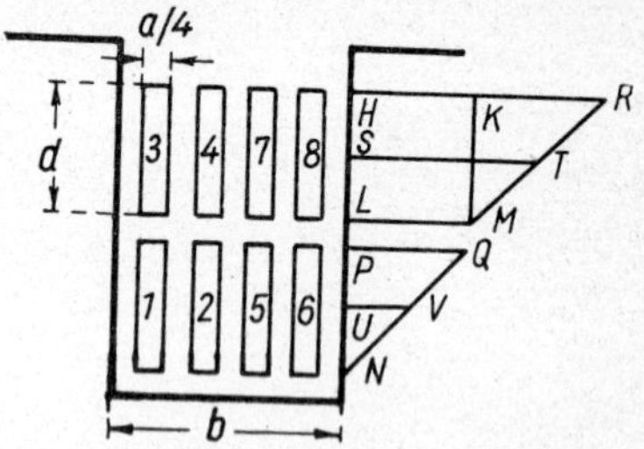

Fig. 9-5

passing through the upper layer of conductors shown in Fig. 9-4, can be replaced, without great error, by one conductor with flux density $\overline{FG}$. The value $\overline{FG} = Z$ can be computed in the following way: the flux density $Z_{\max}$ determined nomographically is multiplied by $f_1(x/h)$ and the latter can be read from Fig. 8-3 for a given value α. If Fig. 8-3 is used for this computation, x is taken as the mean height of the conductor. For the computation of the reduced densities of the eddy currents with Eq. (9-41) the values $\Delta Z_m = Z_m - Z_{m-1}$, obtained according to the method of section 8-3, are used as the magnitudes $\Delta B_n = B_n - B_{n-1}$.

B) Transverse slot fluxes between adjacent teeth, due to loading current

The said flux due to loading current in the armature conductors is distributed according to Fig. 9-5 and, in the period of commutation (i.e. when the current changes in some conductor), creates eddy currents in all windings in the slot.

On the strength of considerations, analogous to those expounded in the preceding section, for the value Z we take the mean flux densities $\overline{ST}$ and $\overline{UV}$ of fluxes $LMRH$ and NQP passing through the upper and the lower layer of the windings.

Obviously $\overline{ST}$ and $\overline{UV}$ will have the following values:

$$\overline{ST} = \frac{3}{4} \frac{0.4 \pi A \tau_s}{b}$$

$$\overline{UV} = \frac{1}{4} \frac{0.4 \pi A \tau_s}{b}$$

Thus the densities of eddy currents due to transverse slot fluxes created by loading current can be determined with the method of section 9-4 even in case of most involved commutation conditions.

The character of the change ΔB_n for one conductor (e.g. conductor 1) should be determined preliminarily, when the current is commutated in one conductor only (say in conductor 3). In the case of ideal commutation the value ΔB_n is constant during the period of commutation and when commutation comes to an end, it equals zero.

Now determine the character of the change ΔB_n for conductor 1 when the current is commutated in another conductor (say conductor 4), etc.. On summing up the simple diagrams thus obtained (Fig. 9-6) with due regard to the phase shift pertaining to the effective shift in time at the beginning of commutation in the different conductors, some stepped curve of the values $\Delta B_n = f(y)$ can be determined for any commutation process. Once the stepped curve is obtained for some conductor, the densities of the eddy currents can readily be calculated with the method explained in the preceding section.

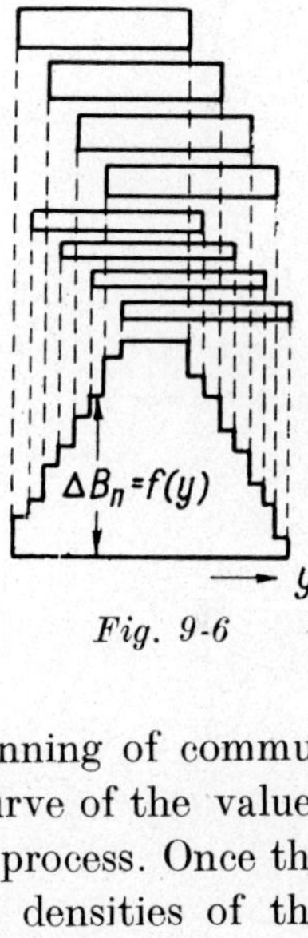

Fig. 9-6

C) Longitudinal slot flux due to the saturation of the teeth

The procedure is analogous to the previous method. One should proceed from the flux density prevailing at mid-height of the conductor in which losses are computed.

Determine b_x at point x corresponding to the mean height of the conductor. Plot the straight line OA on the nomogram so that the tangent of angle AOL should equal $0.4\pi\, b'/b_x\, \gamma l$. Use $\Phi_{\tau m}$ and V_m respectively to denote Φ_τ and V obtained nomographically for the tooth pitch under the pole centre. Determine then nomographically the value H_{xm}, i.e. the field strength in the tooth at x, as the ordinate of point C lying on curve $\varrho = 1$ at a horizontal distance $\Phi_{\tau m}/b_x\, \gamma l$ from the line OA.

Introducing

$$\frac{H_{xm}}{V_m} h = V \tag{9-45}$$

and assuming that the relation of the field strength in the tooth H_x to the potential difference V is constant for all teeth, we can say that the density of the transverse flux at x in any slot is $0.4\pi\, LV_n/h$. Having determined from the nomogram all values $V_n/h = (\overline{CK})_n$, we can compute the required densities of eddy currents with the above method.

D) Transverse slot flux due to potential differences in the air gap

Differentiating P_1' in the Eq. (4-13), taking into account Eq. (4-17), writing the result in a form similar to Eqs. (4-10 and 4-11), assuming $n = 1$, i.e. taking into account the fundamental alone (the effective value $1/\sqrt{2}$) instead of

$$\sin \frac{\pi}{b} y$$

we get the following formula:

$$B = 0.45\, \Phi_\tau \frac{1}{\tau_s l} k_c \left(1 - e^{-2\pi\delta/b}\right) e^{-\pi(h-x)/b} \tag{9-46}$$

Since the losses in the individual elements of the copper volume are proportional to the square of flux density, the losses in the entire conductor will have the same magnitude, as if they were caused by a homogeneous longitudinal flux with a density of

$$B = 0.45\, \Phi_\tau \frac{k_c (1 - e^{-2\pi\delta/b})}{\tau_s l} e^{-\pi(\ -x)/b} \sqrt{\frac{\mathrm{sh}\frac{\pi d}{b}}{\frac{\pi d}{b}}} \tag{9-47}$$

The fluxes Φ_τ pertaining to the different positions of the conductor under the pole can be determined nomographically. Calculating then the flux density at x in every slot, the densities of the eddy currents can be determined by using the method of section 9-4.

It should be stressed that in determining the eddy current densities for the longitudinal flux due to the saturation of the teeth, the ratio a/b should be taken as the relation of the total height of all conductors in which the losses are to be determined to the value h. In order to compute the densities of eddy currents induced by the longitudinal flux due to the air gap, the ratio a/b should be taken as the relation of the total height of the conductors to the value $h + \delta$, where δ is the length of the air gap with which Φ_τ is computed at a given point.

E) Symmetrical transverse slot flux due to the saturation of the teeth (Figs. 9-7a and 9-7b)

This flux passing through the wall of the teeth within the range of heights x_1 to x_2 equals the difference $\Phi_{sx1} - \Phi_{sx2}$, i.e.

$$0.4\,\pi\, b' \frac{V}{h} l\,(L_1 - L_2)$$

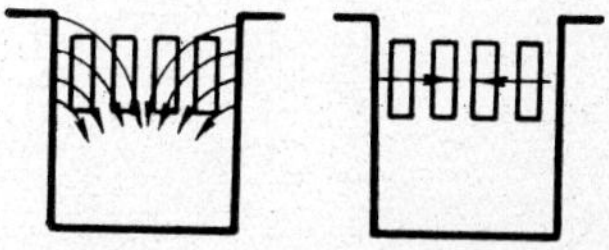

Fig. 9-7

Here L_1 and L_2 can be calculated with Eq. (9-45) by taking as a basis the values H_{x1m} and H_{x2m} pertaining to the heights x_1 and x_2. Assuming that its flux density is uniformly distributed along the height of the conductor, we can say that near the wall of the tooth at a height

$$\frac{x_1 + x_2}{2}$$

it will be

$$\frac{0.4\,b'l}{2}\,\frac{(L_1 - L_2)}{(x_2 - x_1)}\,\frac{V}{h}$$

Assuming that the said flux density decreases linearly to zero toward the symmetry axis of the slot, we can say without great error that the effective flux density (Fig. 9-7b), responsible for the losses in the conductors in the slot between the heights x_1 and x_2, is

$$B = 0.36\,b'\,\frac{(L_1 - L_2)}{(x_2 - x_1)}\,\frac{V}{h} \tag{9-48}$$

Having determined L_1, L_2 and V/h, we apply the method suggested for determining the density of eddy currents induced by longitudinal fluxes.

F) Symmetrical transverse slot flux due to the potential difference in the air gap (Figs. 9-8a and 9-8b)

The potential P'_I in the slot due to the flux of the air gap can be determined with Eq. (4-13). Assuming $n = 1$, differentiating this expression according to y and replacing $\sin \pi y/b$ by $1/\sqrt{2}$, we obtain the formula

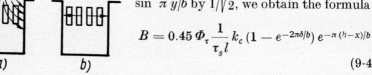

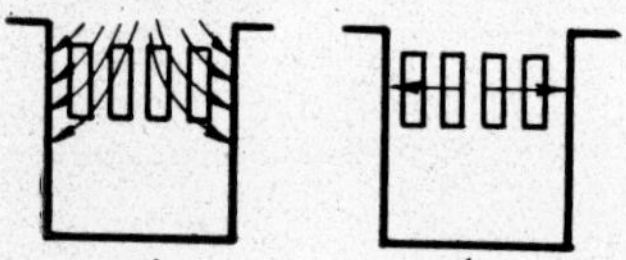

Fig. 9-8

$$B = 0.45\, \Phi_\tau \frac{1}{\tau_s l} k_c \left(1 - e^{-2\pi\delta/b}\right) e^{-\pi(h-x)/b} \tag{9-49}$$

for the density of this flux, similarly to Eq. (9-46).

Constructing the curve, representing the dependence of this flux density on x within the range from $x - k/2$ to $x + k/2$, determining its fundamental and computing the effective value of the flux density, we get the following formula:

$$B = 0.57\, \Phi_\tau \frac{k_c}{\tau_s l} \left(1 - e^{-2\pi\delta/b}\right) e^{-\pi(h-x)/b} \frac{b^2}{k^2 + b^2} \operatorname{ch} \frac{k\pi}{2b} \tag{9-50}$$

The value $1 - e^{-2\pi\delta/b}$ can be determined from curve 1 of Fig. 9-9 for the abscissa $u = 2\pi\delta/b$; the value $e^{-\pi(h-x)/b}$ from curve 2 of Fig. 9-9 for the abscissa $u = \pi(h - x)/b$; the value

$$\sqrt{\frac{\operatorname{sh} \frac{\pi d}{b}}{\frac{\pi d}{b}}}$$

from curve 3 of Fig. 9-9 for the abscissa $u = \pi d/2b$ and the value

$$\operatorname{ch} \frac{k\pi}{2b}$$

from curve 4 of Fig. 9-9 for the abscissa $u = k\pi/2b$.

Thus, having determined from the nomogram the value Φ_τ, we can compute the density of the eddy currents induced by this transverse flux, by using the method of section 9-4.

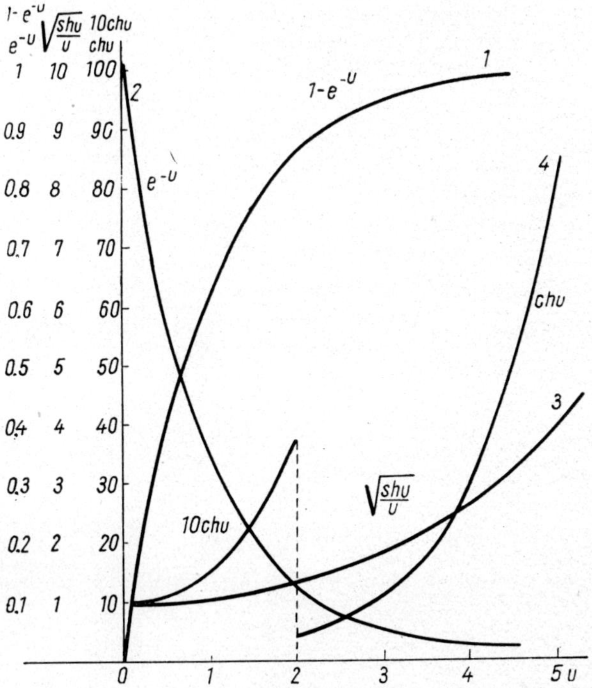

Fig. 9-9

G) Computation of losses due to eddy currents in copper conductors

The losses due to the fluxes investigated in sections *A)* and *B)* of this chapter, can be computed by the algebraic addition of the ordinates of curves $j_n = f(t)$ and by the application of the method of section 9-4.

The same procedure should be followed for computing the losses caused by the fluxes examined in sections *C)* and *D)*, as well as for calculating those due to the fluxes examined in sections *E)* and *F)*.

Then the losses due to these three groups of fluxes are added up.

Thus the method developed for the computation of eddy current losses has proved generally valid and can be applied for computing the losses for any time curve of magnetic fluxes, howewer complicated their course may be, for any demand and spatial distribution of the transverse or longitudinal slot fluxes due to different causes.

A similar method can, obviously, be applied for computing electric circuits with complicated distribution of the impedances fed by non-sinusoidal voltages.

CHAPTER TEN

PERSPECTIVES OF APPLYING THE NOMOGRAPHIC METHOD FOR SOLVING OTHER SIMILAR PROBLEMS

The nomographic method developed in this book can be used not only to compute electric machines and devices but also to solve different theoretical problems occurring in other fields of electromagnetic computations, whose discussion would go beyond the scope of this book. Nevertheless we shall quote a few examples of such tasks.

10-1. The Exact Determination of Systems with Permanent Magnets

For the computation of such systems a family of curves $V/h = f(B)$ can be constructed on the basis of the demagnetizing curve of the given ferromagnetic substance. Each of these curves will correspond to the magnetic relations for the different configurations characterized by different factors ϱ. This method makes it possible to study more thoroughly certain important phenomena in machines and devices with permanent magnets.

10-2. The Nomographic Determination of Dynamic Reluctance

The basic idea of solving the complicated problem expounded in chapter 8 is that the result can be obtained nomographically with an error so small that the unknown errors in flux density, fluxes, magnetic potential differences, etc. may be regarded as proportional to one another. Thus a system of linear equations can be set up for these unknown magnitudes and can be solved with the use of constants found nomographically. The idea underlying such a solution may, obviously, be developed further and extended to other cases. Here are a few examples:

a) Let us assume that in a four-pole machine, owing to the non-uniformity of the corresponding parts of the air gap, or to the non-uniformity of the magnetomotive force of the different excitation windings, the corresponding four branches of the magnetic flux will not be uniform either. By assuming the uniformity of the gaps and the magnetomotive forces all magnetic relations can be determined nomographically, including the relation between the changes in V and the pertaining values Φ at different points of the magnetic circuits. Thus "dynamic reluctances" are obtained which are constant if the deviation of the magnetomotive forces and gaps from the required values are not considerable. With the help of these dynamic reluctances linear equations can be set up for the individual branches of the flux and their analytical solution will yield the actual magnetic relations.

b) On the basis of similar considerations even the difficult problem of the mutual influence of armature saturation on leakage fluxes and also the problem of the effect of this saturation upon the flux of the commutating pole can be found. Owing to the smallness of these fluxes as compared to the excitation flux, the dynamic reluctances for the individual sections of the magnetic circuit can be determined nomographically if these fluxes are neglected and then compute the latter analytically by means of the constants obtained.

c) On the strength of similar considerations another very complicated problem can also be solved, i.e. the computation of the effect of the ventilation ducts upon the magnetic relations in the armature of the rotor. The ferromagnetic parts between the ducts, together with the parallel-connected parts of the ducts, show a configuration like $DD'C'C$ in Fig. 4-8a. Since the reluctances of the other parts are very small in comparison to the reluctance of the said elements, the armature can be considered as a net whose parts consist of elements having a form like $DD'C'C$, i.e. a reluctance that can readily be represented nomographically. By estimating the approximate distribution of fluxes in the rotor, the corresponding dynamic reluctances of the said elements can be determined nomographically and linear equations can be set up with their help for the entire magnetic net. If the solution of the equations shows that the difference between the actual and the assumed flux distribution still lies within the range, in which the dynamic reluctances can be regarded as constant, then the problem may be considered solved. If the said difference lies without this range, the computation should be repeated nomographically, starting from a more accurate flux distribution.

The method of the nomographic determination of dynamic reluctances can be used also for solving other problems occurring in connection with electrical machines and devices.

10-3. The Nomographic Investigation of the Effect of the Changes in Construction upon Reluctance

It has been pointed out in chapter 8 that within a certain range the relationship between some change in ϱ, characterizing the configuration of the teeth, and the change in the pertaining fluxes and potential differences, may be regarded as linear and expressed by the aid of the factor k_ϱ taken from the nomogram.

This method can, obviously, be generalized and used for the solution of a great many problems. Since the nomogram takes into account the relation of the magnitudes V_0, V, Φ_τ, Φ_s and Φ_t not only to the value ϱ but also to the dimensions h, b_0, l, b', δ, τ_s etc., the relationship between the changes in any of these parameters and the corresponding change in magnetic values can be determined nomographically. This relationship can be regarded as linear within a certain range. Thanks to the linear relationship, the effect of a simultaneous change in several geometrical parameters can be obtained by adding up the changes in each parameter.

Thus the effect of some change in configuration upon the magnetic values can be examined analytically, i.e. improved variants of configuration can be found. If the changes in the different values are regarded as differentials, the limit values, such as for instance the optimal conditions, can be found.

10-4. The Changes of the Electromagnetic Relations in Time

The nomographic-analytical method can be used to find the ranges within which linear relations are valid and thereby to solve the problems of transient processes in saturated machines.

The greatest difficulty encountered in solving such problems is that the ratio $d\Phi/dV$, upon which the factor of self-inductance and the value of the eddy currents, due to $d\Phi/dt$, depend, is unknown.

Yet the nomographic method can be instrumental in determining the values $d\Phi/dV$, which are constant within a certain range of flux changes in time, and in obtaining thus a system of linear differential equations representing the transient process taking place within this range. Here the curves ϱ indicate the limits within which the said factors may be taken for constant. Beyond this limit there is another range that can be determined nomographically, with another transient process which can be connected with the previous one by means of the boundary conditions.

10-5. The Possibility of Finding New Nomographic Rules

In chapter 3 we have explained the rule referring to the mutual position of the individual curves in the nomogram. The latter may, obviously, be used for the further simplification of the nomographic system. If, for instance, the requirements of accuracy are not very strict, a single mean curve ϱ can be substituted for all the other curves by altering correspondingly their abscissae, i.e. the values Φ_τ, Φ_s, Φ_t and δ pertaining to point C. The application of such a nomogram requires only one mean curve (for instance, $\varrho = 1.44$) to be found, and for the determination of the factors, by which the said values should be multiplied, it is sufficient to find only one point on each of the remaining curves. It is clear that if all the curves are replaced by a single curve, it is easy to find the analytical expression of this curve within the ranges in question.

A close inspection of the nomogram will also reveal that an analytical expression for the relationship between the values ϱ and the abscissae can readily be found. The possibility of finding these or other relationships may considerably extend the field of application of the nomographic-analytic method for solving different problems.

The few examples quoted above reveal the vast possibilities of the further development of our nomographic system. It seems that some of these examples may also be used for solving problems of other (non-magnetic) complicated non-linear relationships.

Thus, in the author's opinion, vast perspectives open up before scientific research workers towards the further extension, generalization and simplification of the nomographic methods developed in this book and towards their application for solving problems in other fields of technical sciences.

LIST OF SYMBOLS

A	specific electric loading (specific ampere-turn)
A_{ea}	loss constant of eddy current in the armature
A_{ep}	loss constant of eddy current in the pole
A_{et}	loss constant of eddy current in the tooth
A_{ht}	loss constant of hysteresis in the tooth
a	ratio of the minimum and maximum width
B	induction, flux density
B_0	flux density in the largest cross-section
$B_{\delta 1}, B_{\delta 2}, B_{\delta 3}$	mean flux densities along the periphery of the armature
$B_{\delta A}$	flux density at the left end of the pole
$B_{\delta D}$	flux density at the right end of the pole
$B_{\delta m}$	flux density in the air gap under the middle of the pole
B_x	flux density at a distance x
$B_{xq\ m-n}$	transverse flux density in the slot passing from the mth tooth into the nth
b_0, b_2	maximum, respectively minimum width of the tooth
b'	effective width of the tooth
b_b	width of the slot at the bottom
b_i	"ideal" width of the pole arc
b_l	width of the slot at the maximum height
b_p	width of the pole shoe
b_{par}	width of the slot
b_s	width of the slot
b_t	width of the tooth
b_x	width of the wedge-shaped body at a distance x
β	angle of a straight line
C_1, C_2, C_3	constants
d	thickness of electrical sheets
δ	width length of the air grap
δ_A	air gap at the left end of the pole
δ_D	air gap at the right end of the pole
$\delta_1, \delta_2, \delta_3$	mean values of air gaps along the periphery of the armature
δ_w	length of air gap with due regard to Carter's coefficient
ε	ratio determined by distribution of induction
$\varepsilon_1, \varepsilon_2 \ldots$	angles of magnetic lines and equipotential lines
F_a	magnetomotive force of the armature reaction
F_{cp}	magnetomotive force of the commutating pole
F_e	magnetomotive force of the field coil

F_{lp} longitudinal magnetomotive force linked with the entire pole arc
F_{qy} transverse magnetomotive force under the pole arc at a distance of ry from the middle of the pole
f magnetization frequency
Φ magnetic flux, main magnetic flux
Φ_e exciting flux
Φ_{e1} flux passing from the pole to armature
Φ_{e2} flux by-passing the air gap
Φ_P main flux
Φ_{par} parallel flux
Φ_{pv}, Φ'_{pv} flux at the pole shoe, flux passing through pole shoe
Φ_q transverse flux
Φ_{sx} slot flux at a height x
Φ_σ, Φ'_σ, Φ''_σ, $\Phi_{\sigma I}$, $\Phi'_{\sigma I}$,... leakage fluxes
Φ_t flux of the tooth
Φ_τ total flux of a tooth and the two halves of the adjacent slots
flux of the tooth pitch
Φ_x tooth flux at a height x
Φ_{xn} flux in the nth tooth
$\Phi_{xq\,m-n}$ transverse flux passing from the mth tooth into the nth
$\Delta\Phi_{xn}$ longitudinal flux difference in the nth tooth
$\Delta\Phi_{xq\,m-n}$ transverse flux difference
G_t weight of a tooth
G_{at} weight of part of the armature pertaining to a tooth pitch
γ filling factor of laminated steel
H field strength
H_x field strength at a distance x
H_{xm} field strength in mth tooth
H_{xs} field strength in the slot at distance x
h height of the body, depth of the slot
j, j_{eff}, j_{I}, j_{effI}, j_{II}, j_{effII},... current densities
ϑ proportionality factor
k coefficient of the flux passing the wedge-shaped body
geometric factor
divisor factor
k_c, k_δ air gap factor
k_{c1} air gap factor of the stator
air gap factor pertaining to δ_1
k_{c2} air gap factor of the rotor
air gap factor pertaining to δ_2
k_c Carter's gap coefficient
L_{ht} hysteresis loss in the tooth
L_{ea} eddy current loss of the armature
L_{ec} copper loss due to eddy current
L_{ep} eddy current loss of the pole by the tooth pulsations of flux density in the air gap
L_{et} eddy current loss of the tooth

$L_{\Delta Tt}$	eddy current losses in the tooth during time interval ΔT
l	length of the body, length of the magnetized body
l_a	width of the armature
$\lambda, \lambda_I, \lambda'_I, \lambda_{II}, \lambda'_{II}, \lambda''_{II}$	conductivity of the leakage flux, permeance
λ_e	specific electrical conductivity
m	value derived from flux density distribution
	number of harmonics
m'	odd harmonics
μ_x	permeability at distance x
n	integer number
P_{AB}	magnetic potential along the line AB
$P_1, P_2, P'_1, P'_2, P_I, P_{II}$, etc.	potencial, magnetic potential
$p_{10,000}$	specific iron loss at flux density 10,000 G
$Q_I, Q_{II}, Q_{III}, \ldots$	cross-section
R_{m1}, R_{m2}	reluctances of ferromagnetic bodies
ϱ	relative value of induction
S	density of magnetic energy
T	material constant
ΔT	time interval
t	time
τ_p	pole pitch
τ_s	size of the slot pitch
τ_t	size of the tooth pitch
V, V', V_0	the difference of the magnetic potentials
V_a	the potential drop in the armature yoke
$V_{pv}, V_{pvI}, V_{pvII}, \ldots$	potential drop along the pole shoe
V_p	potential drop in the pole
V_{st}	potential drop in the stator yoke
Ψ_I, Ψ_{II}	distribution coefficient
Z	transverse flux density
Z	maximum of transverse flux density
ΔZ	difference of transverse slot fluxes entering and leaving the tooth
ζ	correctional factor

Responsible for the publication
GYÖRGY BERNÁT
Director of the Publishing House of the Academy of Sciences

*

Responsible editor
G. P. DIENES

*

Technical editor
I. HÚTH

*

Manuscript received on 12 April 1961
with 86 figures and 3 supplements

*

Printed in Hungary by the Academy Press, Budapest V, Gerlóczy utca 2
Responsible manager: György Bernát